CW00586744

A Mineralogy of Wales

RICHARD E. BEVINS

Department of Geology, National Museum of Wales, Cardiff

AMGUEDDFA GENEDLAETHOL CYMRU

NATIONAL MUSEUM OF WALES

GEOLOGICAL SERIES NO. 16

Cardiff, May 1994

© *National Museum of Wales 1994*

ISBN 0 7200 0403 9

REFERENCES TO THIS VOLUME

It is recommended that reference to this volume should be made in the following form:

BEVINS, R.E. 1994. *A Mineralogy of Wales.* 146pp. National Museum of Wales, Geological Series No. 16, Cardiff.

Front cover: Radiating goethite pseudomorphs after hematite from Mwyndy Mine, Llantrisant, Mid Glamorgan. The field view is 12 mm across. NMW specimen 85.131, donated to the Cardiff Museum by S. Vivian towards the end of the last century.

Back cover: Radiating aggregates of serpierite crystals up to 1 mm long from Ystrad Einion Mine, in the Central Wales Mining District. J. S. Mason Collection, specimen JMYE006.

  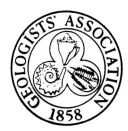

Copyright notice
All Rights Reserved. No part of this publication may be reproduced, stored in a retrieval system or transmitted in any form by any means, electronic, mechanical, photocopying, recording or otherwise, without the prior written permission of the publisher, National Museum of Wales, Cardiff CF1 3NP, Wales, U.K.

FOREWORD

In 1982 the National Museum of Wales published a picture booklet of *Welsh Minerals* (Geological Series No. 4, by R.E. Bevins and T. Sharpe, in English and Welsh versions), which illustrated only a very small selection of specimens from the museum's collections. Despite its limited scope, however, this attractive introduction to the subject provided a suitable emphasis to the fact that a wide variety of minerals occurs in Wales, some of which have been of considerable economic importance. This latter point was also emphasised in an earlier National Museum publication entitled *Mining for Metals in Wales* (by F.J. North, 1962), which concentrated on the historical and more recent industrial exploitation, although inevitably touching also on the range of ores present throughout the Principality.

Given that minerals and mineralogy have been subjects of collection and study since the Museum made its first acquisitions in 1912, it is perhaps somewhat surprising that those two publications are the only ones written by staff to address these interests. The present book is therefore a most welcome and much needed contribution, both as a scientific study in its own right, and as an important database for the mineralogy of Wales; it is the first ever attempt to make such a comprehensive compilation of all the known mineral species in this region, which has experienced a long and varied geological history. The acquisition and interpretation of these kinds of data as a means of disseminating information on the geological framework and evolution of Wales are some of the key objectives and roles of the Department of Geology at the National Museum.

Exploration for, and exploitation of minerals in the Principality have taken place since the Bronze Age. The Romans mined gold here, and at the heyday of the Industrial Revolution copper from Parys Mountain on Anglesey dominated the world market. Much of the database is therefore of long antiquity, but there has been an exponential increase in the last thirty years or so. New technology and sophisticated analytical techniques have permitted more detailed investigations to be made of mineral veins and deposits, and have recalled a hitherto unexpected diversity. The same applies equally to the various secondary products resulting from the alteration of primary minerals. A diverse suite of secondary minerals has been detected by studies in Snowdonia and the Central Wales Mining District in particular. Commonly these alteration products are found only on a microscopic scale (so-called microminerals), and it is testimony to the expertise of a small number of collectors that the existence of this fascinating suite has been highlighted.

Concomitant advances in petrological techniques, with better microscopes and the refinement of electron microprobe analysis, have also made significant contributions. As a result, we now have a much greater appreciation of the mineralogical components of widespread suites of igneous, metamorphic and sedimentary rocks in Wales.

The Museum collections themselves contain only about 50% of the mineral species known in Wales. They have been drawn on heavily in the compilation and illustration of this book, emphasising in some cases the relative importance of some specimens as perhaps the only or finest examples yet known. A valuable side product has been the identification of gaps in our holdings, which helps to define more clearly a rational collecting policy to acquire reference material for the database. It also follows that the information published here has relied on numerous other sources, both as verified published records and on the invaluable support given by many amateur and professional mineralogists in making their collections available.

The Museum has received considerable financial assistance as loans and grants to bring this project to fruition. We are especially appreciative of the help given by the Geologists' Association via a loan from the Curry Fund, and of a grant from the Countryside Council for Wales (CCW). The former organisation has long fostered the interests of amateur geologists, so it is fitting that their contribution should ensure that this work is brought to as wide an audience as possible. The involvement of CCW is welcome in that it is the governmental statutory adviser in Wales on wildlife, countryside (including geological) and maritime matters, and has executive authority for the conservation of habitats and wildlife. CCW now has responsibility for protection of Welsh sites among the 3000 selected, through the Geological Conservation Review (GCR), in the UK, and given the designation as Sites of Special Scientific Interest. Many of the occurrences referred to in this book are from GCR sites, selected for their rare or unique mineralogies. This database is an essential prerequisite in making decisions over the priorities for conservation of sites in the countryside. It makes an invaluable contribution to our knowledge of the Welsh mineral resource and of localities which constitute an undisputed national and international heritage. The National Museum of Wales is similarly committed in its policies towards protection of the environment, which makes our cooperation with CCW even more rewarding.

Prof. M.G. Bassett
Keeper, Department of Geology
National Museum of Wales

Dedicated to my father, who introduced me to minerals in the wilds of Derbyshire and the Caldbeck Fells.

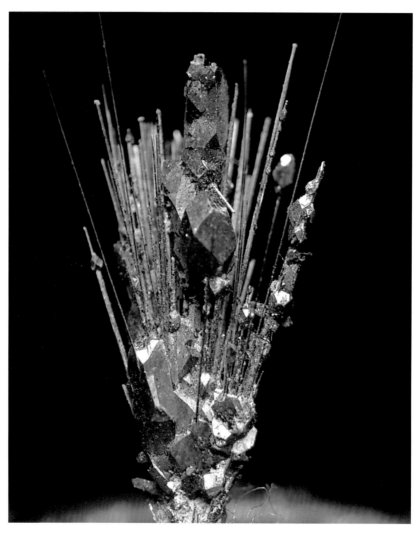

A radiating spray of acicular millerite crystals up to 10 mm long, encrusted with galena, from Cymmer Colliery, Porth, Mid Glamorgan. National Museum of Wales specimen 48.264.GR175. *ex* Cymmer Welfare Library and Institute.

CONTENTS

INTRODUCTION

The mineralogy of Wales is diverse, with over 340 different mineral species being recorded, although in fact this constitutes only about 10% of the 3,500 or so minerals currently known to science from worldwide localities. However, future investigations will no doubt reveal the presence of additional species new to Wales, and perhaps new to the British Isles. It is also probable that species completely new to science will be discovered in Wales, as techniques for analysing specimens become ever more sophisticated. In recent years, for example, detailed investigations have identified two new minerals from Wales, namuwite from the Aberllyn Mine, near Betws-y-Coed (Bevins *et al.*, 1982), and lanthanite-(Ce), from the Britannia Mine, at the foot of Snowdon (Bevins *et al.*, 1985). Prior to these reports, eight other minerals had been first discovered in Wales. All of the minerals first recorded from Wales are listed in Table 1. In addition, first British Isles reports for 67 other mineral species were from Wales; these are listed in Table 2. In this book, details are presented for all mineral species currently known to occur in Wales.

Table 1. Minerals first described from Wales

Anglesite	Cymrite
Banalsite	Dickite
Bannisterite	Lanthanite-(Ce)
Brammallite	Namuwite
Brookite	Pennantite

The first part of this book describes the modes of occurrence of minerals in Wales, with specific details of some of the more unusual or interesting records. The second part of the book provides a listing of all mineral species currently known to occur in Wales, along with brief details of occurrence. The information presented has been gathered through a survey of published literature, a review of specimens in public and private collections, information supplied by many amateur and professional mineralogists, and through primary research. The list is, of course, not exhaustive; much information on the mineralogy of Wales lies as yet undetermined or unpublished. However, the list is as comprehensive as possible at the time of writing.

Where possible, identifications have been verified by use of a determinative technique, principally X-ray diffraction, but also electron probe micro-analysis, optical microscopy, scanning electron microscopy, and infra-red spectrophotometry. Sometimes, definitive identifications have not been possible because of a lack of sufficient material. However, a programme of verification is continuing at the National Museum of Wales, and additional information or revisions to the listings

Table 2. First British Isles mineral occurrences from Wales

Aeschynite	Lawsonite
Agardite-(Y)	Manganhumite
Aleksite	Matildite
Alleghanyite	Nagyagite
Altaite	Paracelsian
Bixbyite	Paragonite
Braunite	Parisite
Calaverite	Parsettensite
Carbonate-hydroxylapatite	Perovskite
Celsian	Pilsenite
Clintonite	Plagionite
Cobalt pentlandite	Platiniridium
Collophane	Polybasite
Cookeite	Pumpellyite
Crossite	Pyrobelonite
Dundasite	Pyrochroite
Electrum	Pyrophanite
Ferro-actinolite	Pyrosmalite
Ferrobarroisite	Ramsbeckite
Ferroglaucophane	Rectorite
Fibroferrite	Riebeckite
Florencite	Romanèchite
Galenobismuthite	Sonolite
Ganophyllite	Stilpnomelane
Georgeite	Strüverite
Glaucophane	Synchysite-(Ce)
Hedleyite	Synchysite-(Y)
Hessite	Szomolnokite
Hollandite	Tapiolite (but whether ferro-
Hydronium jarosite	tapiolite or mangantapi-
Iridosmine	olite is not certain)
Jacobsite	Tephroite
Jamborite	Tetradymite
Kobellite	Tucekite
Kutnohorite	Winchite

recorded. Details of new or additional occurrences, or of verifications would be gratefully received by the author for inclusion in a later revision. Terminology used here chiefly follows that presented by Fleischer and Mandarino (1991) in their 6th edition of the 'Glossary of the Mineral Species 1991'.

Acknowledgements

The people who have contributed to this volume are almost too many to list, and I offer sincere apologies to anyone inadvertently omitted. In particular, however, I must acknowledge the free and liberal information received from a host of professional and amateur colleagues, including Dick Braithwaite, Trevor Bridges, Mick Cooper, Paul Eakin, John Francis, Neil Hubbard, Rob Ixer, David Jenkins, Anton Kearsley, John Mason, Jon Naden, Steve Rust, George Ryback, Roy Starkey, Bob Symes, and Brian Young. Others who have helped are recognised by personal communication remarks in the text. In the end, however, I must bear responsibility for inaccuracies and errors. Roy Starkey and John Mason both provided thoughtful yet polite comments on an early draft of the manuscript.

From the Department of Geology at the National Museum of Wales, I thank Jana Horák and Sara Chambers for many hours spent checking records or verifying occurrences, Paula Knapman and Rachel Dyke for typing the endless versions of the manuscript, Gaye Evans for drafting the figures, and Mike Lambert for all of his technical support.

Generous financial support towards the cost of publication was received from the Countryside Council for Wales and the Curry Fund of the Geologists' Association, and in this respect I thank Nick Pearce and Eric Robinson for their keen interest in the project.

Finally, I am grateful to Sheila and Gareth for tolerating so many lost hours.

Photograph credits: R.E. Bevins, Figs 2-4, 6-12, 58, 66, 86, 95; M.P. Cooper, Front cover, Back cover, Figs 28, 31-53, 55-56, 59-60, 62-65, 67-71, 74-78, 80-82, 84-85, 88-94, 96-114, 116, 118-123; W. Gibbons, Figs 73, 87; Gwynedd Archaeological Trust, Fig. 26; R.A. Ixer, Figs 54, 61, 79, 83; D.A. Jenkins, Fig. 15; A.T. Kearsley, Figs 27, 30, 115; B.P. Kokelaar, Fig. 5; J.S. Mason, Figs 57, 72, 118; T. Sharpe, Figs 18, 24; C.J. Stanley, Fig. 29.

Photograph copyright: M.P. Cooper, Figs 33, 47, 121, 123; W. Gibbons, Figs 73, 87; Gwynedd Archaeological Trust, Fig. 26; R.A. Ixer, Figs 54, 61, 79, 83; D.A. Jenkins, Fig. 15; A.T. Kearsley, Figs 27, 30, 115; J.S. Mason, Figs 57, 72, 117; Oxford University Press, Fig. 5; T. Sharpe, Figs 18, 24; C.J. Stanley, Fig. 29; all others National Museum of Wales.

8

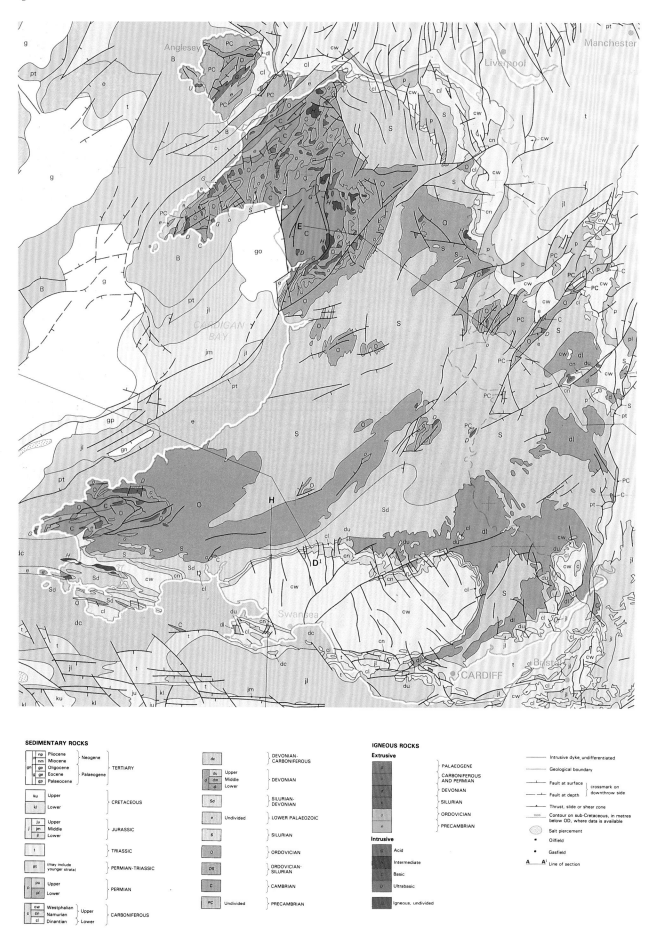

Figure 1. Geological map of Wales. Based on the British Geological Survey 1:1 000 000 sheet Geology of the United Kingdom, Ireland and the adjacent Continental Shelf (1991). Reproduced by permission of the Director, British Geological Survey: NERC copyright reserved. Topography based on Ordnance Survey mapping: Crown copyright.

MINERAL OCCURRENCES IN WALES

The minerals described in this book are found in a wide variety of geological settings. Many occur as constituents of rocks, the so-called rock-forming minerals, others are found in mineral deposits either lying within the strata or in veins cutting through pre-existing rocks. Many of the mineralized zones are associated with a range of alteration minerals, related to processes such as hydration and oxidation of primary sulphide minerals. Finally, a suite of minerals occurs as a component of the superficial materials overlying the solid rock, such as in glacial sands, the soils which have developed since the last glaciation, and river sediments.

Rock-Forming Minerals

Rocks are divided into three categories, igneous, sedimentary and metamorphic. These rocks are made up almost entirely of the rock-forming minerals, chiefly silicates, which are composed principally of the Earth's most common elements, namely Si, Al, Ca, Mg, Fe, Na, and K, along with the substitution of lesser amounts of minor and trace elements such as Ti, Mn, V, Cr, Ni, Rb, Sr, and Ba. The geochemical character of an element is related principally to its arrangement of electrons, which dictates whether it has an affinity for metallic iron, sulphide, silicate, or for the atmosphere in a gaseous form. These varying affinities are reflected in the abundance of individual elements on Earth. Those with an affinity for silicate, the so-called lithophile elements, are found largely in the rock-forming minerals. Because the lithophile elements are abundant, so are the minerals made up of those elements.

Figure 2. Thin section of a dolerite from the St. David's Head Intrusion, composed chiefly of plagioclase feldspar (grey) and clinopyroxene (coloured). Crossed polarized light. Photograph is 4 mm across.

Igneous rocks

Igneous rocks form from molten magma, which rises through the Earth's crust, erupting at the surface to produce lava flows, or crystallizing beneath the surface, to produce dykes, sills, or, on a larger scale, plutons. A variety of magmatic compositions occurs, resulting in igneous rocks ranging from basic (relatively poor in Si but high in Mg and Fe), through intermediate, to acidic (relatively high in Si, but low in Mg and Fe). The varying magma compositions result in contrasting mineralogies in the crystallized rocks.

Basic igneous rocks of Ordovician age are widespread in Wales (Fig. 1), magmas having been intruded at high levels in the crust, producing sills and dykes, and also erupted on land and under the sea as lava flows. The

Figure 3. The St. David's Head Intrusion, near St. David's, Dyfed, a thick intrusion composed of a variety of gabbro types.

largest sills, composed of gabbro, are exposed in the St. David's area of Dyfed (Roach, 1969; Bevins *et al.*, in press), and at Rhiw, on Llŷn (Hawkins, 1970; Cattermole, 1976). Plagioclase feldspar and clinopyroxene dominate the mineralogy of the various gabbros of these intrusions (Fig. 2), combined with lesser amounts of olivine and orthopyroxene. Plagioclase minerals range in composition across the full spectrum of the series, from the Ca-rich member anorthite (An_{90-100}), through bytownite, labradorite, andesine, and oligoclase, to the Na-rich member albite (An_{0-10}). Clinopyroxene compositions also vary, although only diopside and augite species occur in these intrusions. In the St. David's Head Intrusion (Fig. 3) olivine is always replaced by low temperature minerals, although in the Rhiw Intrusion olivine of a forsterite composition (Fo_{86}-Fo_{79}) is preserved. Indeed, at some levels in the intrusion olivine is extremely abundant due to sinking and accumulation of crystals in the solidifying magma, resulting in an ultrabasic rock with very low Si and high Mg contents, known as picrite. Orthopyroxene is not present in the Rhiw Intrusion, but it does occur in the St. David's Head Intrusion, reflecting minor differences in chemistry between the parental magmas of the two intrusions. Although usually altered, analyses of pristine orthopyroxene in the St. David's Head Intrusion indicate that it is enstatite. In both intrusions minor amounts of biotite, spinel, ilmenite, magnetite and amphibole are present. In the St. David's Head Intrusion the biotite is fox-red in plane light under the microscope (Fig. 4), reflecting a high content

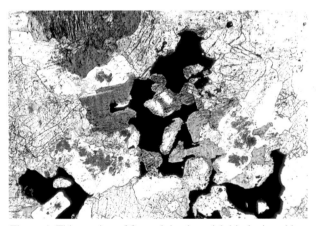

Figure 4. Thin section of fox-red titanium-rich biotite in gabbro from the St. David's Head Intrusion, Dyfed. Plane polarized light. Photograph is 4 mm across.

of Ti. The amphiboles in this intrusion are pargasite and hastingsite, and similarly contain high Ti. Accessory minerals, which are most abundant in the more evolved gabbros, include apatite, titanite and zircon, which relate to the fact that elements such as P, Ti, and Zr, major components of these accessory minerals, are not readily accommodated into the crystal structure of the common rock-forming minerals such as plagioclase or pyroxene. As a result, concentrations of these elements build up in the magma as the early formed minerals crystallize. Eventually, their concentrations reach the point where crystallization occurs of minerals composed chiefly of these so-called incompatible elements. During cooling of these large igneous bodies, late stage magmatic fluids

rich in water circulate through the largely crystalline mass, leading to hydration of early-formed minerals, and the production of new minerals, in particular amphiboles. The presence of tschermakite and magnesiohornblende in the Rhiw and St. David's Head Intrusions most probably relates to such events.

Basaltic lavas are common in Wales, many of Ordovician age but others of late Precambrian and also Silurian age. The mineralogy of these basalts is more restricted than their gabbroic counterparts, reflecting the rapid cooling of magmas of broadly constant composition. Essentially, they are composed of plagioclase feldspar and clinopyroxene. Lavas of the Rhobell

Figure 5. Thin section of pargasite (yellow) and diopside (grey) phenocrysts in basalt from the Rhobell Volcanic Group, Rhobell Fawr, Gwynedd. Crossed polarized light. Photograph is 6 mm across. Reproduced from Kokelaar (1986), by permission of Oxford University Press.

Volcanic Complex, exposed near Dolgellau, in southern Snowdonia, however, are noticeably different, containing abundant phenocrysts of the amphibole pargasite (Fig. 5), and also of diopside (Kokelaar, 1986). These relate to the distinct composition of the magma parental to the Rhobell lavas. Basalts in the Fishguard area are pillowed as a result of eruption under the sea (Fig. 6). In this environment erupted magmas are quenched on coming into contact with the cold sea water, and crystals grow very rapidly. The chief result is production of the distinctive morphologies of quench crystals, with plagioclase crystals developing elongate and hollow shapes,

Figure 6. Pillowed basalts, erupted under the sea over 400 million years ago, exposed near Fishguard, Dyfed.

with characteristic 'swallow tail' terminations, while clinopyroxenes form dendritic crystals. In addition, the chemistry of the crystals, in particular the clinopyroxenes, is affected. Normally as a crystal grows it is selective about which elements it incorporates into it's structure. As a particular element is depleted from the area surrounding the growing crystal, so diffusion of that element into the area occurs. If growth is rapid, diffusion may be too slow to replace the appropriate elements and 'other' elements may be included into the crystal. The Fishguard lavas show anomalously high contents of Ti and Al, the former giving the crystals a pronounced purple colour in plane light under the microscope instead of their usual colourless character (Bevins, 1982).

Basic igneous rocks younger than Silurian age are rare in Wales. A diatreme pipe and related feeder dyke exposed near Usk (Boulton, 1911; Cox, 1954; Eyles and Blundell, 1957; Haslett, 1992) cuts through Devonian strata at the present level of erosion, but carries blocks of Carboniferous age; on this evidence, it is generally assumed that activity occurred during Carboniferous times. The dyke rock and pipe breccia contain a variety of mantle-derived ultramafic xenoliths, including magnesian peridotites, pyroxenites, and biotite-pyroxenites, as well as clinopyroxene and biotite megacrysts. The magnesian peridotites comprise forsteritic olivine (Fo_{90}), enstatite, emerald-green chrome diopside, chromite and spinel. Unfortunately, all the pyroxenites are heavily altered. Analysis indicates that the biotite is phlogopitic (D.T. Moffat, *personal communication*). The host dyke rock is basanite, which again is heavily altered; however interstitial areas contain analcime and

natrolite (Haslett, 1992), while thomsonite is recorded from vesicles (D.T. Moffat, *personal communication*).

Northwest-southeast trending Tertiary dolerite dykes cut through Carboniferous and older rocks across Snowdonia and Anglesey (Greenly, 1919; Williams, 1924; Williams, 1930), and can be traced offshore to the north-west of Anglesey by their aeromagnetic signature (Kirton and Donato, 1985; Lee *et al.*, 1990). Generally these dyke rocks are fresh, although some are intensely weathered, and show spectacular spheroidal patterns (Fig. 7). Williams (1924) described the olivine dolerite of the Marchlyn Mawr dyke, in Snowdonia and recorded the presence of olivine, plagioclase, augite and magnetite, along with analcime and thomsonite infilling vesicles. Later, Williams (1930) reported the presence of natrolite also as an infilling to vesicles in supposed Tertiary dykes in the same area.

At the opposite end of the compositional spectrum, acidic rocks do not show the same or indeed the range in mineralogy displayed by the basic rocks. This relates principally to the contrasting and more restricted range of chemical elements present in acidic magmas. Generally Si, Al, Na and K account for more than 95 wt% of the oxides present in such magmas, leading to a simple mineralogy, dominated by feldspar (either a sodic plagioclase or orthoclase, or both), quartz and mica (muscovite or biotite). In some cases, however, parental magmas with a slightly abnormal composition lead to variations in this restricted mineralogy, for example intrusions which crystallize from peralkaline magmas, characterized by unusually high contents of Na and K and relatively low contents of Al. In such cases non-

Figure 7. Spheroidal weathering pattern in a Tertiary dyke exposed near Bangor, Gwynedd.

aluminous alkaline minerals, such as aegerine and riebeckite, crystallize, as in the Mynydd Mawr Intrusion, in Snowdonia (Nockolds, 1938). Peralkaline magmas also contain high contents of incompatible elements such as Zr, as well as the halogens F and Cl. In the Mynydd Mawr Intrusion, high contents of F led to the presence of fluorite as inclusions in the riebeckite crystals. Other riebeckite-bearing acidic rocks are found in western Llŷn, for example at Mynytho Common (Croudace, 1982).

The Tan-y-Grisiau Microgranite Intrusion, exposed near Blaenau Ffestiniog, is also mineralogically distinct in that it contains allanite as an important accessory phase. In addition, allanite up to 10 mm long is found in veins or pipes cutting through the microgranite, associated with pyrophyllite and molybdenite (Bromley, 1964; Roberts, 1979).

Rhyolitic lavas (Fig. 8) and high-level rhyolitic intrusions are widely developed across Wales, but again show a rather monotonous assemblage of plagioclase and/or

Figure 8. Flow folded rhyolite of Ordovician age, Llanberis Pass, Gwynedd.

orthoclase (or another potassium feldspar), and quartz. Generally the lavas are peraluminous (high in Al), and mafic minerals are absent, although Williams (1922) reported the presence of almandine garnet in Ordovician lavas in the Capel Curig district. However, an interesting suite of accessory primary minerals is typically present, chiefly apatite, zircon, titanite and allanite (eg. Bevins, 1982), as well as rare monazite and xenotime.

Metamorphic rocks

Metamorphic rocks result from changes in temperature and pressure, which lead to the growth of new minerals in pre-existing rocks. The effects of significant increases in these parameters are usually very obvious; however, where the changes are only slight the effects are incipient, and often difficult to see without recourse to microscopic investigations.

Alteration of sedimentary rocks adjacent to igneous intrusions as a result of contact metamorphism is of restricted extent in Wales. This is partly because many of the sediments were unlithified at the time of magma intrusion, and heat was dissipated rapidly from the hot magmas into the plentiful water around. There are, however, exceptions; petrographic evidence indicates

that andalusite and cordierite developed in aluminium-rich rocks adjacent to the St. David's Head Intrusion (Roach, 1969) and the Tan-y-Grisiau Intrusion (Bromley, 1969), leading to the development of so-called spotted slates. However, subsequent low grade regional metamorphism has resulted in alteration of the contact minerals to aggregates of muscovite and chlorite. In the contact aureole of the St. David's Head Intrusion, spessartine garnet crystallized in manganese-rich mudstones, although this mineral is still present because it was stable at the temperatures and pressures of the later regional metamorphic event. An interesting contact metamorphic assemblage is developed in Ordovician mudstones at Blaen-y-nant, in Snowdonia, adjacent to the Bwlch y Cywion Intrusion. Williams (1930) described the development of a fine grained, dark green almandine-biotite-magnetite-topaz rock, apparently reflecting alteration of an 'arkosic' sandstone.

Tertiary dolerites exposed across Snowdonia and Anglesey generally show little contact effects. However, Henslow (1822) and Harker (1887) described the presence of grossular garnet and analcime in Carboniferous limestones adjacent to a dyke exposed at Plas Newydd, on Anglesey. Unfortunately, the dyke and it's contact rocks are no longer exposed.

The majority of Lower Palaeozoic rocks in Wales have been affected by low grade regional metamorphism, although effects are rarely seen in hand specimen. Following cooling and crystallization, the Precambrian and Lower Palaeozoic basic rocks of Wales suffered alteration and metamorphism. The effects of relatively high grade metamorphism, in excess of 400°C, are obvious, producing rocks with totally different mineral assemblages and commonly displaying a pronounced fabric. The lower temperature effects, up to about 350°C, however, are not so obvious, and are less pronounced in the field, although the original dark grey to black colour of the basalts and finer grained intrusives (dolerites) is replaced by a pervasive green colour due to the growth of abundant chlorite or chlorite-like minerals; hence these rocks are sometimes known as 'greenstones'. Although not usually visible to the naked eye, a range of new minerals accompanies the growth of chlorite, including prehnite (Fig. 9), pumpellyite (Fig. 10), actinolite (Fig. 11), ferro-actinolite, epidote (Fig. 12), titanite

Figure 9. Thin section of prehnite (coloured) in altered Ordovician dolerite from the St. David's Head Intrusion, Dyfed. Crossed polarized light. Photograph is 4 mm across.

Figure 10. Thin section of pumpellyite (coloured) in quartz, along with minor prehnite (top right), in altered Ordovician dolerite from the Fishguard area, Dyfed. Crossed polarized light. Photograph is 1.7 mm across.

titanite and stilpnomelane. Such minerals are widespread across Wales (Bevins and Rowbotham, 1983; Bevins and Robinson, 1993). Occasionally, veins carrying these minerals occur, as in the case of epidote at Marloes Bay, in Dyfed, while lavas containing prehnite and pumpellyite at Llanelwedd Quarry, Builth Wells are cut by veins which carry analcime, laumontite and saponite (Metcalfe, 1990), suggesting a late stage alteration episode in this area at very low temperatures. Very rarely, axinite is present in veins in Wales, such as at Carreg Ddu, near Porth Dinllaen, Llŷn, at Llanddwyn Bay, Anglesey (Greenly, 1919), at Garn Turne Rocks, south of Fishguard, and in the Penmaenmawr Intrusion,

near Conwy (Sargent, 1916, 1925).

Like the basic rocks, acidic rocks of Lower Palaeozoic age have been altered as a result of low grade metamorphism, although because of a lack of calcium, iron and magnesium, the range of secondary minerals is not

Figure 12. Thin section of epidote from Marloes Bay, Dyfed. Crossed polarized light. Photograph is 4 mm across.

extensive. Generally muscovite mica develops, in some cases to such an extent that the rocks become strongly foliated. In North Pembrokeshire, Ordovician rhyolites in the Treffgarne area have been intensely altered by hydrothermal fluids, leading to intense silicification and pyritization (Brown and others, 1987); the presence of minerals such as alunite, corundum and kaolinite suggest that the rhyolites also interacted with very acidic waters

Figure 11. Thin section of actinolite (blue rhombs) in altered Ordovician dolerite from the Cadair Idris area, Gwynedd. Crossed polarized light. Photograph is 1.7 mm across.

at some stage in their history. In North Wales, Howells *et al.* (1991) reported the presence of aeschynite, lanthanite-(Ce), larsenite-fayalite, monazite, parisite, synchysite, thorite, xenotime and gadolinite (or spencite) occurring as anhedral crystals and intergrowths in veins in rhyolitic rocks, a range of minerals which they considered to be of secondary, possibly hydrothermal origin.

Rocks showing the highest grades of metamorphism in Wales are exposed on Anglesey, and are of Precambrian age. The geology of this area is extremely complex, with rock units of contrasting lithology occurring adjacent to each other, separated by mylonitic fault zones. These tectonic contacts appear to separate several discrete terranes (Gibbons, 1983, 1987), which were brought into place in late Precambrian times as a result of lateral movements along the fault zones. A 5 km wide belt of blueschists, basalts and sediments affected by high pressure blueschist facies metamorphism in a subduction zone, is found in the southeastern part of Anglesey. The altered basalts contain amphiboles with green cores, falling in the barroisite-ferrobarroisite-winchite range, and blue rims, falling in the crossite-glaucophane-ferroglaucophane range (Gibbons and Gyopari, 1986). Minerals developed in associated sedimentary rocks include phengitic mica, lawsonite and spessartine garnet (Gibbons and Mann, 1983). Much of Central Anglesey comprises a unit known as the Coedana Complex. Of particular interest in the Coedana Complex is a sequence of rocks exposed in the Nebo Inlier, in the northeast of Anglesey. Here, calcium-rich sedimentary rocks have been converted at high temperatures to calc-silicate gneisses, containing the Mg-rich clinopyroxene diopside, grossular garnet and the Fe-rich clinopyroxene hedenbergite (Horák, 1993). In associated aluminium-rich sediments the Al_2SiO_5 polymorph sillimanite developed. In other parts of the Coedana Complex, basic igneous rocks have been converted to amphibolites as a result of the transformation of igneous pyroxenes to metamorphic amphiboles.

Finally, a suite of ultrabasic and basic intrusions and associated basic lavas belonging to the New Harbour Group, exposed on Holy Island and adjacent parts of Anglesey, have been metamorphosed and deformed, resulting in a range of metamorphic lithologies (Greenly, 1919; Maltman, 1977). The ultramafic rocks underwent serpentinization, resulting in the development of lizardite and antigorite, although primary diopside is preserved locally. The basic intrusions have been altered to rocks containing abundant epidote, tremolite and chlorite, while occasionally blades of apophyllite are present. Calcium metasomatism occurred locally, producing rodingites, with up to 50% grossular garnet. Associated rock types include chlorite-magnetite schists, tremolite schists, talc-brucite schists, and a peculiar rock dominated by the pyroxene diopside.

Sedimentary rocks

Sedimentary rocks are chiefly composed of pebbles, sand, silt and mud, derived from the erosion of pre-existing rocks, and transported by the agents of gravity, water, wind, and ice. Accordingly, their mineral constituents in the first instance relate to the source area, that is the nature of the pre-existing rocks which were being eroded. Softer materials are degraded during transport, and hence mature sediments, those which have been carried considerable distances, tend to be composed chiefly of harder minerals, such as quartz. In extreme cases, rocks are composed almost entirely of quartz grains, such as the Holyhead Quartzites, of Precambrian age, exposed on Anglesey. In Snowdonia, certain sandstone horizons in the Caradoc sequences contain a high proportion of magnetite, which is present in sufficient quantities to produce an aeromagnetic anomaly (Evans and Chacksfield, 1987). Other sandstones in Wales contain diverse suites of accessory minerals, such as the Denbigh Grits Group (Warren *et al.*, 1984), which contains zircon, tourmaline, apatite, brookite, rutile, titanite and garnet, while cordierite and corundum have been recorded from the highly micaceous Pennant sandstones of Carboniferous age in South Wales (Heard, 1922).

Following deposition of sediments, new minerals grow. In sands, minerals are precipitated from fluids circulating through pore spaces. In many cases silica is precipitated, while in some sands clay minerals, such as kaolinite, develop. Many sandstones of Carboniferous age in North Wales contain the clay mineral dickite (Brown and Smithson, 1953; Smithson, 1954; Smithson and Brown, 1957). This process of lithification is also known as diagenesis.

As sediments become buried more deeply they are subjected to increases in temperature and pressure, and further new minerals develop, passing with transition into the field of very low grade metamorphism. Quartz is a very stable mineral, and is unaffected by these low grade metamorphic effects. In contrast, finer grained sedimentary rocks, in particular mudstones, undergo considerable changes in respect of the contained clay minerals. Detailed investigations of changes in clay minerals in Lower Palaeozoic low grade metamorphosed mudstones in Wales have shown a change from regular mixed-layer illite/smectite at the lowest (diagenetic) grades, through a 1Md illite associated with the discrete paragonite at anchizonal grades, to a $2M_1$ illite with paragonite at the highest, so-called epizonal grades (Robinson and Bevins, 1986). Studies of low grade mudstones from Snowdonia and Llŷn, have revealed varied assemblages, containing a range of phases, including pyrophyllite, paragonite, chlorite, corrensite and rectorite (Merriman and Roberts, 1985). Locally, chloritoid is developed in Snowdonia (Brearley, 1988; Smith, 1988), while biotite is a component of fine grained metamorphosed mudstones and tuffaceous rocks in Snowdonia and the Harlech Dome area (de Béthune, 1972; Roberts 1981). Investigations of clay minerals in Upper Palaeozoic rocks in Wales include those by Robinson *et al.* (1980) for sequences in western Dyfed, and those by Gill *et al.* (1977) and White (1993) for the South Wales Coalfield region. Gill *et al.* (1977) reported the occurrence of pyrophyllite in association with illite/smectite in the western part of the South Wales Coalfield, where coals are anthracitic, while kaolinite along with illite/smectite is recorded from the eastern area of the coalfield, where coal ranks are lower. The Na-

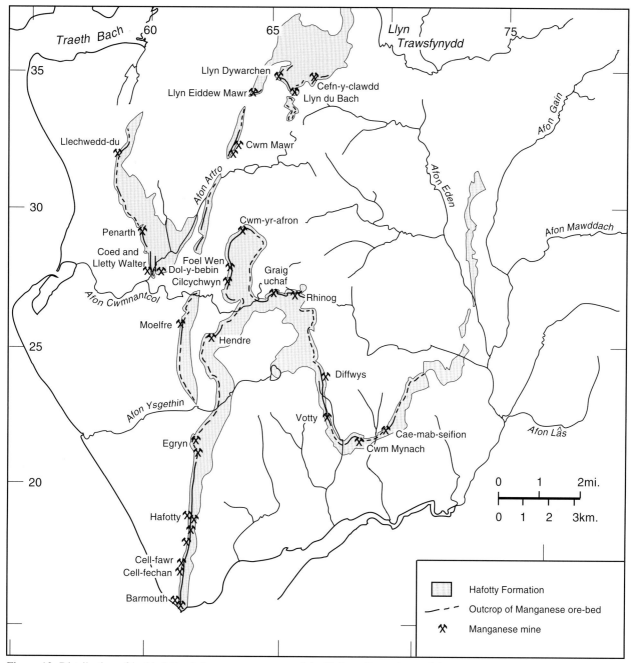

Figure 13. Distribution of bedded Cambrian manganese ore of the Hafotty Formation and former manganese mines in the Harlech Dome area of southern Snowdonia. Based on Down (1980) and Allen and Jackson (1985), by permission of the Director, British Geological Survey: NERC copyright reserved.

rich illite mineral brammallite was first described by Bannister (1943) from Llandebie, in the anthracite zone of the coalfield.

Other sedimentary rocks are formed by precipitation of calcium carbonate directly from warm, shallow sea waters. These rocks are limestones, and are composed chiefly of calcite. Typically, limestones comprise fine grained aggregates of calcite (micrite), and little crystalline material is observable to the naked eye. However, sometimes limestones contain cavities which show well-formed calcite crystals. Excellent scaleno-hedral calcite crystals are found in limestones of the South Wales area, for example at Taff's Well, north of Cardiff. Some of the Carboniferous limestones of Wales

possess cavities, generated as a result of volume reduction during dolomitization, and contain well-formed dolomite crystals, typically showing curved faces. Excellent dolomite crystals are found at the Great Ormes Head, Llandudno.

Certain horizons within the Lower Palaeozoic successions of Wales are characterized by marked increases in particular elements, especially manganese and iron, resulting in bedded ores of these minerals, which have in the past been exploited commercially.

In the Harlech Dome area in southern Snowdonia, and on the St. Tudwal's Peninsula, Llŷn, manganese enrichment is present in sedimentary rocks of Cambrian age (Woodland, 1939a, 1956; Mohr, 1964; de Béthune,

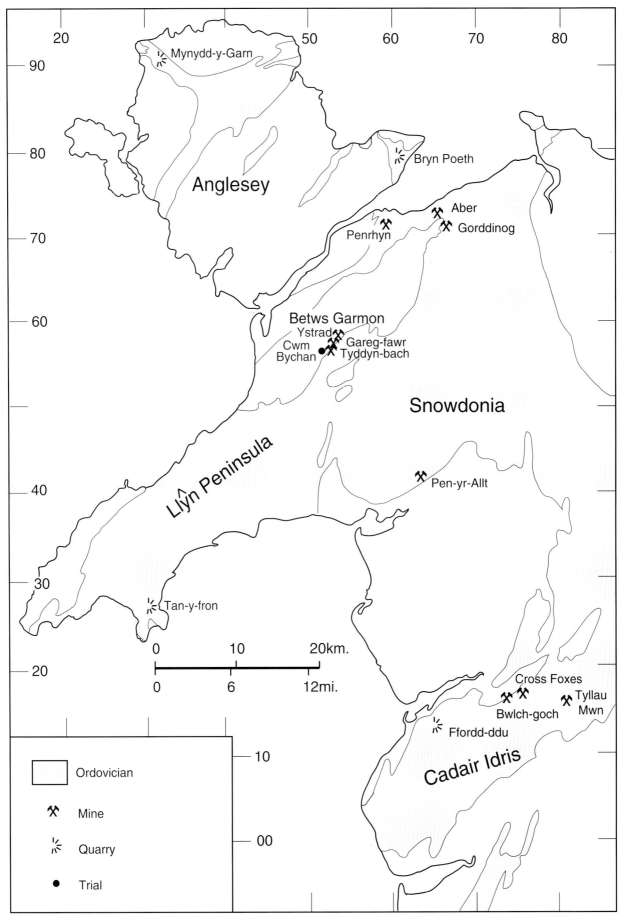

Figure 14. Distribution of former iron mines in North Wales working Ordovician oolitic ores. Based on Trythall (1988).

Figure 15. The opencast pit at Parys Mountain, Anglesey, the site of intensive copper extraction between 1750 and 1850.

1972; Glasby, 1974; Binstock, 1977; Bennett, 1987a, b). On the St. Tudwal's Peninsula, the matrix of a 5 m thick greywacke unit is composed largely of Ca-Mn-Fe-Mg carbonates, while in contrast manganese mineralization in the Harlech Dome occurs in the form of a discrete bed (Fig. 13), made up of alternating red laminated bands and yellow concretionary bands (Bennett, 1987a, b). The red bands are composed chiefly of spessartine and quartz, along with calcium-manganese carbonates (mainly kutnohorite, but also rhodochrosite), chlorite, magnetite, hematite, albite, ferropyrophanite, apatite, barite, and rare manganese-rich humite group minerals. The yellow concretions are made up almost entirely of manganese-rich carbonates (chiefly rhodochrosite), along with minor quartz and garnet. There has been considerable discussion concerning the origin of this mineralization. Woodland (1939a) and Mohr (1964) considered that the Harlech ores related to extreme weathering of volcanic rocks, while de Béthune (1972), Glasby (1974) and Binstock (1977) suggested that the ores were of diagenetic origin. Most recently, Bennett (1987 a, b) has argued that the manganese was most probably of submarine exhalative origin, deposited chiefly in oxide form, with later diagenetic remobilization to produce the variety of manganese carbonates. A range of minerals has been recorded from these bedded manganese ore deposits, including collophane, kutnohorite, manganhumite, pennantite, pyrophanite, parsettensite, rhodochrosite, rhodonite, scheelite, sonolite, spessartine, stilpnomelane and todorokite.

Oolitic ironstones of Ordovician age occur across North Wales. They are present as discontinuous, concordant lenses within fine grained shelf siliclastic sediments, and have been the subject of extensive studies (Strahan et al., 1920; Hallimond, 1924, 1925; Pulfrey, 1933; Weinberg, 1973; Trythall et al., 1987; Trythall, 1988, 1989; Young, 1989, 1991). The ironstones were mined chiefly during the 19th century, from numerous mines across North Wales, from Anglesey to Cadair Idris (Fig. 14). However, about one third of the ore was recovered from Betws Garmon, in northern Snowdonia. The ironstones are chiefly chamositic, although other minerals recorded include carbonate-fluorapatite, chlorite, hematite, magnetite, pyrite, quartz, siderite and stilpnomelane (see, for example, Matthews and Scoon, 1964).

Many fine grained sedimentary rocks in Wales contain high proportions of pyrite. For example, Cambrian sediments exposed at Penrhyn Quarry contain well formed pyrite crystals, while similar age pyritic mudstones are found in the Harlech Dome area (Woodland, 1938c). Further south, at Dolaucothi, in Dyfed, pyrite-rich sediments of late Ordovician to early Silurian age are auriferous, the gold occurring for the most part as inclusions in arsenopyrite and pyrite, as well as in quartz-carbonate veins cutting the sedimentary rocks. Annels and Roberts (1989) suggested that during the early stages of the Caledonian orogeny gold was leached from underlying basement igneous rocks by contemporary circulating fluids.

Mineralization

A variety of mineral deposits occurs in Wales. A number

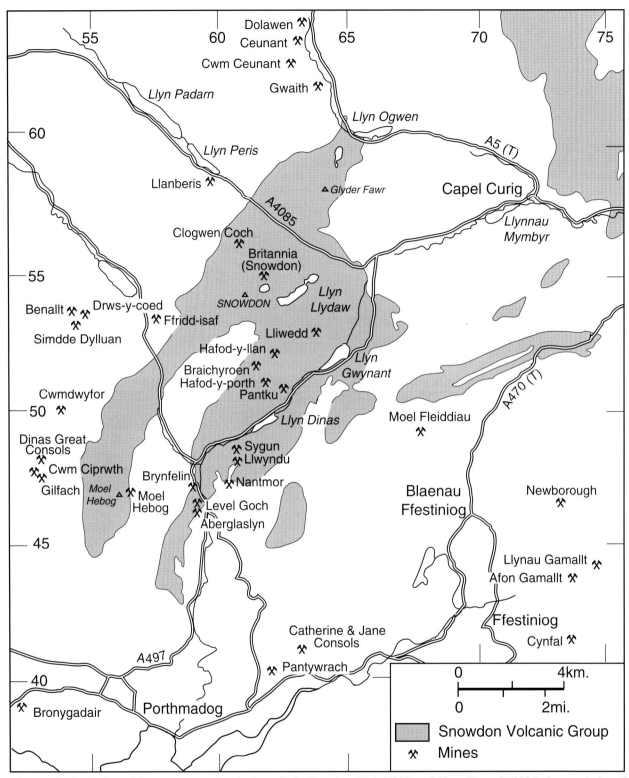

Figure 16. Distribution of former copper mines in Snowdonia. Based on Bick (1982) and Howells *et al.* (1991), by permission of the Director, British Geological Survey: NERC copyright reserved.

are intimately associated with igneous rocks, in particular with volcanic and high-level intrusive rocks. The Parys Mountain deposit, on Anglesey (Fig. 15), is composed principally of massive ore of galena, sphalerite and chalcopyrite and is thought to result from the exhalation of hot mineralizing fluids into the sea during Ordovician times (Pointon and Ixer, 1980), probably in the form of black smokers. Sulphide

minerals were precipitated from the fluids as a result of the dramatic changes in temperature and pH. The sulphide minerals accumulated on the sea-floor, to produce a massive ore body broadly condordant with the associated sediments. The mineral fluids were thought to be derived from sea water circulating through the underlying rocks, being heated by volcanic activity. Such ore bodies are known as volcanogenic massive sulphide

(VMS) deposits. Silica-rich mineralized rocks, making up the so-called White Rock, associated with the Parys Mountain mineral deposit are thought to be siliceous sinter deposits (Pointon and Ixer, 1980), although alternatively Nutt *et al.* (1979) considered them to relate to late-stage epithermal veining. Copper was extensively expoited at Parys Mountain from around 1750. At that time a thick alteration capping, known as gossan, occurred over the site of the present-day opencast pit (Lentin, 1800). This gossan was particularly rich in the sulphate of lead, originally called 'vitriol de plomb' (see Monnet 1779), but later named anglesite, after the locality (Beudant, 1832). Excellent specimens are preserved in the Mineral Collection of the National Museum of Wales. Although galena, sphalerite and chalcopyrite are the chief sulphide minerals, various studies have identified the presence of other metallic minerals, including arsenopyrite, bismuthinite, bournonite, galenobismutite, gold, jordanite, kobellite, native bismuth, pyrite, pyrrhotite, tennantite and tetrahedrite (Thanasuthipitak, 1974; Sivaprakash 1977; Pointon and Ixer, 1980). Alteration of these minerals has led to a variety of secondary minerals in addition to anglesite, including chalcocite, clinoclase, covellite, cuprite, native copper and tenorite, while various iron-bearing sulphate minerals, such as halotrichite, hydronium jarosite, jarosite and melanterite, have been deposited on the walls in various levels and adits (D.A. Jenkins, *personal communication*). These relate to the breakdown of sulphide minerals, in particular pyrite. Additional reports of the Parys Mountain mineral deposit include those by Wheatley (1971), Southwood (1982, 1984) and Westhead (1993).

In central Snowdonia, sulphide mineralization is intimately associated with Ordovician volcanic rocks, occurring mainly in NE-SW oriented veins along the axis of an apical graben within a caldera which developed during Caradoc times (Reedman *et al.*, 1985). Veins in this area were worked from a number of mines including

the Britannia, Sygun, Lliwedd, and Hafod-y-Llan Mines (Fig. 16). Reedman *et al.* (1985) reported five ore-bearing assemblages, which variably comprise chalcopyrite, sphalerite, galena, pyrite, pyrrhotite, marcasite, hematite, magnetite, quartz and calcite. Mineralization is thought to have related to intense hydrothermal activity, with heat from the magmatic system driving a convection system (Fig. 17). Incorporated metals were most probably leached from the underlying volcanic succession. Alteration of the primary minerals has led to a host of secondary minerals (Bevins *et al.*, 1985; Pollard *et al.*, 1989), including malachite, brochantite, posnjakite, georgeite, chalcoalumite and carbonatian connellite, while Britannia Mine is the type locality for lanthanite-(Ce). Outside of the apical graben area, lead-zinc-copper mineralization is recognised at a number of other old mines, including Drws-y-Coed, in the Nantlle Valley, Ceunant and Gwaith, in Nant Ffrancon, Tal-y-sarn, near Llanllyfni, and Coed-y-Dinas, near Bethesda. In the Nantlle Valley, east-west trending veins cut Cambrian and Ordovician sedimentary rocks. The veins carry chalcopyrite, sphalerite, galena, pyrrhotite, arsenopyrite and rare millerite, while secondary minerals reported from this area include langite, malachite, wroewolfeite and so-called woodwardite (recently identified as the Cu-analogue of glaucocerinite).

In northern Snowdonia, antimony-bearing mineral veins exposed at Deganwy cut through Ordovician silicic volcanic rocks, and are probably volcanogenic in nature. Russell (1944) reported stibnite, jamesonite, semseyite, bindheimite and stibiconite from this mine, while more recently, Bevins *et al.* (1988) also described the presence of boulangerite, plagionite, robinsonite, zinkenite, and probable kermesite.

Further east, a massive pyrite mineral deposit occurs at Cae Coch, near Trefriw, considered by Ball and Bland (1985) to be a Kuroko-type ore body, formed by exhalation of metal-rich brines onto the sea-floor, the heat to drive the convection system being supplied by associated, high-level magmas. Pyrite tubes, 5-10 mm across, occurring 0.5 m below the top of the ore body, are thought to represent fossilized 'black smokers' (Howells *et al.*, 1991). Recently, however, Bottrell and Morton (1992) have questioned this interpretation, suggesting, on the basis of isotopic investigations, that the deposit is of syn-diagenetic inhalative origin. Also of interest at Cae Coch are the copious amounts of iron sulphate minerals precipitated on the mine walls and floor, dominated by jarosite, fibroferrite, melanterite and copiapite (Jenkins and Johnson, 1993). The highly acidic environment in the mine has resulted in a remarkable microbiology (Johnson *et al.*, 1979).

Another mineral deposit intimately associated with Ordovician volcanic activity occurs in southern Snowdonia, in the Coed-y-Brenin area, north of Dolgellau (Fig. 18). Here, copper, in the form of chalcopyrite, along with molybdenite, occurs disseminated in dioritic rocks associated with lavas of the Rhobell Volcanic Group (Rice and Sharp, 1976). Such ore bodies are known as porphyry-copper deposits. It has been estimated that the deposit contains up to 200 million tons of ore at 0.3% copper (O. Miller, *personal*

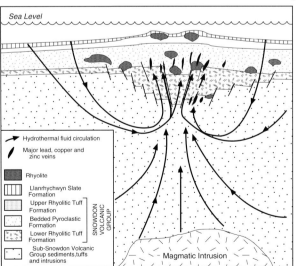

Sea Level

Hydrothermal fluid circulation

Major lead, copper and zinc veins

Rhyolite

Llanrhychwyn Slate Formation

Upper Rhyolitic Tuff Formation

Bedded Pyroclastic Formation

Lower Rhyolitic Tuff Formation

SNOWDON VOLCANIC GROUP

Sub-Snowdon Volcanic Group sediments,tuffs and intrusions

Magmatic Intrusion

Figure 17. Schematic representation of the Ordovician hydrothermal system in Snowdonia which gave rise to the copper-bearing mineral veins, showing its relationship to the rocks of the Snowdon Volcanic Group. Adapted with permission of the Geological Society of London from Reedman *et al.* (1985).

Figure 18. The Coed-y-Brenin area north of Dolgellau, the site of a disseminated copper deposit containing up to 200 million tons at 0.3% copper.

communication). The sulphide minerals most probably precipitated from the island arc-type magmas, while later mineralization in veins carrying gold, silver and antimony was probably related to an epithermal hydrothermal system (O. Miller, *personal communication*), in which meteoric (ground) waters circulated through the volcanic pile, leaching elements from one area, concentrating them in the fluid, and depositing them in hydraulic fractures. Of particular interest in the Coed-y-Brenin area, and intimately associated with the porphyry-copper deposit, is the so-called 'Turf Copper' (Rice and Sharp, 1976). This is a peat deposit heavily impregnated with native copper and various copper sulphates derived from the adjacent volcanic rocks. In the early part of the 19th century, peat cut from this area was burnt, and the copper extracted, before being sent for processing in smelters at Swansea (see Allen and Jackson, 1985).

On Llŷn, important manganese deposits occur near Rhiw (Fig. 19), where ore was recovered from the Nant and Benallt Mines (Dewey and Dines, 1923; Groves, 1947, 1952; Woodland, 1956; Down, 1980). Ore was mined from the Nant Mine in the period 1902-1925, and at Benallt at various times in the period 1886-1928, although during the Second World War, Benallt was worked once again for a short period. The ore occurs as a series of elongate lenses lying within the Ordovician mudstones and associated with basic lavas and sills. Important studies of the minerals and mineralization from these deposits include those by Russell (1911), Hey (1932), Woodland (1939b), Spencer (1942), Campbell

Smith *et al.* (1944a, b), Campbell Smith (1945), Campbell Smith *et al.* (1946), Campbell Smith and Claringbull (1947), Campbell Smith (1948), Campbell Smith *et al.* (1949), Bannister *et al.* (1955), Smith and Frondel (1968), and Peacor *et al.* (1974). These studies identified a number of new minerals, including banalsite, bannisterite, cymrite and pennantite. A more recent review, by Brown and Evans (1989), concluded that the ore was related to the submarine exhalation of manganese-rich fluids into the sea during Ordovician

Table 3. *Rarer minerals reported from the Benallt and Nant Mines, Llŷn*

Alleghanyite	Manganosite
Analcime	Natrolite
Banalsite	Neotocite
Bannisterite	Paracelsian
Bementite	Paragonite
Birnessite	Pennantite
Bixbyite	Piemontite
Braunite	Pyrochroite
Celsian	Pyrolusite
Collophane	Pyrophanite
Cymrite	Rhodochrosite
Ganophyllite	Rhodonite
Harmotome	Romanèchite
Hausmannite	Spessartine
Hematite	Strontianite
Jacobsite	Tephroite
Manganite	

times. Less common minerals known to occur at the Benallt and Nant Mines are listed in Table 3.

Minerals occurring in veins are relatively widespread in Wales, cutting through rocks ranging from Precambrian to Jurassic age. The majority, however, are found in rocks of Lower Palaeozoic and Upper Palaeozoic age.

Minerals veins cutting Precambrian rocks are relatively rare in Wales. On Anglesey, chalcopyrite and various secondary minerals occur in a mineralized fault at Pant-y-Gaseg, near Amlwch (Greenly, 1919). This is the locality from where the kaolinite-serpentine group mineral dickite was first described (Ross and Kerr, 1930).

In southern Snowdonia, gold occurs in mineral veins cutting through sedimentary rocks of Cambrian age, in the so-called Dolgellau Gold Belt. The first published account of gold in this area was as late as 1844 (see Dean, 1845), although there are earlier records of gold in

the area. Hall (1975) noted that gold was worked by the Romans, while a painting in the Welsh Industrial and Maritime Museum depicts gold panning in the Afon Mawddach around 1795. At the peak of production, between 1900-1905, over 20 mines were operative (Fig. 20). Gold mineralization occurs in steeply-dipping quartz veins which typically trend NE-SW (between 030-060°). Gold is concentrated where the veins cut through black shales of the Clogau Formation. A variation in the sulphide mineralogy of the gold-bearing veins occurs across the gold belt region. Gilbey (1968) reported that in the southwest of the area the veins are dominated by pyrrhotite-chalcopyrite-pyrite-arsenopyrite/cobaltite, while in the northeast they are characterised by assemblages dominated by pyrite-sphalerite-galena. In addition towards the southwest the veins also carry a range of bismuth and tellurium-bearing minerals. Recent studies of the gold-belt mineralization include those by Gilbey (1968), Bottrell (1986), Naden (1988), Bottrell and Spiro

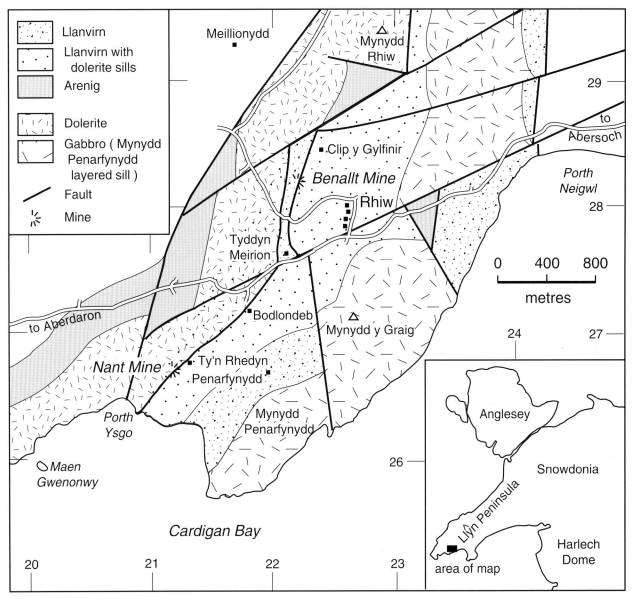

Figure 19. The location of important manganese mineralization at the Nant and Benallt Mines, on Llŷn. Based on the British Geological Survey 1:10 000 series Sheet SH22NW, Rhiw, by permission of the Director, British Geological Survey: NERC copyright reserved.

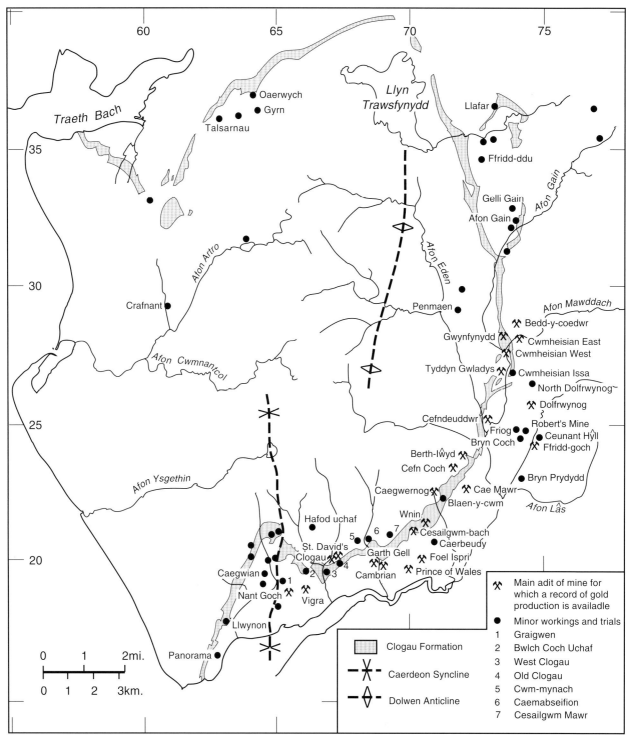

Figure 20. Distribution of former gold mines in the Dolgellau Gold Belt, showing the close relationship with black shales of the Cambrian Clogau Formation. Based on the British Geological Survey 1:50 000 series Sheet 135, Harlech, by permission of the Director, British Geological Survey: NERC copyright reserved.

(1988), Bottrell *et al.* (1988), Bottrell and Miller (1990), Bottrell *et al.* (1990), and Bevins and Stanley (1990), while Shepherd and Bottrell (1993) provided a thorough review of the mineralization. Current concensus is that gold mineralization occurred as a result of dewatering of underlying Precambrian and Cambrian strata during uplift in end Silurian times. As the fluids rose along NE-SW oriented faults, quartz was deposited into open fractures. Where the fluids reached the graphitic Clogau shales, methane and nitrogen were taken into the fluid,

which led to deposition of the gold. A wide range of minerals is recorded from this area, including the primary ore and related minerals, a variety of secondary minerals which developed as a result of alteration of the various primary minerals and which crystallized *in situ* on the mine walls and on the spoil heaps, and finally minerals occurring as detrital grains in the rivers of the district. A list of these minerals is presented in Table 4, drawn principally from the works quoted above, as well as earlier studies by Readwin (1860, 1862, 1864, 1888),

Table 4. Rarer minerals recorded from the Dolgellau Gold Belt

Acanthite	Mackinawite
Aleksite	Matildite
Altaite	Mimetite
Arsenopyrite	Molybdenite
Bismuth	Nagyagite
Bismuthinite	Osmium
Boulangerite	Pentlandite
Bournonite	Pickeringite
Calaverite	Pilsenite
Cobaltite	Platinum
Covellite	Polybasite
Cubanite	Pyrargyrite
Electrum	Pyromorphite
Erythrite	Pyrrhotite
Freibergite	Rhodochrosite
Goethite	Rhodonite
Gold	Tetrahedrite
Halotrichite	Ullmannite
Hedleyite	Vanadinite
Hessite	Wroewolfeite
Iridium	

Smyth (1862), Forbes (1867), and Andrew (1910).

Across much of Wales, Ordovician and Silurian sedimentary rocks host lead, zinc and copper sulphide vein mineralization. In eastern Snowdonia, such mineralization occurs in the Llanrwst district, where ores were

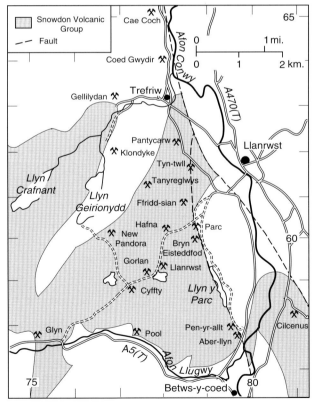

Figure 21. Distribution of old metal mines in the Llanrwst district of eastern Snowdonia. Based on Dewey and Smith (1922) with geology from Howells *et al.* (1991), by permission of the Director, British Geological Survey: NERC copyright reserved.

worked from mines such as Parc, Cyffty, Hafna, Llanrwst, Aberllyn, Gorlan, and Welsh Foxdale (New Pandora), and Trecastell, further to the north (Fig. 21). The principal ore minerals worked at these mines were galena and sphalerite, with minor chalcopyrite, accompanied by marcasite, pyrite and quartz. A range of secondary minerals developed subsequently on the mine walls and floors, as well as on the mine dumps, including allophane, anglesite, cerussite, dundasite, hydrozincite, and namuwite (Prior, 1906; Russell, 1944; Alwan and Williams, 1979; Bevins *et al.*, 1982 a, b).

A small number of mines worked lead from veins in the Denbigh Moors area of Clwyd, for example at Llanfair Talhaiarn, south of Abergele. To the east, at the Pennant Mine, near St. Asaph, galena and sphalerite are associated with a gangue of barite and witherite (Carruthers *et al.*, 1915).

Further to the south, lead-zinc mineral veins occur in the Llangynog district of Powys, where ore has been recovered from about 12 mines, including the Cwm Orog, Craig Rhiwarth, Ochr Graig, Craig-y-Mwyn and Llangynog Mines (Fig. 22). Associated with galena, sphalerite and minor chalcopyrite are gangue barite and witherite (Carruthers *et al.*, 1915) and secondary minerals such as aurichalcite, hemimorphite, pyromorphite, and smithsonite. Harmotome is also recorded from these mines.

Across much of North Wales, and locally in Central Wales, Lower Palaeozoic rocks are cut by Alpine-type mineral veins, dominated by quartz, but also variably carrying albite, anatase, apatite, brookite, monazite, rutile, synchysite-(Ce) and xenotime-(Y). Notable occurrences include Fron Oleu near Tremadog, Arenig Station Quarry near Arenig, Manod Quarry at Blaenau Ffestiniog, Minffordd Quarry near Porthmadog, Hendre Quarry near Glyn Ceiriog, and further south at Brynyrafr Mine, near Llanidloes.

In Central Wales, eastnortheast-westsouthwest orientated fault-related sulphide-bearing mineral veins cut through Ordovician and Silurian sedimentary rocks in the Central Wales Mining District (Jones, 1922; Raybould, 1976). Lead, zinc and copper were worked from over 50 different veins, at over 130 mines (Fig. 23). Exploitation of these mineral veins has a long history, dating back to Bronze Age times at Cwmystwyth (Fig. 24). The principal sulphide minerals are galena, sphalerite and chalcopyrite, associated with pyrite, and more locally marcasite, and gangue quartz and ankerite. In addition, numerous accessory sulphide minerals are present, along with a wide range of secondary phases, listed in Table 5. Accounts describing various aspects of these secondary minerals include those by Jones and Moreton (1977), Braithwaite (1982a, b), Jones (1987), Rust and Rust (1987), and Rust and Mason (1988). In the eastern part of the Central Wales Mining District, northwest of Llanidloes, the mineral veins are characterized by the presence of barite, witherite and harmotome. Carruthers *et al.* (1915) reported barite or witherite (or both) at the Aberdaunant, Bryntail, Gorn and Pen-y-Clun Mines. Multiple episodes of mineralization are indicated by later mineral veins carrying breccias composed of earlier mineralized veins, as well as by contrasting parageneses. Recent lead isotope modelling has indicated two

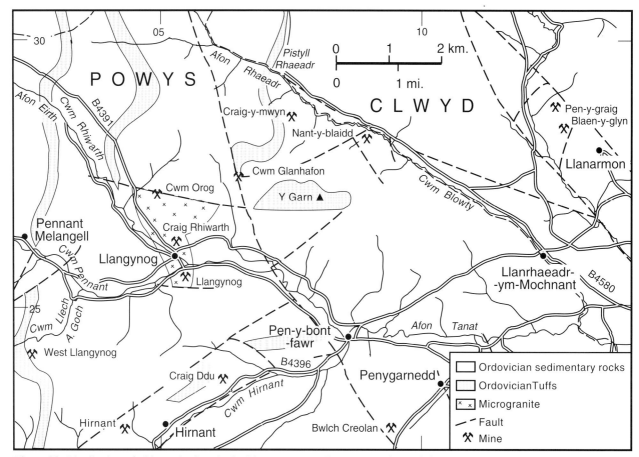

Figure 22. Distribution of old metal mines in the Llangynog area, Powys. Based on Williams (1985) and British Geological Survey 1:250 000 series Sheet 52°N-04°W, Mid-Wales and Marches, by permission of the Director, British Geological Survey: NERC copyright reserved.

Table 5. Rarer minerals recorded from the Central Wales Mining District

Agardite-(Y)	Chrysocolla	Hydrocerussite	Ramsbeckite
Anglesite	Cinnabar	Hydrozincite	Rosasite
Antigorite	Cobaltite	Ktenasite	Schmiederite
Apatite	Cobalt pentlandite	Langite	Schulenbergite
Aragonite	Connellite	Lautenthalite	Serpierite
Arsenopyrite	Copper	Leadhillite	Siegenite
Aurichalcite	Covellite	Linarite	Smithsonite
Azurite	Cuprite	Litharge	Susannite
Beaverite	Descloizite	Malachite	Tenorite
Beudantite	Devilline	Matheddleite	Tetrahedrite
Bindheimite	Dickite	Millerite	Tucekite
Bornite	Dundasite	Mimetite	Tyrolite
Bottinoite	Electrum	Olivenite	Ullmannite
Boulangerite	Elyite	Parnauite	Witherite
Bournonite	Erythrite	Pharmacosiderite	Woodwardite
Brochantite	Freibergite	Phlogopite	Wroewolfeite
Caledonite	Gold	Plumbojarosite	Wulfenite
Cerussite	Greenockite	Posnjakite	
Chalcocite	Harmotome	Pyromorphite	
Chalcophyllite	Hemimorphite	Pyrrhotite	

episodes of mineralization, at 390 Ma and from 360 to 330 Ma (Fletcher *et al.*, 1993). J.S. Mason (*personal communication*) identified an 'Early Complex' paragenesis and a 'Late Simple' paragenesis, which could correlate with the two events indicated by isotope modelling.

South of the Central Wales Mining District, lead-bearing mineral veins cutting through Lower Palaeozoic strata occur in the Rhandirmwyn area, as well as near Carmarthen, and also further west at Llanfyrnach. At the Vale of Towy (Nant) and Cystanog Mines, near Carmarthen, galena and sphalerite are the principal sulphide minerals, occurring with gangue barite (Carruthers *et al.*, 1915), while secondary minerals recorded include brochantite, cerussite, linarite, malachite and pyromorphite.

Lead, zinc and copper-bearing mineral veins cutting through Carboniferous rocks are found in both North and South Wales. The so-called Northeast Wales Orefield stretches from Prestatyn in the north to the Llanelidan Fault in the south, with extensions across to Great Orme in the northwest, and to Minera, and eventually Llanymynech, in the south (Fig. 25). Mineralization is hosted chiefly by Carboniferous Limestone. The principal mining areas were in the Holywell-Halkyn-Maeshafn and the Minera districts. It is thought that the ore fluids were connate brines expelled from adjacent sedimentary basins (Irish Sea and Cheshire Basins) during Variscan times (see Ixer and Vaughan, 1993). The chief sulphide minerals are galena and sphalerite, while chalcopyrite is abundant locally, as at mines at the Great Ormes Head, Llandudno (Fig. 26), from where copper has been extracted since Bronze Age times (see Lewis,

1990). A range of gangue and secondary minerals have been reported from this area. In the Halkyn area, fluorite is an important gangue mineral (Smith, 1973), while cerussite, hemimorphite, phosgenite, pyromorphite and smithsonite are found as secondary minerals. At the Great Orme, a diverse mineral assemblage has been identified, including, in addition to chalcopyrite, azurite, chalcocite, cuprite, digenite, djurleite, erythrite, goethite, malachite, native copper, nickeline, olivenite, spionkopite and tenorite (Vivian, 1859; Jenkins and Johnson, 1993; R.A. Ixer, *personal communication*). Hydrocarbon minerals are recorded at the Great Orme, intimately associated with annabergite, gersdorffite and uraninite (P. Eakin, personal communication; Parnell, 1988). Uraniferous hydrocarbons hosted by Carboniferous Limestone are found at numerous other localities in North Wales, including Minera, Llandulas, Halkyn, and Llanarmon (Parnell, 1988; Eakin, 1989; Eakin and Gize, 1992). In the Llanymynech district, near Oswestry, secondary minerals reported include aurichalcite, azurite, malachite and rhodochrosite.

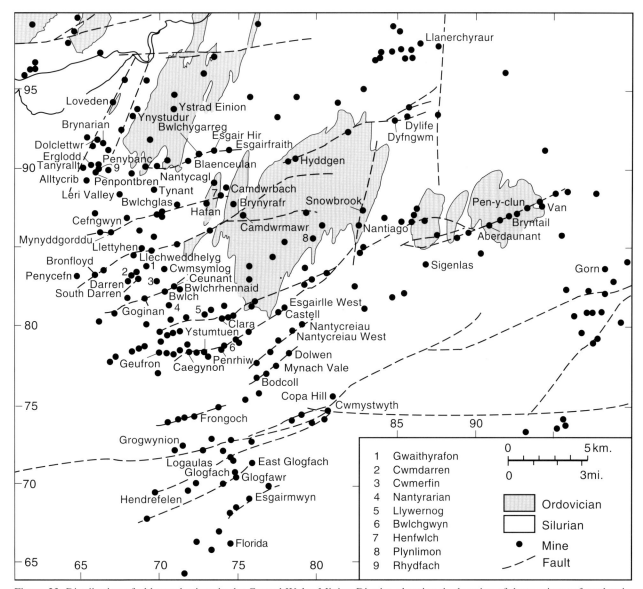

Figure 23. Distribution of old metal mines in the Central Wales Mining District, showing the location of those mines referred to in the text. Based on Ball and Nutt (1976), by permission of the Director, British Geological Survey: NERC copyright reserved.

Figure 24. Cwmystwyth Mine, in the Central Wales Mining District, the site of copper mining since Bronze Age times.

In South Wales, galena, sphalerite and chalcopyrite occur in veins in Carboniferous Limestone exposed on the south crop of the coalfield region. Gangue minerals include calcite and barite, while secondary minerals recorded to date are anglesite, aurichalcite, bindheimite, hemimorphite, malachite, rosasite, and smithsonite. Locally, fluorite is found, for example at Risca, as well as on the north crop of the coalfield, at Vaynor. Further west, chalcopyrite, along with malachite, is found in veins in Carboniferous Limestone at Mynydd-y-Garreg, northeast of Kidwelly. Galena from these mineral veins give Triassic and Jurassic model ages (Fletcher *et al.*, 1993), and it is likely that they pass upwards into the more disseminated mineralization seen in Triassic and Jurassic rocks in the Vale of Glamorgan (see below). In contrast to the vein mineralization cutting the Carboniferous strata of South Wales, sulphide minerals, including millerite, galena, sphalerite, chalcopyrite, pyrrhotite and siegenite occur in clay ironstone nodules in shales of Coal Measures age (North and Howarth, 1928; Bevins and Horák, 1985). The nodules are lined with siderite, and are also notable for containing the organic compound hattchetine. In fractures in the shales themselves, and particularly on the walls of coal mines, occur a range of minerals, including amesite, aragonite, epsomite, melanterite, nacrite and szomolnokite, which mostly relate to the circulation of acid waters resulting from the breakdown of pyrite in the shales. Of particular interest is the recent report of colloform gold in cleats (fractures) in coal-bearing strata of the western part of the South Wales Coalfield (Gayer and Rickard, 1993).

Also along the south crop of the South Wales

Coalfield occur several bodies of hematite-goethite, hosted by Carboniferous Limestone. These were formerly worked from the Garth, Llanharry, Mwyndy, Bute and Trecastle Mines (Sibly, 1919; Sibly and Lloyd 1927). The iron mineralization occurs in part as conformable units and in part as bodies crosscutting the shallow-dipping limestones. On the basis of a fluid inclusion investigation, Rankin and Criddle (1985) concluded that the mineralizing fluids were composite in nature, resulting from mixing of descending ground-waters, enriched in iron as a result of leaching of the overlying Triassic beds, with fluids derived from the adjacent Coal Measures basin. Apparently, the fluids were channelled along Hercynian faults during late Triassic times.

Further west, at Tŷ Coch, near Porthcawl, goethite occurs associated with various manganese minerals in an ore body at the Carboniferous Limestone/Triassic boundary (Watson, 1859; Vivian, 1885). Criddle and Symes (1977) reported a range of minerals from this locality, including braunite, hausmannite, pyrobelonite, romanèchite, palygorskite and vanadinite, while more recently Braithwaite and Lamb (1986) recorded the presence of wulfenite at Tŷ Coch.

Triassic rocks in South Wales show evidence of mineralization, with galena, sphalerite, pyrite and rare chalcopyrite occurring in thin (up to 8 cm) joints or faults cutting through rocks of the Dolomitic Conglomerate unit (Bowler and Kingston, 1971). Gangue minerals include calcite, witherite, dolomite and barite, while secondary oxidation minerals present include covellite, chalcocite, anglesite, cerussite,

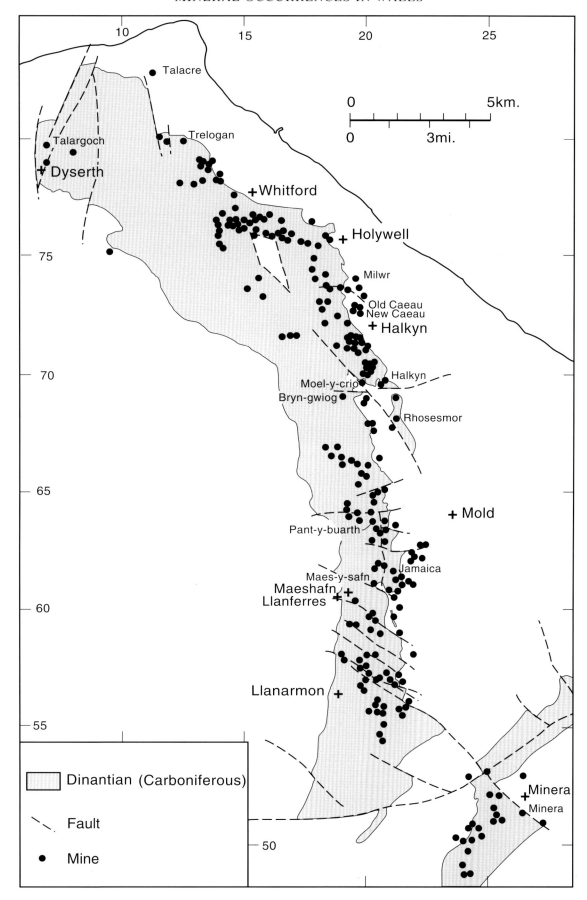

Figure 25. Distribution of old metal mines in northeast Wales. Based on Lewis (1967) and British Geological Survey 1:250 000 series Sheet 53°N-04°W, Liverpool Bay, by permission of the Director, British Geological Survey: NERC copyright reserved.

Figure 26. Great Ormes Head, Gwynedd, the site of copper extraction since Bronze Age times.

digenite, cuprite, native copper, malachite, goethite, limonite, and smithsonite. Dolomite-lined geodes in the conglomerates, which may be up to 30 cm across, contain coarsely crystalline calcite and witherite. Recently, Alabaster (1990) reported alstonite both as a component of the gangue mineralization and also in the geodes. Commonly, the alstonite is partly altered to aragonite. On isotopic evidence Fletcher *et al.* (1993) considered this mineralization to be related to a major mineralizing event between 240 Ma and 200 Ma (ie mid Trias to early Jurassic), which is manifest as discrete veins in the underlying Carboniferous Limestone.

The youngest rocks in Wales to show evidence of mineralization are of Jurassic age, exposed in South Wales. Disseminated galena occurs as a cement in conglomerates and sandstones at scattered localities in the neighbourhood of Bridgend, having been exploited from a number of mines, the most notable being Llangan. Fletcher (1988) described disseminated galena mineral-ization in cavities in basal Liassic breccias at Ogmore-by-Sea, which he considered to be of exhalative origin, the mineralizing fluids being exhaled into Liassic sediments while they were only semilithified. Fletcher *et al.* (1993) obtained an age for this mineralization on isotopic evidence from galena in early Jurassic strata at nearby Southerndown. The age determined is broadly equivalent to the age of the host sediments, supporting the field evidence for contemporary sedimentation and exhalation for metal-rich fluids in early Jurassic times.

Minerals in superficial deposits

Minerals are also found as components of the superficial deposits, that is those deposits which occur as unconsoli-dated or poorly consolidated blankets over the Earth's solid rocks. Such deposits include the ubiquitous soils, glacial clays, sands, and gravels, and the sediments found in rivers.

Soils are typically composed of a variety of clay minerals and quartz, but also commonly contain so-called 'heavy minerals'. Jenkins (1964), for example, reported the presence of anatase, rutile, titanite, zircon, tourmaline, garnet, zoisite, clinozoiste, epidote, augite, various amphiboles, chlorite-type minerals, magnetite, and ilmenite in soils overlying various igneous rocks in Snowdonia. Jenkins and Ball (1964) described the presence of pumpellyite in Snowdonian soils in more detail.

Glacial deposits sometimes have quite varied mineral assemblages, depending on the nature of the rocks in the source area. In Wales, exotic mineral assemblages are considered characteristic of the so-called 'Irish Sea Drift', deposits carried into the area during Pleistocene times from the Irish Sea region, but with original source areas most probably much farther afield. For example, Griffiths and Stuart (1940) reported a range of minerals in sandy boulder clay of Irish Sea origin at Ludchurch, Dyfed, including diaspore, kyanite, staurolite, andalusite and zircon. Other reports of the mineralogy of glacial deposits in Wales include those by Strahan *et al.* (1909), Thomas (1909b), and Griffiths (1939).

River sands and gravels, like those of glacial origin,

have mineral suites related to the nature of the rocks being eroded in the source area. In rivers, however, dense grains tend to be concentrated in sediments deposited in low energy environments, such as the inside of river meanders, or in estuary regions. In some cases, sufficient concentrations of valuable minerals occur to give rise to 'placer' mineral deposits. In Wales, gold in the sediments of the Afon Mawddach and the Mawddach Estuary provides a classic example of such a placer mineral; and infact, there was a recent proposal to dredge the estuary sediments for their contained gold. Readwin (1888) also recorded the presence of platinum, iridosmine (= osmium) and platiniridium (= platian iridium) from the Afon Mawddach. Interesting occurrences of detrital monazite in stream sediments from a number of areas in Wales, including the Harlech Dome, Berwyn Dome and the Central Wales region, were described by Cooper et al. (1983), who attributed its presence to erosion of underlying Lower Palaeozoic mudstones and siltstones containing diagenetic monazite nodules.

THE MINERALS

Acanthite   Monoclinic
Ag_2S

A rare silver sulphide mineral, dimorphous with argentite. Acanthite occurs in hydrothermal veins, usually in association with other silver-bearing minerals and also in zones of secondary enrichment.

Pryor (1988) has provided the only report of acanthite in Wales to date, describing its occurrence along with sylvanite replacing chalcopyrite and pyrrhotite in a late stage low temperature assemblage at Gwynfynydd Mine, near Dolgellau, Gwynedd.

Actinolite   Monoclinic
$Ca_2(Mg,Fe+^2)_5Si_8O_{22}(OH)_2$

A calcium magnesium iron silicate hydroxide. A member of the amphibole group which forms a series with tremolite and ferro-actinolite. Actinolite typically develops in metamorphosed basic igneous rocks which have been subjected to the effects of low to medium grade (greenschist facies) metamorphism.

In Wales actinolite is widely developed in altered basic igneous rocks, although typically it is seen only on a microscopic scale. Early reports include those by Greenly (1919) from Anglesey, and Williams (1922) from Snowdonia, while Cox and Wells (1920) reported 'wisps of hornblende' (now identified as actinolite) in dolerites from the Cadair Idris region. More recently Bevins and Rowbotham (1983) reported that actinolite occurs in metabasites in the Mynydd Preseli district of Dyfed, and in the Aran Mountains, in addition to the Cadair Idris and central and southern Snowdonia districts, in Gwynedd. It occurs as a groundmass mineral, most commonly as small needles overprinting chlorite, or as epitaxial overgrowths on clinopyroxene. Kokelaar (1977, 1986) described the presence of actinolite in pargasite-bearing mafic cumulates from the Eglwys Rhobell Formation, Rhobell Volcanic Group, exposed to the northeast of Dolgellau, Gwynedd. Actinolite has also been reported from the Tal y Fan Intrusion in Gwynedd by Bevins and Merriman (1988). Electron microprobe analyses of actinolite are presented by Bevins and Rowbotham (1983), Kokelaar (1977) and Bevins and Merriman (1988).

A mineral from the actinolite-tremolite series occurs in a vein on Moel Hebog, near Beddgelert, Gwynedd (Natural History Museum X-ray no. 7349F), while actinolite is recorded from a trial working near Ogof

Owain Glyndwr, north of Moel Hebog, on National Museum of Wales specimen NMW 72.36G.M1 (see Langford, 1973); these occurrences are probably the same.

Aegirine (synonym acmite)   Monoclinic
$NaFe^{3+}Si_2O_6$

A sodium iron silicate belonging to the pyroxene group. Aegirine is found in igneous rocks of alkaline affinity.

The identity of acicular crystals, up to 0.30 mm in length and 0.06 mm in width, occurring with riebeckite in the Mynydd Mawr microgranite, Gwynedd, could not be resolved by either Harker (1888a) or Bonney (1888). It was not until much later that they were identified by Nockolds (1938), on the basis of their optical properties, as aegirine.

Aeschynite   Orthorhombic
$(Ce,La,Y,Ca,Fe,Th)(Ti,Nb)_2(O,OH)_6$

An uncommon rare earth element-bearing titanium niobium oxide hydroxide. Typically it is found as a minor component in alkaline pegmatites.

Aeschynite occurs as small euhedral crystals in matrix and intergrown with Fe-, Mn-, and Sc-rich Ti and Nb oxides in altered Ordovician rhyolites in Central Snowdonia, Gwynedd (for example at Gallt y Wenallt,

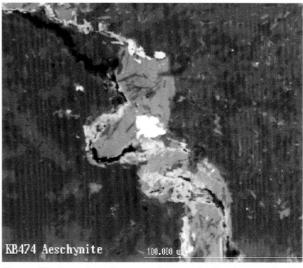

Figure 27. Scanning electron micrograph showing aeschynite (white) in a thin vein in altered Ordovician intrusive rhyolite from Beddgelert Forest, in central Snowdonia, Gwynedd. British Geological Survey specimen KB474.

Carnedd y Cribau, and Beddgelert Forest). Identification is on the basis of back-scatter energy dispersive analysis (Howells *et al.*, 1991). The exact species present in Snowdonia has yet to be determined, although as the heavy rare earth elements are dominant it is likely to be aeschynite-(Y). This represents the first occurrence of aeschynite in the British Isles.

Agardite-(Y)   Hexagonal
$(Y, Ca) Cu_6 (AsO_4)_3 (OH)_6.3H_2O$
An yttrium calcium copper arsenate hydroxide hydrate belonging to the mixite group of minerals. Agardite typically develops in the oxidized zone of copper deposits.

Agardite-(Y) has been identified from the Gwaithyrafon Mine, in the Central Wales Mining District, where it forms green acicular crystals in black oxide matrix. Identification was confirmed at the National Museum of Wales by X-ray diffraction, combined with energy dispersive analysis. This represents the first record of agardite-(Y) in the British Isles.

Albite   Triclinic
$NaAlSi_3O_8$
A sodium aluminium silicate belonging to the feldspar group. Albite is the sodic end member of the plagioclase series, with An_{0-10}. It is characteristically developed in acid igneous rocks of both intrusive (granite, granodiorite) and extrusive (rhyolite, dacite) origin. It is also widely developed in low-grade metamorphic rocks of more basic composition, resulting from the decomposition of high temperature calcic plagioclase feldspars. In addition, albite is found in low temperature Alpine-type veins, associated with quartz.

In Wales albite is a characteristic mineral in altered basic igneous rocks which have suffered the effects of low-grade metamorphism (Bevins and Rowbotham, 1983), occurring as pseudomorphs after original calcic plagioclase. In such cases, electron microprobe analyses show that it is typically nearly pure albite. Albite is also an important component of many of the more acidic igneous rocks in Wales, such as the St. David's Granophyre (Bloxam and Dirk, 1988), as well as granophyric gabbros and aplite veins in the St. David's Head Intrusion (Roach, 1969).

In addition, albite is found associated with quartz and various other minerals in low temperature Alpine-type veins cutting low-grade metamorphic rocks of Lower Palaeozoic age. Examples include veins bearing brookite and anatase at Fron Oleu, near Tremadog, Arenig Station Quarry, near Arenig, and Manod Quarry, near Blaenau Ffestiniog, quartz-bearing veins at Llyn-y-dywarchen, Rhyd-ddu, and calcite- and quartz-bearing veins at Minffordd Quarry, Minffordd, all in Gwynedd. Recently Starkey *et al.* (1991) have described small (up to 2 mm x 2 mm) colourless to white crystals of albite from joints in dolerite at Hendre Quarry, near Glyn Ceiriog, Clwyd, while an account of Alpine-type mineral veins from Brynyrafr Mine, in the Central Wales Mining District,

Figure 28. Albite and quartz from an Alpine-type vein at Minffordd Quarry, Minffordd, Gwynedd. The albite crystal is 5 mm in length. NMW specimen 27.111.GR374, *ex* G.J. Williams Collection.

containing albite and apatite appears in *British Micromount Society Newsletter* No. 35.

Aleksite   Pseudotrigonal
$PbBi_2Te_2S_2$
A rare lead bismuth tellurium sulphide.

Previously, aleksite has been recorded only from the Alekseyev deposit, in the Stanovoy range, Russia. However, silvery-grey masses up to 200 μm across intergrown with galena and tellurobismuthite in a quartz matrix in a specimen collected between 1982 and 1983 from St. David's Mine, Bontddu, near Dolgellau, Gwynedd have recently been shown, on the basis of X-ray diffraction, optical determinations and electron microprobe analytical evidence to be aleksite (Bevins and Stanley, 1990). This represented the first record of aleksite in the British Isles, and only the second world occurrence of the mineral.

Allanite   Monoclinic
$(Ce,Ca,Y)_2(Al,Fe^{+3})_3(SiO_4)_3(OH)$
Allanite is a rare earth element-bearing member of the epidote group, occurring as an accessory mineral in acidic igneous rocks such as granite and aplite.

In March 1908 W.G. Fearnsides discovered an

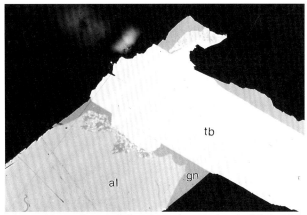

Figure 29. Reflected light photomicrograph of aleksite (al) associated with tellurobismuthite (tb) and galena (gn) from St. David's Mine, Gwynedd. The aleksite crystal shows partial replacement by galena, and by an intergrowth of galena and tellurobismuthite. Photographed under oil immersion. Horizontal dimension of photograph is 200 μm. Specimen E1309 in the Natural History Museum.

"unfamiliar" mineral in a narrow vein cutting the Tan-y-Grisiau microgranite in the northwest face of the Ffestiniog Granite Quarry at Cefn-Bychan, near Ffestiniog, Gwynedd. This "unknown and very interesting mineral" was later also found by members of the Geologists' Association field excursion to North Wales in 1909 (Fearnsides, 1910), and analysis proved the mineral to be allanite (Thomas, 1909a). Subsequently Bromley (1964) demonstrated that allanite is present not only in veins cutting the microgranite, but also is present as an accessory mineral throughout the groundmass of the microgranite itself. Bromley described two modes of occurrence: firstly associated with quartz, chlorite, calcite, epidote and ore minerals in veins (up to 2.5 cm across) and cavities (up to 30 cm across), forming black to dark grey, compositionally zoned, prismatic or tabular crystals 1-10 mm in length; and secondly in the groundmass of the microgranite, forming small, euhedral crystals up to 1 mm in length closely associated with or

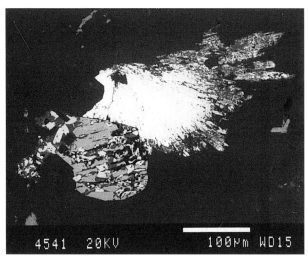

Figure 30. Scanning electron micrograph of radiating allanite (white) on degraded titanite, in altered intrusive rhyolite of Ordovician age from Bwlch Ehediad, central Snowdonia, Gwynedd. British Geological Survey specimen KB 454.

Figure 31. Allanite crystals in alteration veins in the Ffestiniog Granite, Blaenau Ffestiniog, Gwynedd. The crystals are up to 3 cm in length. NMW specimen 27.111.GR435 ex G.J. Williams Collection.

enclosed by chlorite, or large, irregular, interstitial masses up to 4 mm across which are in optical continuity with large masses replacing the potassium feldspar of adjacent microperthite crystals. Cox (1920) reported the occurrence of allanite as an accessory phase in the Cregenen granophyre near Dolgellau, while Williams (1927) described a pleochroic (pale green to deep chestnut brown) epidote in certain dolerites from central Snowdonia, which he thought was probably allanite.

More recently allanite has been identified as a significant mineral of both primary and secondary origin in the Ordovician acidic lavas, intrusions and pyroclastic rocks in Snowdonia, for example at Carnedd y Cribau [SH 6657 5333], Cerrig Coehion [SH 6622 5193] and Castell Yr Arddu [SH 6382 4780] (A.T. Kearsley, *personal communication*; Howells *et al.*, 1991).

Possible allanite was reported from the hornblende gneisses of the Mona Complex of Anglesey by Greenly (1919), although no specific localities are mentioned. Horák (1993), however, confirmed this occurrence, describing small, anhedral to euhedral golden-yellow crystals as inclusions in amphibole, and larger (up to 1.2 mm) pale brown crystals in the groundmass or in amphibole. Horák (1993) illustrates allanite from Y Werthyr and from Craig yr Allor, on Anglesey.

Finally, zoned 'epidote' crystals in the Tal y Fan Intrusion, Gwynedd have dark brown cores which show low element totals which, coupled with their high Mg contents, indicates the probable presence of high rare earth element concentrations; hence these epidotes may be allanitic (Merriman *et al.*, 1986).

Alleghanyite   Monoclinic
$Mn_5(SiO_4)_2(OH)_2$
A manganese silicate hydroxide, dimorphous with ribbeite and belonging to the humite group of minerals. A rare mineral found in manganese ore bodies.

Alleghanyite was found as individual crystals or, more commonly, composite crystals with tephroite on the footwall side of the no. 1 ore-body, by no. 1 Chute, '50-

60 feet west of the main shaft', and about '10-20 feet above the 130 foot level' at Benallt Mine, Llŷn, Gwynedd (Campbell Smith *et al.*, 1944b). The composite alleghanyite/tephroite crystals are up to 2 cm in length and vary in thickness from 2 mm down to microscopic size. The alleghanyite is clove-brown in colour, and crystals are blade-like in form. It differs from alleghanyite from the type locality (Bald Knob, Alleghany County, North Carolina, USA) in being Ti-rich (with up to 4.8 wt% TiO_2; see Campbell Smith *et al.*, 1944b). A second occurrence of alleghanyite from Benallt Mine, occurring near the footwall of no. 2 orebody, some '40 to 80 feet west of the Court Shaft', was also described by Campbell Smith *et al.* (1944b), and again is found intimately associated with tephroite. The occurrences described by Campbell Smith *et al.* (1944b) represented the first account of alleghanyite in the British Isles.

Allophane

An amorphous hydrous aluminium silicate occurring as massive or powdery aggregates in mineral veins.

Prior (1906) described the presence of allophane from Welsh Foxdale (= New Pandora) Mine, near Trefriw, Gwynedd, where it occurs as small glassy spherules associated with dundasite and cerussite. Identification was on the basis of a chemical analysis. Subsequently Russell (1944) reported gum-like brownish-yellow allophane associated with dundasite, cerussite, quartz, and anglesite from Gorlan Mine, also near Trefriw. Elsewhere in North Wales allophane has been recorded at the iron mines at Betws Garmon, in Snowdonia (Jenkins and Johnson, 1993).

A specimen of allophane (B.M.1918,403) from a level driven on a marcasite vein at Cwm Dwyfnant, near Llangammarch Wells, Powys, is in the collections of the Natural History Museum; again identification was by chemical analysis by G.T. Prior and by X-ray diffraction (Natural History Museum X-ray no. x1663).

Almandine   Cubic
$Fe_3^{2+}Al_2(SiO_4)_3$
An iron aluminium silicate of the garnet group which forms two series, with pyrope and with spessartine. Almandine generally develops as a result of medium to high grade metamorphism of mudstones and sandstones, although more rarely it is found as a primary mineral in some igneous rocks.

Williams (1922) described the development of aggregates of almandine garnet in rhyolitic lavas of the Capel Curig district in Snowdonia, where it is associated with secondary quartz related to extensive silicification; no analyses, however, are available. Further west, near Blaen-y-nant, at the northern end of the Nant Ffrancon Pass, sediments adjacent to the Bwlch y Cywion Intrusion have been contact metamorphosed, resulting in the development of a garnet-biotite rock (Williams, 1930). These garnets belong to the almandine-spessartine series (Annual Report of the Institute of Geological Sciences for 1976).

In Dyfed, almandine garnet forms a component of the

Dutch Gin Schists, a suite of Precambrian regionally metamorphosed mudstones and sandstones occurring in contact with various igneous rocks of the Johnston Plutonic Complex, exposed near Talbenny (Claxton, 1963). Again, however, no analyses have been determined.

Alstonite   Triclinic
$BaCa(CO_3)_2$
A rare barium calcium carbonate, trimorphous with barytocalcite and paralstonite.

Two specimens (NMW 83.41G.M5489 and NMW 83.41G.M5493) in the Mineral Collection of the National Museum of Wales are labelled as alstonite from Pennant Mine, near St. Asaph, Clwyd; however the provenance of these specimens is dubious (B. Young, *personal communication*), bearing marked resemblance to material from the type locality. Alstonite does occur, however, in the Llantrisant area, in Mid Glamorgan, being found at an old mine site [ST 063 824], as well as at the southern end of the Llantrisant by-pass roadcutting. It forms colourless to pale pink bipyramidal, striated crystals up to 6 mm in length associated with witherite, calcite, barite and various sulphide minerals in dolomite-lined cavities in Triassic conglomerates, and also as a minor component

Figure 32. Bipyramidal alstonite crystals up to 2 mm in length, collected in 1990 from a cavity in Triassic conglomerates from a roadcutting on the A4119 south of Llantrisant, Mid Glamorgan. I. Jones Collection.

in brecciated ore veins (Alabaster, 1990). Many of these alstonite crystals are actually pseudomorphed by barite, along, in some cases, with aragonite.

Altaite   Cubic
PbTe

A rare lead telluride mineral occurring in veins with gold, various sulphides and other telluride minerals.

The presence of altaite in Wales was first recorded by Des Cloizeaux (1893) in his *Manuel de Minéralogie,* occurring 'à Bontddu, entre Dolgelly et Barmouth, Galles du Nord', which represented the first occurrence of the mineral in the British Isles. The occurrence was verified by Gilbey (1968) on the basis of optical and electron microprobe investigations, who identified the mineral from Clogau Mine, near Dolgellau, Gwynedd, occurring as granular to sub-rounded inclusions in tellurobismuthite, always present in association with hessite, either as a rim or as a dual inclusion. More recently the presence of altaite at Clogau Mine has been confirmed by Naden (1988), occurring in tellurobismuthite-dominated assemblages in an ore shoot on the 4th level of the Llechfraith section of the mine.

Alunite   Trigonal
$KAl_3(SO_4)_2(OH)_6$

A potassium aluminium sulphate belonging to the alunite group of minerals. Alunite typically develops by sulfotaric activity in volcanic regions, and indicates the presence of very low pH (acidic) conditions.

Alunite has been identified in altered rhyolitic rocks of the Roch Rhyolite Group encountered in a borehole near Treffgarne, Dyfed (Brown *et al.,* 1987).

Alunogen   Triclinic
$Al_2(SO_4)_3.17H_2O$

An aluminium sulphate hydrate, formed usually as a result of alteration of pyritic ores.

Three specimens in the Mineral Collection of the National Museum of Wales, from Cymmer Colliery, Porth (Mid Glamorgan), Deep Navigation Colliery, Treharris (Mid Glamorgan), and Parys Mountain, Anglesey (Gwynedd) were originally labelled alunogen. However, recent X-ray diffraction investigations have shown all of them in fact to be halotrichite. Whether alunogen occurs in Wales therefore presently remains uncertain.

Amesite   Triclinic
$Mg_2Al(Si,Al)O_5(OH)_4$

A magnesium aluminium silicate hydroxide belonging to the kaolinite-serpentine group.

A mineral reported from the Dulais Seam, Cefn Coed Colliery, West Glamorgan has been identified by X-ray diffraction (Natural History Museum X-ray No. x2724) as 'amesite or chrysotile'.

Analcime   Cubic
$NaAlSi_2O_6.H_2O$

A sodium aluminium silicate hydrate mineral of the zeolite group which forms a series with pollucite. It typically develops in vesicles in altered volcanic rocks, generally of basaltic composition, as a result of low temperature alteration. Rarely analcime occurs as a primary igneous phase.

The first description of analcime in Wales appears to be that by Henslow (1822), from the contact aureole of the Plas Newydd Dyke on Anglesey. Henslow described perfectly-formed faceted crystals with a trapezoidal form. An analysis in Henslow (1822) indicated that the crystals are 'analcime with excess of iron'. Harker (1887) remarked that the analysis in Henslow implied that the analcime is half converted to prehnite, although more recent X-ray diffraction work has confirmed the presence of analcime (Natural History Museum no. 2500 - 1979 P75). Greenly (1919) also referred to the occurrence of analcime in the contact metamorphic rocks surrounding the Plas Newydd Dyke.

Elsewhere in North Wales, glassy, colourless analcime is present as vesicle infillings in a suite of olivine-dolerite dykes exposed between Marchlyn Mawr Reservoir and Blaen-y-nant to the west of Nant Ffrancon, in Snowdonia (Williams, 1924, 1930), while Campbell Smith (1946) identified analcime in veins cutting massive ore in the Tŷ Canol Incline at Benallt Mine, Llŷn.

The presence of analcime has also been confirmed from Gimlet Quarry, near Pwllheli on the basis of X-ray diffraction analysis (NMW - X57) on specimen NMW 27.111.GR377 from the Mineral Collection of the National Museum of Wales.

In Mid Wales analcime has been found associated with quartz, calcite, and laumontite in veins cutting altered Ordovician lavas at Llanelwedd Quarry, near Builth Wells, Powys (Metcalfe, 1990).

In South Wales analcime has been identified by Boulton (1911) in a monchiquitic intrusion at Golden Hill, near Usk (Gwent), forming colourless, euhedral to anhedral crystals in the groundmass, an identification also made more recently by Haslett (1992) for a similar mineral from monchiquite exposed at nearby Glen Court.

Anatase   Tetragonal
TiO_2

A titanium dioxide mineral, trimorphous with rutile and brookite. Anatase occurs as an accessory mineral in acidic igneous rocks, in low-grade metamorphic rocks, and in low temperature Alpine-type veins along with minerals such as quartz, albite, chlorite, and brookite.

One of the earliest records of anatase in Wales was by Sowerby (1838) who remarked that he had found two crystals of anatase in a mineral vein containing brookite, quartz and albite at a locality 'on the road side between Beddgelert and Tremaddoc, Carnarvonshire, about 8 miles from Snowdon'. This locality was no doubt in the Prenteg area, from where many excellent crystals have been recovered subsequently from quartz veins cutting altered dolerites. Other localities in Gwynedd where anatase crystals are found in quartz-bearing veins include Arenig Station Quarry, Manod Quarry (near Blaenau Ffestiniog), Hendrehenydd, near Penrhyndeudraeth, and

Figure 33. Anatase, 1.5 mm long, from Hendre Quarry, near Glyn Ceiriog, Clwyd. Collected January 1988. N. Hubbard Collection.

near Tanygrisiau. X-ray diffraction determinations by the Natural History Museum also confirm the occurrence of anatase on Crib-goch Ridge, Snowdon and at Cwm Meillionen, near Beddgelert. In Clwyd anatase has been recorded in mineral veins cutting altered dolerite at Hendre Quarry, near Glyn Ceiriog (Wedd *et al.*, 1929; Starkey *et al.*, 1991).

Pointon and Ixer (1980) described the presence of anatase in altered volcanic rocks at Parys Mountain, Anglesey, where it forms 10 μm boxworks or laths after original iron-titanium oxides.

In Gwent, anatase has been collected from Christchurch Quarry, near Newport (Natural History Museum X-ray no. x15179).

Andalusite   Orthorhombic
Al_2SiO_5
An aluminium silicate, trimorphous with sillimanite and kyanite. Andalusite is a metamorphic mineral which typically develops in contact aureoles.

Greenly (1919) described the presence of andalusite at various localities in the aureole of the Coedana Granite, on Anglesey, although each individual description actually remarks that the andalusite has been retrogressively metamorphosed and that only pseudomorphs after

andalusite occur. Similarly andalusite pseudomorphs are recorded from contact aureoles around the Tan-y-Grisiau Granite, Gwynedd (Bromley, 1969), and the St. David's Head Intrusion, Dyfed (Roach, 1969).

Andalusite is present, however, as a component of glacial sands and tills from various parts of Wales, including those at Castell-tôch, near Llansadurnen, Dyfed (Strahan *et al.*, 1909), at Ludchurch (Griffiths and Stuart, 1940), and elsewhere in the region between the rivers Neath and Tywi (Griffiths, 1939). Also it is recorded from numerous localities in drift and beach blown sand in Dyfed (Thomas, 1909b). The presence of andalusite, along with other relatively exotic minerals, in the glacial deposits of South Wales has been taken to indicate the former advance of Irish Sea ice into this region.

Thomas (1909b) also listed one occurrence of detrital andalusite from glacial sands at Bagillt, Clwyd.

Andesine   Triclinic
$(Na,Ca)Al(Al,Si)Si_2O_8$
A sodium calcium aluminium silicate belonging to the feldspar group. Andesine is a member of the plagioclase series, with An_{30-50}. Typically it is found as a rock-forming mineral in basic to intermediate igneous rocks.

In Wales andesine is widespread, occurring as an alteration product of more calcic plagioclase feldspars in dolerites and basaltic lavas of Ordovician age, as, for example, in the Tal y Fan Intrusion near Conwy, Gwynedd (Bevins and Merriman, 1988), as well as being a primary mineral in igneous rocks of more intermediate character.

Andradite   Cubic
$Ca_3Fe_2^{+3}(SiO_4)_3$
A calcium iron silicate member of the garnet group. Andradite is most typically developed in contact metamorphic aureoles in calcium-rich rocks, such as limestones.

The only record of andradite in Wales to date is by Archer and Elliott (1965) who identified the mineral forming honey-yellow crystals on joint faces in lodes adjacent to the northeast side of two dykes (of Tertiary age) on No. 3 level, Parc Mine, near Llanrwst, Gwynedd. Identification was confirmed by X-ray diffraction techniques.

Anglesite   Orthorhombic
$PbSO_4$
A lead sulphate of the barite group which typically develops in the oxidized zone of lead-bearing ore bodies.

Anglesite was named after the Island of Anglesey by Beudant in 1832 in his *Traité élémentaire de Minéralogie*. However the occurrence of this lead sulphate, previously known as 'vitriol de plomb', at Parys Mountain on Anglesey, had been known already for some years, being mentioned by Monnet (1779) in his *Nouveau Système de Minéralogie*. Greenly (1919) gave further account of anglesite from Parys Mountain, where it occurs as discrete, euhedral, milky white to yellow crystals up to 10 mm in length on ferruginous

Figure 34. Rich yellow anglesite crystals in gossan from Mona Mine, Parys Mountain, Anglesey. Crystals reach up to 10 mm in length. NMW specimen 86.83G.M1.

gossan (an example of such material is preserved in the Mineral Collection of the National Museum of Wales, specimen NMW 77.36G.M18). A further specimen in the Mineral Collection of the National Museum of Wales (specimen no. NMW 91.6G.M1) was collected from 'Parry's Copper Mine' in 1784.

Elsewhere in North Wales, anglesite has been identified from Llanengan Mine, on Llŷn, Gwynedd

Figure 35. Pale yellow to colourless anglesite crystals up to 4 mm in length from Parys Mountain, Anglesey. NMW specimen 91.12G.M5, originally from the R.W. Barstow Collection, and later in the R. Sutcliffe Collection.

Figure 36. Anglesite crystals up to 9 mm in length from Machen Quarry, Mid Glamorgan. NMW specimen 85.62G.M1, collected in 1985.

(Natural History Museum X-ray no. 7049F).

Anglesite has been identified from other parts of Wales, being of widespread occurrence in the Central Wales Mining District, for example at Nantycagl (Eaglebrook) Mine (Braithwaite, 1982a), Bwlchglas Mine (Braithwaite, 1982b; Rust and Mason, 1988), Ystrad Einion Mine (*British Micromount Society Newsletter*, No. 21), Bwlchrhennaid (*British Micromount Society Newsletter*, No. 18), Glogfawr Mine (*British Micromount Society Newsletter*, No. 16), Geufron Mine (*British Micromount Society Newsletter*, No. 15), Frongoch Mine (*British Micromount Society Newsletter*, No. 15), South Nantycar Mine (*British Micromount Society Newsletter*, No. 34), Dylife (Rust and Rust, 1987; Natural History Museum X-ray nos. 6976F and 8000F), Darren Mine (Natural History Museum X-ray no. 7619F), Esgair Hir Mine (Natural History Museum X-ray no. 7008F), and Cwmystwyth (Natural History Museum X-ray no. x15329), to name but a few. J.S. Mason (*personal communication*) has recorded blocky, white anglesite crystals up to 7 mm long from Nantycagl Mine, and also attractive, colourless microcrystals, less than 1 mm long, from Frongoch Mine.

Spectacular euhedral, colourless anglesite crystals, up to 11 mm in length, were collected at Machen Quarry, Mid Glamorgan in 1985 from a cavity in a galena vein cutting Carboniferous Limestone; these crystals are preserved in the Mineral Collection of the National Museum of Wales as specimens NMW 85.62G.M1 and M2. Anglesite is also recorded from Rhyd-y-Gwern Mine, near Machen, confirmed by X-ray diffraction no. x15750 at the Natural History Museum, and from Hendy Quarry, Miskin (*British Micromount Society Newsletter*, No. 35).

Finally, Russell (1944) described a single anglesite crystal from Bwlch Mine at Deganwy, Gwynedd, occurring in a cavity in semseyite.

Note: Rust and Rust (1987) recorded a suite of micro-minerals from Dyfngwm Mine. Subsequently, however, this suite is recognised as having been collected from the Pen Dylife section of Dylife Mine (S.A. Rust, *personal communication*).

Anhydrite Orthorhombic
$CaSO_4$
Calcium sulphate. Generally anhydrite occurs as an evaporite mineral in arid regions; more rarely it is found in syngenetic sulphide-bearing ore bodies of exhalative origin (so-called Kuroko-type deposits).

Pointon and Ixer (1980) described the presence of anhydrite forming cores to voids in siliceous sinter from the Carreg-y-doll lode zone, at Parys Mountain, Anglesey.

Certain horizons in the Triassic of South Wales, such as near Sully in South Glamorgan, show replacement features indicating that evaporites, including anhydrite were present originally (Tucker, 1977; Waters and Lawrence, 1987).

Ankerite Trigonal
$Ca(Fe^{+2},Mg,Mn)(CO_3)_2$
A calcium iron carbonate mineral belonging to the dolomite group, and forming two series, with dolomite and with kutnohorite. It develops typically in hydrothermal mineral veins.

Ankerite is probably of widespread occurrence in Wales although specific records are few. North and Howarth (1928) described the presence of ankerite in clay ironstone nodules from the South Wales Coalfield, although the nodule mineralogy was considered by Firth (1971) to be dominated by "siderite". Recent X-ray studies in the National Museum of Wales, however, have confirmed the presence of ankerite.

Russell (1944) reported ankerite from Bwlch Mine, near Deganwy, Gwynedd, where it occurs in altered rhyolitic ash-flow tuffs of Ordovician age, in association with stibnite and various lead-antimony sulphosalt minerals. Ankerite is also thought to be the chief gangue mineral in veins of the Central Wales Mining District (Raybould, 1976; Fletcher *et al.*, 1993), although J.S. Mason (*personal communication*) considers the phase in fact to be ferroan dolomite.

Annabergite Monoclinic
$Ni_3(AsO_4)_2.8H_2O$
A nickel arsenate hydrate, which forms a series with erythrite, and is a member of the vivianite group. Usually annabergite occurs as an alteration product of primary nickel minerals.

The only recognised occurrence of annabergite in Wales to date is as coatings associated with gersdorffite on fractures within hydrocarbon at Great Ormes Head, Llandudno, Gwynedd (P. Eakin, *personal communication*).

Anorthite Triclinic
$CaAl_2Si_2O_8$
A calcium aluminium silicate belonging to the feldspar group trimorphous with dmisteinbergite and svyatoslavite. Anorthite is the calcium-rich end member of the plagioclase series, with An_{90-100}. It is a high temperature plagioclase feldspar occurring in lavas and intrusive rocks of basic and ultrabasic composition.

Greenly (1919) suggested that some of the plagioclase crystals in post-Carboniferous age dykes of Anglesey approach anorthite, although no particular occurrences are detailed, while more recently Cattermole (1976) indicated that plagioclase of An_{90} is present in the plagioclase-heteradcumulates of the Rhiw Intrusion, Llŷn, although compositions are based only on optical determinations.

Anorthoclase Triclinic
$(Na,K)AlSi_3O_8$
A sodium potassium aluminium silicate belonging to the feldspar group. A rock-forming mineral, being a constituent of intermediate to acidic lavas.

Greenly (1919) reported anorthoclase, along with albite, in folded pegmatitic quartz augen in the Precambrian Gwna beds exposed in the vicinity of Craig-y-don house, near Menai, Anglesey.

Antigorite Monoclinic
$(Mg,Fe^{+2})_3Si_2O_5(OH)_4$
A magnesium iron silicate hydroxide of the kaolinite-serpentine group. Typically antigorite develops as a result of alteration of ultrabasic rocks.

Greenly (1919) described antigorite from various localities on Holy Island, Anglesey, resulting from serpentinization of a suite of basic and ultrabasic intrusions belonging to the Mona Complex of Precambrian age. Specific occurrences reported include antigorite associated with garnet in the serpentinite of the Mynachdy Intrusion, in an ophicalcite unit associated with serpentinite cropping out SW of Llanfechell, in a massive limestone at Tre-gele, and from the peninsula west of Four Mile Bridge. Maltman (1977) also briefly mentioned the presence of antigorite associated with lizardite from the serpentinites of Holy Island, Anglesey.

More recently antigorite has been identified associated with secondary copper and lead minerals (brochantite, linarite and cerussite) from Esgair Hir Mine, Dyfed, where it forms rare, white to blue/green platey rosettes and crystal groups up to 1 mm (Rust and Mason, 1988); confirmed by X-ray diffraction (Natural History Museum X-ray no. 7177F).

Antimony Trigonal
Sb
Native antimony is a member of the arsenic group. Usually antimony is found in hydrothermal veins, associated with silver, arsenic and other antimony ores.

Native antimony has been reported from the Dolgellau Gold Belt, Gwynedd, by Readwin (1888), although this record requires verification.

Apatite Hexagonal
$Ca_5(PO_4)_3(F,OH,Cl)$
A group name for calcium phosphates containing varying proportions of fluoride, hydroxide and chloride, sometimes also containing carbonate. Apatite forms in a wide variety of environments, but commonly occurs as an accessory mineral in igneous rocks. Fluorapatite is the most common species.

Apatite is widely developed in Wales, chiefly in igneous rocks of basic, intermediate and acidic composition. It occurs, for example, in the St. David's Head Intrusion (Roach, 1969), being most abundant in the more fractionated rocks (granophyric gabbros and aplites), in the more fractionated gabbros in the Fishguard area (Bevins, 1982), in plagioclase-apatite-hornblende mesocumulates in the Rhiw Intrusion, Llŷn (Cattermole, 1976), and in microtonalites of northern Llŷn (Croudace, 1982). Apatite is also found in certain sedimentary rocks (see carbonate-hydroxylapatite and hydroxylapatite).

Apatite is a minor component of mineral veins at Hendre Quarry, near Glyn Ceiriog, Clwyd, forming small (maximum 0.5 mm) colourless crystals, sometimes showing complex forms (Starkey *et al.*, 1991). Matthews and Scoon (1964) and Starkey and Robinson (1992) recorded fluorapatite from Tyllau Mwn, near Dolgellau and Prenteg, Gwynedd, respectively (see fluorapatite). Apatite has also been recorded sparingly in Alpine-type mineral veins at Brynyrafr Mine, in the Central Wales Mining District (*British Micromount Society Newsletter*, No. 35).

Apophyllite   Tetragonal
$KCa_4Si_8O_{20}(F,OH).8H_2O$

A potassium calcium silicate fluoride hydroxide hydrate; a group name, comprising fluorapophyllite, hydroxyapophyllite, and natroapophyllite. Commonly apophyllite develops in amygdales or secondary veins in altered basic igneous rocks, often in association with zeolite group minerals.

Maltman (1977) reported the presence of blades of apophyllite in altered gabbros of the Mona Complex exposed on Holy Island, Anglesey.

In the Mineral Collection of the National Museum of Wales white pseudocubic apophyllite crystals up to 7 mm across occur associated with pectolite on specimens NMW 27.111.GR263-265 and 27.111.GR530 from Hendre Quarry, near Glyn Ceiriog, Clwyd (specimen NMW 27.111.GR265 is illustrated in Starkey *et al.*, 1991). This occurrence has been confirmed by X-ray diffraction at the National Museum of Wales. In addition, specimen NMW 27.111.GR262 is apophyllite with pectolite from Gimlet Quarry, at Pwllheli, Gwynedd.

Aragonite   Orthorhombic
$CaCO_3$

A calcium carbonate mineral belonging to the aragonite group, and trimorphous with calcite and vaterite. Aragonite is metastable under normal conditions, reverting to the more stable form calcite. It occurs most commonly in limestone caves and fractures, in limestone rock, and also in spring deposits.

References to aragonite in Wales are few. Kendall (1988) reported the presence of aragonite forming speleotherms in Ogof Daren Cilau, Mynydd Llangattwg, Gwent, with identification confirmed by X-ray diffraction (NMW X-ray nos. X-323 and X-324). Elsewhere in South Wales, Alabaster (1990) reported

Figure 37. Apophyllite on pectolite from Hendre Quarry, near Glyn Ceiriog, Clwyd. The specimen measures 8 cm x 5.5 cm. NMW specimen 27.111.GR265, *ex* G.J. Williams Collection.

aragonite replacing alstonite in cavities and veinstones, forming felted overgrowths and radiating sprays of acicular crystals from a small mine dump near Llantrisant. Aragonite has also been found at a number of mines in South Wales, including Bedwas Colliery, at Trethomas, Mid Glamorgan, identified by X-ray diffraction (X-ray no. 16582) on Natural History Museum specimen B.M. 1971, 363, Windsor Colliery, near Senghenydd (idenified by X-ray diffraction at the National Museum of Wales, X-ray no. X-775), Marine Colliery, Cwm Colliery, Deep Navigation Colliery, Ferndale Colliery, and Gelli Colliery (I. Jones, *personal communication*).

In Mid Wales aragonite occurs at the Dolaucothi Mine near Pumsaint, Dyfed, forming stalactitic masses, and also has been identified in association with brochantite, langite, malachite, and linarite at the Esgairfraith Mine in the Central Wales Mining District (Jones and Moreton, 1977), and in altered ferroan dolomite at South Nantycar Mine (*British Micromount Society Newsletter*, No. 34). J.S. Mason (*personal communication*) has recorded small aragonite crystals up to 10 mm in altered ferroan dolomite at the Castell Mine, near Ponterwyd, as well as aggregates up to 15 mm at Henfwlch Mine, both in the Central Wales Mining District.

Starkey *et al.* (1991) referred to the presence of tapering prismatic aragonite crystals up to 3 mm in length in quartz and ankerite, and of aggregates up to 8 mm across associated with chlorite from Hendre Quarry, near Glyn Ceiriog, Clwyd. Elsewhere in North Wales pale blue botryoidal masses and radiating colourless needles of aragonite occur in association with malachite at the Ty Gwyn Mine, Llandudno, Gwynedd.

Arsenolite Cubic

As_2O_3

An arsenic oxide, dimorphous with claudetite. A secondary mineral resulting from the alteration of primary arsenic-bearing minerals.

Arsenolite was reported as occurring in the Dolgellau Gold Belt, Gwynedd by Readwin (1888).

Arsenopyrite Monoclinic

FeAsS

An iron arsenic sulphide of hydrothermal origin which develops in mineral veins, commonly associated with other sulphides such as galena, sphalerite and chalcopyrite.

In Gwynedd minor amounts of arsenopyrite are

Figure 38. Striated and iridescent arsenopyrite crystal measuring 15 mm x 7 mm, from St. David's Mine, near Dolgellau, Gwynedd. NMW specimen 27.111.GR286, *ex* G.J. Williams Collection.

developed at Parys Mountain (Pointon and Ixer, 1980) and Rhôs-mynach Mine, on Anglesey. At Parys Mountain it forms zoned, rhombic or lath-shaped crystals associated with tetrahedrite group and bismuth-bearing minerals. In Snowdonia arsenopyrite was formerly mined from Cambrian sandstones at Tan-y-garth Mine near Bethesda (Dewey, 1920), while it is also relatively abundant at Drws-y-Coed Mine (Braithwaite, 1982a), and at Simdde Dylluan Mine, both in the Nantlle Valley.

In the Dolgellau Gold Belt, in southern Gwynedd, arsenopyrite is a widespread but relatively minor component of the vein assemblages (see Andrew, 1910), forming idiomorphic rhombs and needles up to 1-2 cm. It occurs in many mines across the area as far apart as Prince Edward and Cwm Prysor in the north, and Clogau and Vigra in the southwest (Gilbey, 1968). Naden (1988), for example, reported arsenopyrite occurring in association with pyrite, pyrrhotite and cobaltite at Clogau Mine.

Further south, in Dyfed, arsenopyrite is an important component of the gold-bearing mineral assemblage at the Dolaucothi Mine at Pumsaint, where it occurs both in pyritic shales and in mineral veins (Annels and Roberts, 1989). Some of the arsenopyrite porphyroblasts contain gold grains typically between 15-30 μm across. In the Central Wales Mining District, however, arsenopyrite is rare; the only recorded occurrence is from Hyddgen Mine, near Nant-y-moch reservoir, where, according to Raybould (1976) it forms small (up to 50 μm) grains in galena, as well as enclosing small (20-30 μm) cobaltite grains; however this occurrence and also that of cobaltite at this mine is dubious (J.S. Mason, *personal communication*).

Asbolan Hexagonal

$(Co,Ni)_{1-y}(Mn^{+4}O_2)_{2-x}(OH)_{2-2y+2x}.nH_2O$

A cobalt nickel manganese oxide hydroxide hydrate which develops as a result of oxidation of cobalt- and nickel-bearing manganese deposits.

Le Neve Foster (1882) gave account of the extraction of cobalt from mineral veins up to 3 m wide cutting Carboniferous Limestone at Moel Hiraddug Mine, Cwm, near Rhyl, Clwyd. The asbolan occurs as soft, black, reniform or botryoidal masses, as large 'as walnuts, or even hen's eggs' set in red clay along with fragments of brown hematite, wad, or Carboniferous Limestone. Ore from this mine was sent to smelters in Swansea.

A zincian asbolan, with a formula approximating to $Mn_{2.0-2.6}Zn_{0.91-1.8}O_{4.1-5.3}(OH)_{1.6-3.4}.(H_2O)_{0.8-3.3}$, forms concretionary deposits in certain abandoned lead and zinc mines in Gwynedd. These nodular growths appear to be of abiotic origin, formed by autocatalytic oxidation (Roberts, 1986).

Augite Monoclinic

$(Ca,Na)(Mg,Fe,Al,Ti)(Si,Al)_2O_6$

A calcium magnesium iron aluminium silicate mineral belonging to the pyroxene group. A common rock-forming mineral occurring in basic igneous rocks.

Augite is a widely developed mineral in Wales, being

one of the primary minerals in igneous rocks of basic composition, occurring associated with plagioclase feldspar; accordingly only a few recent descriptions are presented. In slowly cooled intrusions, such as the Tal y Fan Intrusion, in Gwynedd, augite forms large ophitic plates enclosing plagioclase (Merriman *et al.*, 1986), while in parts of the St. David's Head Intrusion it is an important primary phase which, along with plagioclase defines a pronounced lamination (Roach, 1969). Pegmatitic patches in the St. David's Head Intrusion have augite crystals up to 12 cm in length. When present in basic lavas it sometimes forms phenocrysts or microphenocrysts, as in the Rhobell Volcanic Complex (Kokelaar, 1986), while in the Fishguard Volcanic Group Ti-rich augites in pillow lavas show spectacular dendritic to fan spherulitic growth forms related to rapid quenching of these lavas when they were erupted subaqueously (Bevins, 1982).

Representative electron microprobe analyses of augites in basic igneous rocks from various parts of Wales are presented by Bevins (1982), Kokelaar (1986), and Merriman *et al.* (1986).

Aurichalcite   Orthorhombic
$(Zn,Cu)_5(CO_3)_2(OH)_6$

A zinc copper carbonate hydroxide which forms in the oxidized zones of copper-bearing ore bodies.

Figure 39. Globular aurichalcite aggregates up to 2 mm in diameter from Ochr Graig Mine, Llangynog, Powys. I. Jones Collection, specimen no. 1333A.

In Wales aurichalcite is a comparatively rare mineral. Jones and Moreton (1977) reported the presence of aurichalcite from only three mines in the Central Wales Mining District, namely Castell Mine, Snowbrook and Dylife, forming small pale green feathery tufts and crusts. Subsequently it has been identified at Henfwlch Mine, near Talybont, as rare pale blue lath-like crystals (*British Micromount Society Newsletter*, No. 15), on the 'Copper Level' at Cwmystwyth (R.E. Starkey, *personal communication*), at South Nantycar Mine (*British Micromount Society Newsletter*, No. 34).

Figure 40. Acicular aurichalcite crystals lining a cavity 10 mm across, collected in July 1993 from bench 9, Machen Quarry, Mid Glamorgan. I. Jones Collection.

Perhaps some of the finest aurichalcite in Wales has been collected from the Craig Rhiwarth and Ochr Graig Mines at Llangynog, Powys, where it occurs in close association with chalcopyrite and more rarely smithsonite. Specimens from this area are preserved in the Mineral Collection of the National Museum of Wales, registration numbers NMW 68.576.GR18 and NMW 82.17G.M1. Aurichalcite is also known from old mine workings in the Llanymynech area of Powys, with several fine specimens in the collections of the National Museum of Wales.

In Clwyd aurichalcite has been reported from Nant-y-Plwm Mine, at Llansannan, and at the Pen-y-Bryn Shaft, Halkyn (R.S.W. Braithwaite, *personal communication*).

More recently, aurichalcite has been recorded from a number of localities in Mid Glamorgan. Fletcher and Young (1988) identified aurichalcite at Bute Quarry, near Llantrisant, where it forms radiating acicular needles associated with calcite in small cavities in limestones of the Hunts Bay Oolite (Carboniferous Limestone), and also from a borehole through Carboniferous Limestone at Locks Common, Porthcawl. In addition, NMW X-ray diffraction investigations have confirmed the occurrence of the mineral at Machen Quarry, Machen (on National Museum of Wales specimen 87.73G.M290) and at Hendy Quarry, Llantrisant (on National Museum of Wales specimen 87.73G.M292). Elsewhere in Mid Glamorgan it has been recorded from old mine workings in the Cwmleyshon area, near Draethen.

Axinite   Triclinic
$(Ca,Mn,Mg,Fe^{+2})_3Al_2BSi_4O_{15}(OH)$

A group name for calcium manganese magnesium iron aluminium borosilicate hydroxide minerals. Commonly it is developed in contact metamorphic aureoles, in particular in limestones. It is also a mineral which develops in low-grade metamorphic rocks.

Sargent (1916) provided the first description of axinite in Wales, occurring in thin veins cutting the Penmaenmawr Intrusion, Gwynedd, although this initial report was based only on loose blocks collected from the waste tips from the Graiglwyd Quarry. In these mineral veins, which are up to 5 cm thick, the axinite is massive,

and mauve in colour, while in fissures and cracks pale brown axinite forms thin radiating blades up to 2.5 cm long. In both modes it occurs in association with prehnite. A more complete description of the associated minerals was provided by Sargent (1925), who reported vein assemblages of axinite + prehnite + quartz, axinite + pectolite, and axinite + zoisite + quartz.

Greenly (1919) reported the presence of axinite in a 15 cm thick vein cutting altered basic lavas at the northern end of Llanddwyn Bay, on Anglesey, but mistakenly attributed this as the first occurrence in Wales.

Axinite is also known from Carreg Ddu, at Porth Dinllaen, on Llŷn, Gwynedd, where it occurs in veins in association with epidote and quartz, cutting altered basic lavas of the Mona Complex (specimens from this locality are preserved in the Mineral Collection of the National Museum of Wales, registration numbers NMW 68.576.GR32 and NMW 89.56G.M1).

In South Wales, axinite has been identified in thin prehnite-quartz-white mica veins cutting altered dacite at Garn Turne Rocks, south of Fishguard, in Dyfed (author's unpublished data).

Azurite   Monoclinic
$Cu_3(CO_3)_2(OH)_2$

A copper carbonate hydroxide which develops in the oxidized zone of copper-bearing ore bodies.

Although usually considered as a common secondary

Figure 41. Azurite on dolomite from Great Ormes Head, Llandudno, Gwynedd. Field of view 8 mm across. NMW specimen 77.36G.M16, *ex* R.W. Barstow Collection.

mineral in the oxidized zone of copper-bearing ore bodies, azurite is not widely developed in Wales. In North Wales fine azurite is found in association with malachite on dolomite at the Ty Gwyn Mine, Llandudno, Gwynedd. On Anglesey, azurite is found associated with malachite at the old copper mine at Pant-y-Gaseg, while a specimen in the National Museum of Wales (registration number NMW 60.250.GR2) is azurite with malachite supposedly from Parys Mountain, but the provenance is dubious.

In the Central Wales Mining District azurite is of rather restricted occurrence, as noted by Mason (1992), although Jones and Moreton (1977) record its presence at a number of mines, including Penrhiw, Darren, Llettyhen (Vaughan), Snowbrook, Cwmystwyth, Dylife, Mynyddgorddu and Esgairfraith. It has also been recorded from the South Nantycar Mine, southwest of Rhayader (*British Micromount Society Newsletter*, No. 34). Many of the blue crusts found in this area, however, comprise other secondary copper minerals, in particular linarite. Crystalline azurite is found, however, at Bwlchrhennaid Mine, forming crusts associated with malachite.

In the Borderlands finely crystalline azurite is known from the old copper workings at Llanymynech (on NMW specimen 83.41G.M4786, for example).

An interesting report of azurite, along with malachite, is from the green and grey sandstones of Devonian age exposed at various localities in south Pembrokeshire (Dixon, 1921), although the identification needs confirmation. More recently Fletcher and Young (1988) recorded azurite along with aurichalcite, rosasite, and zincian malachite from the Locks Common borehole, at Porthcawl, Mid Glamorgan, while the presence of azurite at Hendy Quarry, Miskin, was reported in the *British Micromount Society Newsletter*, No. 35.

Banalsite   Orthorhombic
$BaNa_2Al_4Si_4O_{16}$
A rare barium sodium aluminium silicate belonging to the feldspar group.

Banalsite was described as a new mineral by Campbell *et al.* (1944a and b) from Benallt Mine, near Rhiw, Llŷn during the Second World War when the mine was re-opened by the Home Ore Department of Iron and Steel Control of the Ministry of Defence. The name banalsite was taken from the chemical composition of the mineral. It was discovered first in July 1943 in ore 'on the footwall side of no. 1 ore-body by no. 1 Chute, 50-60 feet west of the main shaft, some 10-20 feet above the 130-foot level'; a little later it was found in the no. 2 ore-body. Still later, crystalline banalsite was found in the no. 5 ore-body (Campbell Smith, 1945). Associated minerals in the Benallt Mine include calcite, barite, tephroite, alleghanyite, jacobsite, biotite, natrolite, and harmotome.

Bannisterite   Monoclinic
$KCa(Mn,Fe^{+2},Zn,Mg)_{20}(Si,Al)_{32}O_{76}(OH)_{16}.4-12H_2O$
A potassium calcium manganese iron zinc magnesium aluminium silicate hydroxide hydrate which is found in manganese ore deposits.

Some of the cinnamon-brown crystals associated with calcite on fracture surfaces in manganese ore from the Tŷ Canol incline at Benallt Mine, Llŷn, described by Campbell Smith (1948) were subsequently shown by Smith and Frondel (1968) to be the new mineral bannisterite.

Barite   Orthorhombic
$BaSO_4$
Barium sulphate. Barite is a common gangue mineral in sulphide-bearing mineral veins.

Barite is widely developed in Wales, occurring in particular as a gangue in mineral veins; accordingly only a few occurrences are described.

In the Central Wales Mining District, barite is particularly abundant at a number of mines to the NW of Llanidloes, including Aberdaunant, Bryntail, Gorn, and Pen-y-Clun (Carruthers *et al.*, 1915). Typically it is associated with witherite and more rarely harmotome. Morgan and Starkey (1991) described barite from Pen-y-Clun Mine as forming 'rough tabular crystals' up to 5-10 mm across, as well as small (1-2 mm), colourless euhedral crystals in cavities in witherite. Further west,

Figure 42. Bladed barite (pink) associated with calcite from Taff's Well Quarry, Mid Glamorgan. The blades are up to 27 mm in length. NMW specimen 87.73G.M42, *ex* A. Dean Collection.

Figure 43. Yellow prismatic barite crystals up to 7 mm in length, collected in 1985 from the Llwyn-saer Engine House dump at Mwyndy Mine, Llantrisant, Mid Glamorgan. I. Jones Collection.

barite is an important component in veins at Bwlchygarreg, on the Esgair Hir lode (J.S. Mason, *personal communication*).

In North Wales barite is found at Pennant Mine near St. Asaph, Clwyd, where it occurs in association with galena, sphalerite and witherite (Carruthers *et al.*, 1915). Further west, on Llŷn, massive barite was extracted at Pompren Mine, near Aberdaron, where it occurs in a fault zone associated with quartz. Elsewhere in North Wales barite is found at a number of mines in the Llangynog district of Powys, in particular Cwm Orog, Craig Rhiwarth, Craig-y-Mwyn, and Llangynog, while Bick (1978) illustrated a clear single barite crystal from an old mine at Galltymain, near Meifod.

Barite is also present at the Weston Mine, near Middletown, Powys, where it forms clear, euhedral, tabular crystals typically up to 1.5 cm across, although a poorly-formed, clear, tabular, single crystal reaching 12 cm across from this locality is in the Mineral Collection of the National Museum of Wales.

In South Wales massive barite is a major component of mineral veins cutting Arenig sandstones at the Vale of Towy (Nant) Mine, near Carmarthen, from which it was once extracted commercially. The veins also contain minor argentiferous galena, chalcopyrite and sphalerite. According to Carruthers *et al.* (1915) it was also mined from the nearby Cystanog Mine, from veins which also contained argentiferous galena, chalcopyrite and sphalerite, as well as 'fahl-ore' (a synonym of tennantite and of tetrahedrite).

Further east, in Mid Glamorgan, barite occurs in lead-bearing veins which cut Liassic strata at Llangan Mine, near Bridgend. In addition, it is found in some abundance in numerous old mines and quarries in the area between Llantrisant and Machen. At Llantrisant, excellent barite specimens were recovered from the old Mwyndy Mine, where they occur as crudely radiating aggregates of colourless, euhedral, stubby tabular crystals up to 3 cm long; similar specimens have also been collected from Cwmleyshon Quarry, near Draethen. Of particular note from the Llantrisant area is a single, well-formed crystal 5 cm in length, now in the collections of the National Museum of Wales. It is said to be from the Mwyndy Mine, and was donated by the Cymmer Colliery Workmen's Institute. Also from the Llantrisant area are well-formed tabular yellow-stained barite crystals up to 2 cm in length, from Llwyn-saer Mine. Recently, Alabaster (1990) reported barite as a gangue component, along with witherite, dolomite and calcite, associated with various sulphide minerals in Triassic rocks of the Llantrisant area. Attractive barite specimens have been collected from Taff's Well Quarry, where they form pink cockscomb aggregates associated with calcite and small, colourless quartz crystals. Individual blades can reach up to 6 cm across. Barite is also a minor component of the mineral assemblage present in clay ironstone nodules from the South Wales Coalfield, having been recorded, for example, form the Lewis Merthyr, Bedwas, and Deep Navigation collieries.

Figure 44. Elongate, 5 cm long, yellow barite crystal from Mwyndy Mine, Llantrisant, Mid Glamorgan. NMW specimen 25.554.GR25, *ex* Cymmer Colliery Workmen's Library.

Further to the south, barite is commonly found in veins cutting Mesozoic strata exposed on the coast between Penarth and Sully.

Barroisite   Monoclinic
$NaCa(Mg,Fe^{+2})_3Al_2(Si_7Al)O_{22}(OH)_2$
A sodium calcium iron magnesium aluminium silicate hydroxide of the amphibole group which forms a series with ferrobarroisite. Barroisite is a rock-forming mineral occurring in metamorphosed basic igneous rocks.

Greenly (1919) reported that blue amphiboles in mica schists of the Mona Complex exposed beneath the Marquis of Anglesey's Monument near Llanfairpwllgwyngyll, on Anglesey possess green hornblende cores. Electron microprobe analyses by Gibbons and Gyopari (1986) have demonstrated, however, that these green amphiboles fall in the range barroisite-ferrobarroisite-winchite. Further occurrences of barroisitic amphiboles were reported by Gibbons and Gyopari (1986) from temporary roadcuttings related to construction of the Llanfairpwllgwyngyll bypass.

Barytocalcite   Monoclinic
$BaCa(CO_3)_2$
A rare barium calcium carbonate, trimorphous with alstonite and paralstonite.

North (1916) described a specimen of barytocalcite in the Mineral Collection of the British Museum presented in 1886 by Colonel Rimington which is said to have come from Glamorgan, although no more specific locality details are given. On the basis of a description provided by G.T. Prior ('as small white crystals and massive material, with pyrites and limonite on ferruginous quartz'), North (1916) thought it most likely that the specimen came from the Mwyndy district, near Llantrisant, Mid Glamorgan. A specimen in the Mineral Collection of the National Museum of Wales (NMW 25.554.GR7; donated by the Cymmer Colliery Workmans Library) is barytocalcite from Llantrisant (confirmed by X-ray diffraction NMW X-397). This specimen consists of colourless to yellowish, transparent bladed crystals and massive material associated with minor pyrite lining a cavity in siliceous iron ore (Alabaster, 1990).

Basaluminite   ?Hexagonal
$Al_4(SO_4)(OH)_{10}.5H_2O$
A rare secondary aluminium sulphate hydroxide hydrate.

The only known occurrence of basaluminite in Wales is that recorded by Ball (1969) from shattered black shales of the Clogau Group, exposed in a small roadside pit [SH 610 329] on the slopes of Moel Goedog, near Harlech, Gwynedd. At this locality a single cavity (*c.* 2x1 cm diameter) was observed, filled with a white earthy mineral, which on the basis of X-ray and differential thermal analysis proved to be basaluminite.

Beaverite   Trigonal
$PbCu^{+2}(Fe^{+3},Al)_2(SO_4)_2(OH)_6$
A lead copper iron aluminium sulphate hydroxide belonging to the alunite group. Beaverite occurs as a secondary mineral in the oxidized zone of lead and copper mineral deposits.

Beaverite has been identified from the Ystrad Einion Mine, near Talybont, in the Central Wales Mining District, with confirmation by X-ray diffraction at the Natural History Museum, London (*British Micromount Society Newsletter*, No. 35).

Bementite   Monoclinic
$Mn_8Si_6O_{15}(OH)_{10}$
A rare manganese silicate hydroxide, occurring in manganese ore deposits.

A specimen in the Natural History Museum, registration number B.M. 1964, R10624, is bementite from the Nant Mine, Llŷn.

Berthierite   Orthorhombic
$FeSb_2S_4$
An iron antimony sulphide which typically occurs in low temperature vein deposits associated with stibnite.

Readwin (1888) reported the presence of berthierite in the Dolgellau Gold Belt, Gwynedd.

Beudantite   Trigonal
$PbFe_3(AsO_4)(SO_4)(OH)_6$
A lead iron arsenate sulphate hydroxide, belonging to the

beudantite group of minerals. It occurs as a secondary mineral in the oxidized zones of lead-bearing ore bodies.

Beudantite has been identified from Ystrad Einion Mine, near Tre'r-ddol, in the Central Wales Mining District (S.A. Rust, *personal communication*), confirmed by X-ray diffraction at the Natural History Museum.

Bindheimite   Cubic
$Pb_2Sb_2O_6(O,OH)$

A lead antimony oxide hydroxide, belonging to the stibiconite group, commonly found in the oxidized zone of lead-antimony ore deposits.

Bindheimite was first described from Wales as a brownish-yellow crust on and replacing semseyite at Bwlch Mine, near Deganwy, Gwynedd (Russell, 1944). The presence of bindheimite at this mine has been confirmed subsequently by infra-red spectroscopy of light brown crusts on stibnite and quartz (G. Ryback, *personal communication*). Jones and Moreton (1977) recorded bindheimite from the Frongoch and Nantycagl (Eaglebrook) Mines, in Dyfed. The former occurrence has been verified by X-ray diffraction investigations (Natural History Museum X-ray no. 13502) while more recently it has also been confirmed from the Bwlchrhennaid and Goginan Mines, near Goginan (Natural History Museum X-ray nos. 6335F and 6718F, respectively). In fact, bindheimite is probably widespread in the Central Wales Mining District. Yellow pseudomorphs of bindheimite after ullmannite occur at Hendrefelen, Frongoch, and Mynyddgorddu (Clark and Rust, 1993; J.S. Mason, *personal communication*).

Yellow coatings on galena from Machen Quarry, Mid Glamorgan have been shown to contain antimony, and are most probably bindheimite also (T.F. Bridges, *personal communication*).

Biotite   Monoclinic
$K(Mg,Fe^{2+})_3(Al,Fe^{3+})Si_3O_{10}(OH,F)_2$

A potassium magnesium iron aluminium silicate hydroxide belonging to the mica group and forming a series with phlogopite. Biotite occurs as a constituent mineral in medium to high grade metamorphic rocks, as well as a minor component in intermediate to acid igneous rocks, such as granite. More rarely it is a late stage magmatic mineral in gabbroic rocks.

Biotite is widespread in Wales, occurring in a variety of different rock types and settings. In the St. David's Head Intrusion, Dyfed, magmatic, titanium-rich biotite associated with titanium-rich pargasite and hastingsite is present as a constituent of laminated olivine gabbros exposed on Carn Llidi (Roach, 1969). Elsewhere in South Wales, biotite is found as megacrysts (up to 5 cm across) in a monochiquitic basanite diatreme at Great House near Usk, Gwent (Boulton, 1911). The biotite is phlogopitic (D.T. Moffat, *personal communication).*

In North Wales biotite was described by Williams (1927) as being an important component of doleritic intrusions in central Snowdonia, including those near Llŷn Teyrn, Llŷn Du'r Arddu and Llŷn Llydaw. Subsequently, Roberts (1981) described a so-called

biotite zone in central Snowdonia, recording biotite also in basic tuffs and lavas in which plates reach up to 0.1 mm across, and characterized optically by a pale yellow to dark olive-green pleochroism. Williams (1930) noted biotite in the Bwlch y Cywion 'granite', in central Snowdonia, occurring as plates up to 3 mm across and showing grass-green to pale greenish-yellow pleochroism. In addition Williams (1930) described an 'interesting rock' at the eastern margin of an intrusive rhyolite exposed near Blaen-y-nant, in Snowdonia, composed of biotite, almandine garnet, magnetite and topaz. The biotite forms crystals up to 0.3 mm long and shows strong pleochroism from straw yellow to dark green.

In northern Snowdonia biotite is a component of certain facies of the Penmaenmawr Intrusion (Sargent, 1924), while further west, on Llŷn, biotite is a primary magmatic phase in the Rhiw Intrusion, where it forms plates up to 2.5 mm across in hornblende-metadolerites and hornblende picrites. It shows strong pale-yellow-brown to dark-red-brown pleochroism, but is commonly partially altered to chlorite (Hawkins, 1970).

Biotite is widely developed on Anglesey (Greenly, 1919), being present for example in granites, amphibolites and calc-silicate gneisses of Precambrian age (Horák, 1993).

Further to the south, Woodland (1938a) noted that biotite is an important component of certain Cambrian mudstones (so-called "bluestones") which also contain chlorite, spessartine and rhodochrosite in the vicinity of the Hendre Mines, on the northwest slopes of Moelfre, in the Harlech Dome. This has been confirmed subsequently by de Béthune (1972), who described small (≤ 40 mm) green-brown, pleochroic biotite porphyroblasts in "bluestone" from the same locality, and presented an electron microprobe analysis.

Birnessite   Monoclinic
$Na_4Mn_{14}O_{27}.9H_2O$

A sodium manganese oxide hydrate. A secondary mineral which develops in manganese deposits following the breakdown of primary manganese minerals.

Birnessite occurs on Natural History Museum specimen B.M. 1944, 28, from Benallt Mine, Llŷn.

Bismuth   Trigonal
Bi

Native bismuth. Bismuth belongs to the arsenic group of minerals. A rare metal, found in hydrothermal veins and, more rarely, pegmatites.

Bismuth was recorded from the Dolgellau Gold Belt in Gwynedd by Readwin (see Andrew, 1910). Subsequently it has been recorded at the Clogau Mine, in the Dolgellau Gold Belt, as small (10-40 μm) inclusions in galena in sulphide-dominated telluride assemblages (Naden, 1988).

Bismuth is also found at Parys Mountain, on Anglesey, where it occurs as small laths (5-10 μm) enclosed in aggregates of bismuthinite and bismuth sulphosalts (Sivaprakash, 1977; Pointon and Ixer, 1980).

Bismuthinite   Orthorhombic
Bi_2S_3
A bismuth sulphide which forms in hydrothermal veins, commonly in association with chalcopyrite.

Greenly (1919) described a foliated to scaly, steel-grey, metallic mineral associated with pyrite, chalcopyrite and quartz from Rhôs-mynach-fawr, on Anglesey which was identified by H.H. Thomas of the Geological Survey as bismuthinite. A specimen of bismuthinite from this locality is preserved in the Mineral Collection of the National Museum of Wales as NMW 27.111.GR476, while another is in the Natural History Museum, being *ex* Russell Collection no. 204. Elsewhere on Anglesey, Pointon and Ixer (1980) have identified very minor bismuthinite containing native bismuth laths in the Parys Mountain copper deposit.

Bismuthinite was recorded from the Dolgellau Gold Belt in Gwynedd by Readwin (1888), and more lately specifically by Naden (1988) from the Clogau Mine as small (50 μm) inclusions in galena, associated with tetradymite, and bismuth in sulphide-dominated telluride assemblages.

Bixbyite   Cubic
$(Mn^{+3},Fe^{+3})_2O_3$
A manganese iron oxide which is found in manganese ore bodies, as well as a minor constituent of certain rhyolitic lavas.

Bixbyite has been identified associated with hausmannite from Benallt Mine, Llŷn, on the basis of X-ray diffraction (Natural History Museum X-ray no. x3543). This represents the first verified occurrence of bixbyite in the British Isles.

Bornite   Orthorhombic
Cu_5FeS_4
A copper iron sulphide which occurs in association with chalcopyrite and pyrite in copper ore bodies.

Records of bornite in Wales are few. Dewey and Eastwood (1925) recorded 'peacock ore' from Drws-y-Coed Mine, near Nantlle and from Cwm Cynfal Mine, east of the old Ffestiniog railway station, both in Snowdonia, while Andrew (1910) noted the presence of bornite at Glasdir Mine, near Dolgellau, in southern Snowdonia. More recent descriptions are lacking but specimens identified as bornite and housed in the National Museum of Wales are from Dinorwic Quarry (confirmed by X-ray diffraction, NMW X-ray no. X828), Tal-y-sarn Quarry, Llanllyfni, Clogau, near Dolgellau, all in Snowdonia, and from Dylife and near to Devil's Bridge, in the Central Wales Mining District. Most of these require confirmation, however, as they may only be tarnished chalcopyrite. Bornite has been identified by optical means, however, from Llechweddhelyg Mine, associated with chalcocite and covellite as an alteration product of chalcopyrite (J.S. Mason, *personal communication*).

Botallackite   Monoclinic
$Cu_2Cl(OH)_3$
A copper chloride hydroxide, trimorphous with atacamite and paratacamite. Botallackite occurs as a secondary mineral in copper-bearing ore deposits.

The first, and so far only, record of botallackite from Wales is as minute turquoise-blue platey crystals and crystalline crusts associated with cuprite occurring as a natural weathering product of grey, vesicular slag from a dump site (now obliterated) at Halkyn, Clwyd. Two specimens from this locality were collected by M.P. Cooper in about 1965 and are preserved in the Mineral Collection of the National Museum of Wales, as registered specimens NMW 87.8G.M1 and NMW 87.8G.M2.

Bottinoite   Trigonal
$Ni[Sb^{5+}(OH)_6]_2.6H_2O$
A rare nickel hydrate antimony hydroxide, which occurs as an alteration product of ullmannite.

Clark and Rust (1993) recorded bottinoite as pale turquoise plates on ullmannite on specimens from Hendrefelen, near Ysbyty Ystwyth, and also on specimens from Mynyddgorddu, in the Central Wales Mining District, with confirmation by X-ray diffraction and electron microprobe analysis at the Natural History Museum, London. These records, along with a simultaneous description of the mineral from Brownley Hill Mine, at Nenthead, Cumbria, represent the first description of bottinoite from the British Isles.

Boulangerite   Monoclinic
$Pb_5Sb_4S_{11}$
A lead antimony sulphosalt mineral which occurs in antimony-bearing mineral veins along with stibnite and other lead antimony sulphosalts.

Boulangerite occurs at the Clogau Mine, near Dolgellau, Gwynedd, where it is present as isolated inclusions in quartz associated with gold and pyrite. Identification has been confirmed by electron microprobe analyses (Naden, 1988) on un-numbered specimens from the Kingsbury Collection in the Natural History Museum. It has also been tentatively identified by electron microprobe analysis from Bwlch Mine, near Deganwy, Gwynedd, in association with stibnite and other lead-antimony sulphosalt minerals (Bevins *et al.*, 1988). It is also recorded as being a component of a polymetallic assemblage from Alltycrib Mine, in the Central Wales Mining District (J.S. Mason, *personal communication*).

Bournonite   Orthorhombic
$PbCuSbS_3$
A lead copper antimony sulphide which forms a series with seligmannite. Bournonite occurs in hydrothermal veins, commonly in association with galena and other lead antimony sulphosalts.

Bournonite is recorded from Parys Mountain, Anglesey, as 5-30 μm grains associated with bismuth, bismuthinite and various bismuth sulphosalts (Wheatley, 1971; Sivaprakash, 1977; Pointon and Ixer, 1980).

At the Clogau Mine in the Dolgellau Gold Belt, Gwynedd, bournonite is found as 40-80 μm isolated inclusions in quartz, commonly associated with gold and pyrite (Naden, 1988).

In the Central Wales Mining District, bournonite is found as part of a polymetallic assemblage, occurring as visible grains in association with tetrahedrite at numerous mines, including Darren, South Darren, Cwmerfin, Cwmsymlog, Ceunant, Goginan, Bwlch, Llechweddhelyg, Pencraigddu, Nantyrarian, Bronfloyd, Esgair Hir, Alltycrib, and Leri Valley (Mason and Hughes, 1990; J.S. Mason, *personal communication*). Elsewhere in the area it occurs as microscopic inclusions in galena, as at Esgair Hir Mine (Rust and Mason, 1988).

Brammallite   Monoclinic
$(Na,H_3O)(Al,Mg,Fe)_2(Si,Al)_4O_{10}[(OH)_2,H_2O]$
A sodium-rich illite mica.

Brammallite was first described as a new mineral from Llandebie, Dyfed by Bannister (1943), forming white infillings to fissures or as coatings on slickensided surfaces in shales overlying the Coal Measures. The soft, fibrous mineral comprises small, compact tufts of elongated plates approximately 0.5 mm long. Identification was on the basis of optical, X-ray and (partial) chemical investigations. The mineral was named after Dr Alfred Brammall, formerly of the Department of Geology, Imperial College of Science and Technology. Brammallite has also been identified from the Dulais Seam, at Cefn Coed Colliery, West Glamorgan (Natural History Museum X-ray no. x2742).

Radiating colourless to white fibres from Pandora Mine, near Llŷn Geirionydd, Gwynedd have an X-ray powder pattern close to that of brammallite (Natural History Museum X-ray no. 19595).

Brannerite   Monoclinic
$(U,Ca,Y,Ce)(Ti,Fe)_2O_6$
A uranium calcium yttrium cerium titanium iron oxide which forms a series with thorutite, and is dimorphous with orthobrannerite. Brannerite occurs chiefly in pegmatites.

Eakin and Gize (1992) suggested that alteration rims on wedge-shaped uraninite from Llanddulas, Clwyd may be brannerite.

Braunite   Tetragonal
$Mn^{+2}Mn_6^{+3}SiO_{12}$
A manganese silicate (although sometimes listed as a manganese silicon oxide) which occurs in hydrothermal veins. It also occurs with manganese oxide minerals as a secondary weathering product.

Braunite occurs in manganese ore from a disused mine at Tŷ Coch, near Porthcawl, Mid Glamorgan where it forms euhedral to subhedral grains associated with hausmannite, interstitial and vug-filling calcite, manganocalcite, ferroan calcite, dolomite, barite and rarer pyrobelonite and vanadinite (Criddle and Symes, 1977). This report represented the first verified and

Figure 45. Bladed brochantite crystals up to 0.5 mm across, collected in 1993 from Lodge Park copper trial, near Tre'r-ddol, in the Central Wales Mining District. Specimen JMLP539 from the J.S. Mason Collection.

Figure 46. Brookite crystal from Fron Oleu, Prenteg, Gwynedd. The crystal measures 20 mm across. NMW specimen 75.38G.M1.

published occurrence of the mineral in the British Isles. However, braunite from Nant Mine, Llŷn, has been confirmed by X-ray diffraction (Natural History Museum X-ray nos. x17911 and x18399) on specimens from the Russell Collection, which were collected prior to the work of Criddle and Symes.

Brochantite   Monoclinic
$Cu_4(SO_4)(OH)_6$

A copper sulphate hydroxide which occurs in the oxidized zone of copper-bearing ore bodies, along with other secondary copper sulphates and carbonates.

Brochantite is quite widely distributed in Wales as a post-mining phase. Jones and Moreton (1977) mentioned only three occurrences in the Central Wales Mining District, namely Nantycagl (Eaglebrook), Dylife and Esgairfraith, but it is known from many more sites including Mynyddgorddu, Copa Hill, Esgair Hir, Geufron, Gwaithyrafon, Hendrefelen (all confirmed by X-ray diffraction at the Natural History Museum and the National Museum of Wales), as well as Ystrad Einion Mine (S.A. Rust, *personal communication*).

Further north, Saich and Rust (1987) recorded rare tabular brochantite crystals from an old trial 1.5 km NW of Bontddu, near Dolgellau. Elsewhere in North Wales brochantite was identified occurring with posnjakite, chalcoalumite, malachite and lanthanite-(Ce) at Britannia Mine, in central Snowdonia (Bevins *et al.*, 1985).

In South Wales the only record of brochantite is in association with linarite and cerussite from dump material at Bonville's shaft, Vale of Towy Mine near

Carmarthen, Dyfed (G. Ryback, *personal communication*).

Brookite   Orthorhombic
TiO_2

A titanium oxide, trimorphous with anatase and rutile. Brookite occurs as an accessory mineral in acidic igneous rocks, in low grade metamorphic rocks, and in Alpine-type mineral veins along with quartz, chlorite, anatase, and albite.

J. Sowerby (1809), in volume III of his book *'British Mineralogy'* figured 'oxide of titanium' (p.197, tab 299). This is certainly the mineral brookite, and the illustrated specimen is preserved in the Mineral Collection of the Natural History Museum as B.M. 31715. The specimen was collected by Wilson Lowry and the locality from which the specimen came is given as 'near Snowdon'.

The first complete description of the mineral brookite was by Lévy (1825), in describing crystals provided for him by Sowerby and collected from 'Snowdon'. The mineral, which had previously been identified variously as rutile and sphene (titanite), was named brookite in honour of H.J. Brooke (1771-1857), the British crystallographer and mineralogist. A few years later G.B. Sowerby (1838) was more specific as to the locality from which the brookite specimen was actually collected, stating that 'it is on the road side between Beddgelert and Tremaddoc, Carnarvonshire, about 8 miles from Snowdon'.

Subsequently, brookite was described from Treffgarne Rocks, in Dyfed (Perceval, 1866b), as small well-

Figure 47. Tabular brookite (2.5 mm across) and anatase from Hendre Quarry, near Glyn Ceiriog, Clwyd. Collected January 1988. Specimen NH1886 from the N. Hubbard Collection.

formed, tabular, brown to honey-yellow bevelled crystals, although previously (Perceval, 1866a) had considered this mineral to be wulfenite. Perceval's specimens are preserved in the Natural History Museum as B.M. 44109 and B.M. 44110.

Brookite is now known to occur in many parts of Wales, in particular in altered igneous intrusions such as dolerites and microgranites, or in quartz veins cutting such rocks, as for example at Prenteg, Gwynedd (see Fearnsides, 1912), Hendre Quarry, Clwyd (Starkey *et al.*, 1991), Bwlch-y-Cywion, Gwynedd (Williams, 1930), Gimlet Quarry, Gwynedd (Harrison, 1894, 1897), Arenig Station Quarry, Gwynedd (G. Ryback, *personal communication*), and Manod Quarry, near Blaenau Ffestiniog, Gwynedd (National Museum of Wales specimens NMW 84.41G.M4 and NMW 87.21G.M7, both *ex* T.F. Bridges Collection). Some of the finest crystals from Wales are from the now classic locality at Fron Oleu (Fronolen on some maps), near Prenteg, Gwynedd, for example National Museum of Wales specimen NMW 75.38G.M1. A detailed account of this locality was recently provided by Starkey and Robinson (1992).

Brookite is also commonly found as a detrital mineral, as for example in the red beds of Anglesey (Greenly, 1919), and the Silurian strata of the Denbighshire Moors region (Warren *et al.*, 1984).

Brucite   Trigonal
$Mg(OH)_2$
A magnesium hydroxide mineral belonging to the brucite group. Brucite typically occurs in serpentinites, metamorphosed limestones and calcareous schists.

To date the only record of brucite in Wales is that by Greenly (1919) who described its presence as bright green scales in talc schists in altered ultrabasic rocks (serpentinites) exposed on a small islet in Rhyd-y-Bont Creek, Holy Island, Anglesey.

Bytownite   Triclinic
$(Ca,Na)Al(Al,Si)_3O_8$
A calcium sodium aluminosilicate belonging to the feldspar group, with An_{70-90}. Bytownite is an important rock-forming mineral in igneous rocks of basic composition.

Due to the effects of low-temperature alteration many bytownite crystals in basic rocks in Wales have been replaced by more sodic members of the plagioclase series, principally albite. Greenly (1919) reported bytownite in post-Carboniferous dykes from Anglesey, although no specific localities are referred to. Hawkins (1970) and Cattermole (1976) both described the presence of bytownite in the Rhiw Intrusion, Llŷn, although determinations were only on the basis of optical properties, as were descriptions of bytownite in olivine dolerite dykes from Parc Mine, near Llanrwst by Archer and Elliot (1965). Similarly, Roach (1969) identified bytownite in certain gabbros of the St. David's Head Intrusion, an identification which has been confirmed subsequently on the basis of electron microprobe analyses (author's unpublished data).

Figure 48. Doubly-terminated, orange-tipped calcite crystal 6 cm in length from Taff's Well Quarry, Taff's Well, Mid Glamorgan. Collected 1981. I. Jones Collection, specimen 1174.

Calaverite   Monoclinic
AuTe$_2$
A rare gold telluride mineral found in gold-bearing mineral veins.

Gilbey (1968) tentatively identified calaverite from Panorama Mine in the Dolgellau Gold Belt, Gwynedd, occurring in galena replacing pyrrhotite. However, it has been suggested that the dumps at Panorama Mine were seeded with material from Clogau Mine (L. Haynes, *personal communication, via* J. Naden), although Naden (1988) specifically noted that no gold tellurides were observed during his investigation of the Clogau Mine mineralization, and hence the record requires validation. If verified, this occurrence would represent the first report of calaverite in the British Isles.

Calciovolborthite   Orthorhombic
CaCu(VO$_4$)(OH)
A calcium copper vanadate hydroxide which belongs to the adelite group and which forms a series with conichalcite.

The only known record of calciovolborthite from Wales is a single specimen in the private collection of C. Hedegaard (Denmark), which is calciovolborthite associated with quartz and chalcocite from 'Bethesda

Slate Quarry', which is presumably Penrhyn Quarry, at Bethesda, in Gwynedd. No further details of this occurrence are known.

Calcite   Trigonal
CaCO$_3$
Calcium carbonate, trimorphous with aragonite and vaterite, and forming a series with rhodochrosite. It belongs to the calcite group of minerals, and is of widespread occurrence and paragenesis, being an important constituent of various igneous, metamorphic, and sedimentary rocks, and additionally a frequent component of hydrothermal veins.

Calcite is very widely developed in Wales in view of the widespread distribution of limestones, principally of Carboniferous age. In these rocks calcite is the main constituent, and vugs and cavities tend to be lined with well-formed crystals. Occurrences are so numerous that only a few of the more notable are described below.

Excellent rhombohedral and scalenohedral calcite specimens have long been known from the Carboniferous Limestone of the South Wales Coalfield area, in particular from Taff's Well Quarry, Castell Coch Quarry, Blaengwynlais Quarry, Creigiau Quarry and the Little Garth Iron Mine (North, 1916), to name but a few. Of particular note from this area is a specimen collected

Figure 49. Nailhead calcite crystals on hematite matrix from Llanharry Mine, Llanharry, Mid Glamorgan. The specimen measures 11 cm x 7 cm. NMW specimen 62.433.GR1.

in 1987 from Taff's Well Quarry, and donated to the National Museum of Wales. On this specimen scalenohedral crystals reach up to 30 cm in length. Attractive 'dog-tooth' calcites from the Llantrisant area are in the Mineral Collection of the National Museum of Wales. Further east, fine scalenohedral crystals have been recovered from Caerwent Quarry, at Caerwent, Gwent.

Calcite is quite widely developed in the Central Wales Mining District, although notable occurrences are few. Nailhead calcite crystals from Logaulas were noted by Greg and Lettson (1858), from where specimens have recently been recovered from Level Fawr (specimens in the National Museum of Wales, collected by J.S. Mason). Elsewhere in the region, excellent crystals are known from Nantiago Mine, while Jones and Moreton (1977) recorded excellent flat rhombohedral calcite from Penrhiw Mine.

Further north attractive calcite crystals are known from various localities. In the Llanrwst area, mineral veins cutting Lower Palaeozoic strata commonly carry well-formed calcite. Of particular note are rhombohedral calcites from Parc and Trecastell Mines, which are commonly coated with pyrite, or contain inclusions of marcasite. Bladed calcite ('schieferspar') is also known from Parc Mine. Further south, well-formed nailhead calcite crystals have been collected from Bwlch-y-Plwm, at Penrhyndeudraeth.

Excellent calcites are also known in North Wales from various areas of the Carboniferous Limestone outcrop. In the Minera district well-formed nailhead and 'iceland spar' crystals are present. Further northwest calcite crystals of various forms and colours are known from the Halkyn Mountain area. Mountain (1924) described and illustrated calcite crystals from Bryn-gwiog Mine. Fine specimens from this area currently in the Mineral Collection of the National Museum of Wales include an aggregate of yellow rhombohedral crystals from Halkyn Mine, and a specimen of white, 'dog-tooth' crystals from Rhosesmor Mine, while a highly vitreous nailhead calcite specimen is from Pant-y-buarth Mine, near Mold.

In the Welsh Borderland, well formed, yellow rhombohedral calcites are known from Weston Mine, near Middletown, Powys.

Caledonite   Orthorhombic
$Pb_5Cu_2(CO_3)(SO_4)_3(OH)_6$
A lead copper carbonate sulphate hydroxide which occurs in the oxidized zone of lead- and copper-bearing ore bodies.

Caledonite is present as light blue to bluish-green prismatic crystals up to 0.7 mm in length, as divergent crystal groups up to 2 mm, and rarely as botryoidal aggregates, associated with leadhillite, cerussite, langite and anglesite at Esgair Hir Mine, Dyfed (Rust and Mason, 1988),with identification confirmed by X-ray diffraction at the Natural History Museum, X-ray no. 4512-F. More recently, caledonite has been confirmed from a number of other mines in the Central Wales

Figure 50. Acicular caledonite crystal aggregates up to 2 mm across from Esgair Hir Mine, in the Central Wales Mining District, Dyfed. Specimen 920 from the S.A. Rust Collection.

Mining District, including Darren, Llechweddhelyg, Esgairmwyn, Hendrefelen and Dylife (S. Rust, *personal communication,* see also Clark and Rust, 1993; all identified by X-ray diffraction at the Natural History Museum), South Nantycar (*British Micromount Society Newsletter,* No. 34), Brynyrafr (*British Micromount Society Newsletter,* No. 35) and Frongoch, Bwlchrhennaid and Glogfawr (R.S.W. Braithwaite, *personal communication*). In all cases in this region, however, caledonite is likely to have been formed on the mine dumps.

Carbonate-fluorapatite (syn. francolite)   Hexagonal
$Ca_5(PO_4,CO_3)_3F$
A calcium phosphate carbonate fluoride belonging to the apatite group of minerals. It is an important constituent of primary phosphatic rocks, and also of certain ironstones.

Trythall (1988) recorded that nodules from Ordovician ironstones exposed across North Wales, although previously referred to as being composed of collophane (amorphous apatite), in fact have X-ray diffraction patterns diagnostic of carbonate-fluorapatite.

Carbonate-hydroxylapatite (syn. dahllite)   Hexagonal
$Ca_5(PO_4,CO_3)_3(OH)$
A calcium phosphate carbonate hydroxide belonging to the apatite group of minerals.

Oakley (1934) reported the presence of 'dahllite' forming pearl-like bodies in cells of fossil corals from Silurian strata exposed at Tŷ Mawr, Rumney, South Glamorgan. This account represented the first record of carbonate-hydroxylapatite in the British Isles. More recently, Niedermeyer and Langbein (1989) have shown that bacteriogenic pebble coats (so-called *'bolopora'*), which occur in rocks of Arenig age over a wide area of Wales, are composed of carbonate-hydroxylapatite.

Cassiterite   Tetragonal
SnO_2
The oxide and principle ore of tin. Cassiterite belongs to the rutile group of minerals. It is usually found in high temperature veins associated with granite. Because of its hardness and high density, however, cassiterite also occurs in placer deposits.

Perceval (1866a) reported the presence of cassiterite at Treffgarne Rocks, Dyfed, although this was later correctly identified as brookite (Perceval, 1866b). More recently very small grains of cassiterite have been identified in a WNW-trending quartz-magnetite-hematite-pyrite vein in Cwm Tregalan, in Snowdonia, cutting rocks of the Snowdon Volcanic Group (Reedman *et al.,* 1985). The vein contains up to 1000 ppm Sn and W.

Celadonite   Monoclinic
$K(Mg,Fe^{+2})(Fe^{+3},Al)Si_4O_{10}(OH)_2$
A potassium-rich member of the mica group, typically developed in altered basic volcanic rocks.

Celadonite has been identified as a thin green coating on altered tuffs of Ordovician age at Llanelwedd Quarry,

near Builth Wells, Powys, and as coatings of similar character on basic lavas of Silurian age in the vicinity of the Mew Stone, on Skomer Island, Dyfed. Both occurrences have been verified by X-ray diffraction investigations (author's unpublished data). Celadonite is also sparingly present in Precambrian volcaniclastic siltstones of the Coomb Volcanic Formation exposed in the Llangynog district of Dyfed (Cope and Bevins, 1993).

Celestine   Orthorhombic
$SrSO_4$
A strontium sulphate mineral belonging to the barite group and which forms a series with barite. Celestine commonly occurs in thin beds and also nodules in sedimentary sequences.

The first record of celestine in Wales was by Conybeare and Phillips (1822) who reported the presence of 'geodes filled with crystals of sulphate of Strontian', from Barry Island, South Glamorgan. Howard (1895) remarked, however, that tabular, rhombic, blue crystals discovered during the excavation of Barry Dock proved to be the variety barytocelestine, quoting an analysis '$BaSO_4$ 43.01, $SrSO_4$ 56.99'. He further remarked that the 'same mineral' also occurred in fibrous form in thin veins cutting Carboniferous Limestone in a series of small quarries across Nell's Point, also on Barry Island, and (on information from J. Storrie) at Bendrick Rock, in the vicinity of Barry. Subsequently, North (1916) reported that celestine was to be found in strata of Lower Lias age in the nearby Penarth Quarries, while Cox and Trueman (1936) refered to the presence of celestine at Cogan.

A later account, by Thomas (1968), described the presence of celestine in road cuttings for the Llantrisant by-pass, Mid Glamorgan, occurring as massive or granular masses in geodes or forming nodules in Triassic Dolomitic Conglomerate. Later studies by Bowler and Kingston (1971) and subsequently by Alabaster (1990), however, have failed to confirm the occurrence of celestine in these exposures. Finally, Alkattan (1976) reported the presence of celestine and barite at Lavernock Point.

Celsian   Monoclinic
$BaAl_2Si_2O_8$
A rare barium aluminium silicate belonging to the feldspar group, dimorphous with paracelsian and forming a series with hyalophane and orthoclase.

The first report of celsian in the British Isles was a short note by Russell (1911) describing 'some finely crystallised mineral specimens from North Wales' which had been sent to him by G.J. Williams, then H.M. Inspector of Mines in Wales. At the time this represented only the second world-wide occurrence of the mineral, although a more complete description was not provided until many years later (Spencer, 1942). In this later account, celsian was described as entirely comprising a massive, granular rock from Benallt Mine, at Rhiw, on Llŷn. Two crystal forms were identified, one being long, slender to acicular prisms, up to 5 mm in length and rarely twinned on the Carlsbad Law, the other being

Figure 51. Twinned celsian crystal 10 mm across from Benallt Mine, near Rhiw, Llŷn. NMW specimen 27.111.GR381, *ex* G.J. Williams Collection.

larger, stout, short-prismatic crystals averaging 1 cm across and 0.05-1.0 mm in thickness, and typically twinned on the Manebach and Baveno Laws.

Cerussite   Orthorhombic

$PbCO_3$

Lead carbonate, belonging to the aragonite group. Cerussite is typically found in the oxidized zone of lead-bearing veins, usually as a coating on galena.

Cerussite is a widespread mineral in the lead-mining areas in Wales, and accordingly only a few of the occurrences are reported below.

The presence of cerussite in Wales was recorded by Thomas Pennant as early as 1778 from 'Flintshire', his so-called 'brown lead ore', or 'caulk' (or 'cauke'), being noted from Talacre Mine, Crecas, 'Claudh Mine, Holywell', and Silver Rake, Halkyn (Campbell Smith, 1913). From this area, cerussite has also been recorded from Jamaica Mine by Greg and Lettsom (1858), while specimens from the North Hendre, Caeau, and Rhosesmor Mines are in the collections of the National Museum of Wales.

In Snowdonia cerussite is known from a number of mines in the Llanrwst district, including Welsh Foxdale (Prior, 1906), Gorlan (Russell, 1944), and Llanrwst and Cyffty (National Museum of Wales collections). Further south, Readwin (1888) listed cerussite from the Dolgellau Gold Belt, although no specific locality details were presented.

Cerussite is widely developed in the Central Wales Mining District. Jones and Moreton (1977) reported its occurrence at a number of mines, including Aberdaunant, Esgair Hir, Nantycagl (Eaglebrook), as needle-like aggregates, Frongoch, as large, crystalline masses of up to several cm across, Logaulas, Copa Hill, Penycefn, Glogfawr, Snowbrook, Geufron and Mynyddgorddu. Specimens referred to by Greg and Lettsom (1858), and currently in the collections of the Natural History Museum, rank amongst the best cerussite specimens known from the British Isles. Other known occurrences include Dylife, Esgairmwyn, Llechweddhelyg, Darren, Bwlchrhennaid (all confirmed by X-ray diffraction at the

Figure 52. Colourless cerussite crystals, 1-2 mm across, on iron-rich matrix from Rhydfach Mine, near Talybont, in the Central Wales Mining District. Specimen JMRF003 from the J.S. Mason Collection.

Natural History Museum and the National Museum of Wales), Bwlchglas (Braithwaite, 1982b), Henfwlch (Mason, 1992), Rhydfach, Pandy, Bodcoll (J.S. Mason, *personal communication*), South Nantycar (*British Micromount Society Newsletter*, No. 34), Brynyrafr (*British Micromount Society Newsletter,* No. 35), Brynarian (Mason, 1992), and Florida Mine (National Museum of Wales collections).

Figure 53. Reticulate cerussite from Frongoch Mine, in the Central Wales Mining District. Field of view 18 mm across. Specimen JMFG510 from the J.S. Mason Collection.

In South Wales, cerussite is recorded from the Vale of Towy (Nant) Mine, near Carmarthen, Dyfed, occurring in association with linarite and brochantite on galena from Bonville's shaft (G. Ryback, *personal communication* and National Museum of Wales collections). Further east, cerussite occurs at Ochrwyth Quarry, near Risca, with confirmation by X-ray diffraction at the Natural History Museum, and at Machen Quarry (Mineral Collection, National Museum of Wales). Finally, excellent acicular cerussite has been collected from Nant-y-Mwyn Mine, at Rhandirmwyn, near Llandovery, Dyfed (National Museum of Wales collections).

Chalcanthite   Triclinic
$CuSO_4.5H_2O$
A copper sulphate hydrate which develops in the enriched zone of copper-bearing ore bodies associated with cuprite, native copper, etc. A member of the chalcanthite group.

Aikin (1797) reported the presence of 'sulphate of copper, crystallized and in solution' from Parys Mountain, on Anglesey. Mention of this occurrence was also made by Greg and Lettsom (1858) and by Hall (1868), who both listed the presence of 'blue vitriol' at Parys Mountain, and subsequently also by Greenly (1919).

Chalcoalumite   Monoclinic
$CuAl_4(SO_4)(OH)_{12}.3H_2O$
A copper aluminium sulphate hydroxide hydrate which develops in the oxidized zone of copper-bearing deposits.

Chalcoalumite is a rare mineral in Wales. Bevins *et al.* (1985) reported its occurrence associated with lanthanite-

(Ce), brochantite and posnjakite from Sneyd's Level at Britannia Mine, Snowdonia. More recently chalcoalumite has been identified forming extremely rare white replacements of laths of devilline, of a tyrolite-like mineral, and of malachite in a trial level near Bontddu, Gwynedd (Saich and Rust, 1987), with identification confirmed by X-ray diffraction at the Natural History Museum, X-ray no. 6256F.

Chalcocite   Monoclinic
Cu_2S
Copper sulphide which forms in the zone of supergene enrichment of copper-bearing ore bodies.

Chalcocite is rarely reported in Wales, but is widespread in the Central Wales Mining District. Jones and Moreton (1977) reported chalcocite from Nantycagl (Eaglebrook) Mine, while specimens in the collections of the National Museum of Wales are from the Frongoch and Llettyhen Mines. In addition, chalcocite is recorded from Llechweddhelyg, Camdwrbach, and Dolwen Mines, altering from chalcopyrite, associated with cuprite, covellite and native copper, and altering to malachite or chrysocolla (J.S. Mason, *personal communication).*

In North Wales chalcocite from Penrhyn Quarry, near Bethesda, Gwynedd has been confirmed by X-ray diffraction, Natural History Museum X-ray no. x16682, while a specimen of chalcocite from this locality is in the private collection of C. Hedegaard (Denmark). Elsewhere in North Wales, chalcocite is recorded from Porth Ysgo, near Aberdaron, Llŷn (Natural History Museum X-ray no. 4673F), from Parys Mountain (Greenly, 1919; Pointon and Ixer, 1980), and from the Great Ormes Head, Llandudno, on a single specimen now in the National Museum of Wales. In addition, Williams (1927) described an interesting occurrence of chalcocite replacing original groundmass in 'copper dolerites' (pillowed basalts) from Cwm Tregalan, in central Snowdonia.

In South Wales, chalcocite has been recorded from the Llantrisant district, in Mid Glamorgan, in association with digenite around galena (Bowler and Kingston, 1971).

Chalcophyllite   Trigonal
$Cu_{18}Al_2(AsO_4)_3(SO_4)_3(OH)_{27}.3H_2O$
A copper aluminium arsenate sulphate hydroxide hydrate. A rare secondary mineral found in the oxidized zone of copper-bearing ore bodies.

Chalcophyllite has been reported from a small number of mines in Wales. At Dylife Mine, Powys, it occurs as minute green crystals up to 0.2 mm associated with brochantite, linarite and langite (Rust and Rust, 1987; *British Micromount Society Newsletter,* No. 19); also at Dylife Mine it forms green, hexagonal platey rosettes up to 0.5 mm across associated with mimetite, and also occurs as encrustations with brochantite and serpierite (*British Micromount Society Newsletter,* No. 24); and finally in a trial level near Bontddu, Gwynedd, it forms thin crusts on joints, occurs as a replacement of malachite, or, very rarely is found as translucent, pale blue to greenish blue stalactites (Saich and Rust, 1987). All these occurrences have been confirmed by X-ray diffraction at the Natural History Museum.

Chalcopyrite   Tetragonal
$CuFeS_2$

A copper iron sulphide which belongs to the chalcopyrite group of minerals and forms a series with eskebornite. It occurs in low temperature hydrothermal veins, commonly in association with other sulphide minerals, in medium temperature deposits, in volcanogenic massive sulphide (VMS) deposits, and in volcanic-related disseminated ore bodies. It is the principal ore of copper.

Chalcopyrite is widely developed in Wales, and has been exploited at numerous mines in North and Central Wales. It is somewhat rarer, however, in South Wales. Commonly chalcopyrite occurs in quartz ± carbonate veins, along with sphalerite or galena. A comprehensive review of its occurrence in Wales is provided by Dewey and Eastwood (1925).

In Snowdonia important copper mines were located principally in central Snowdonia, such as the Britannia and Sygun mines, or the Simdde Dylluan and Drws-y-Coed mines in the Nantlle Valley further to the west. A few mines also operated in Cwm Pennant, to the southwest. In all these cases massive chalcopyrite was the main ore mineral and the host veins cut Ordovician sedimentary and volcanic rocks (see Reedman et al., 1985).

At Llandudno chalcopyrite associated with calcite and dolomite and commonly replaced by the secondary copper carbonates azurite and malachite is found at Great Ormes Head in veins cutting the Carboniferous Limestone. Well-formed tetrahedral-shaped crystals are known from this locality. The antiquity of this mine has been shown to date back to Bronze Age times (see, for example, Lewis, 1990).

On Anglesey, copper was the principal ore at the great Parys Mountain opencast site and at the nearby Mona Mine. It occurs both as massive chalcopyrite and as a component of bluestone ore in which chalcopyrite typically occurs as blebs in sphalerite forming a texture known as 'chalcopyrite disease' (Greenly, 1919; Pointon and Ixer, 1980).

Chalcopyrite was also an important mineral in many of the gold-bearing veins of the Dolgellau area in southern Snowdonia, such as at the Vigra and Clogau Mines. In the same district, however, other interesting occurrences of chalcopyrite are as low-grade disseminations in the Coed-y-Brenin porphyry copper deposit (Rice and Sharp, 1976), and in a mineralised breccia pipe at Glasdir (Allen and Easterbrook, 1978).

In the Central Wales Mining District chalcopyrite is relatively widespread, for example at Dylife, Esgairfraith and South Darren mines, occurring in mineralized faults cutting Ordovician and Silurian strata, and most commonly being associated with ferroan dolomite

Figure 54. Chalcopyrite (rich yellow, bottom left), associated with pyrite (pale yellow), galena (pale blue-white, top left), and sphalerite (grey, right), the latter showing 'chalcopyrite-disease'. Typical ore from Parys Mountain, Anglesey. Field of view 1.2 mm across. Specimen PM14, R.A. Ixer Collection.

Figure 55. Chalcopyrite from the Great Ormes Head, Llandudno, Gwynedd. The specimen measures 13.5 mm across. NMW specimen 77.35G.M47, *ex* R.W. Barstow.

gangue. Blister copper is recorded from Cwmystwyth, Geufron and Snowbrook by Jones and Moreton (1977).

In South Wales chalcopyrite is comparatively rare. It is recorded from mineral veins cutting Carboniferous Limestone in the Mynydd-y-Garreg district, near Kidwelly (Strahan *et al.,* 1909), in calcite-lined vughs at Bute Quarry, Llantrisant and in a borehole at Locks Common, Porthcawl (Fletcher and Young, 1988). It is also found in septarian clay ironstone nodules of the South Wales Coalfield region (Firth, 1971), in association with millerite, galena, sphalerite and siegenite. Although crystals in these nodules are small they are typically well formed tetrahedra with well-developed sphenoidal faces (Firth, 1971).

Chamosite   Monoclinic
$(Fe^{+2},Mg,Fe^{+3})_5Al(Si_3Al)O_{10}(OH,O)_8$
An iron magnesium aluminium silicate oxyhydroxide belonging to the chlorite group. Chamosite is dimorphous with orthochamosite, and forms a series with clinochlore. Following the nomenclature for the trioctahedral chlorites of Bayliss (1975), chamosite is a common mineral in Wales.

In reporting the first occurrence of stilpnomelane in Great Britain, at the Pen-yr-allt Mine, near Penrhyndeudraeth, Gwynedd, Hallimond (1924) remarked that oolites of the oolitic iron ores of Ordovician age exposed across North Wales, from Anglesey in the north, to the Cadair Idris area in the south, were composed of concentric layers of magnetite

set in a chamosite matrix. Further reference to these iron ores is provided by Hallimond (1925), and by Fearnsides (in Williams, 1930), while full locality information is given in Pulfrey (1933). Brief mention is also made by Matthews and Scoon (1964) describing a new occurrence of stilpnomelane at Tyllau Mwn, near Drws-y-nant, Dolgellau, in chamosite-bearing oolitic ironstones at the same stratigraphic horizon as that described by Hallimond and Pulfrey.

Chamosite is also widely developed as a secondary mineral in altered igneous rocks throughout Wales, forming pseudomorphs after primary mafic minerals such as olivine or pyroxene, as well as occurring in vesicles, veins and replacing groundmass. Descriptions of these chlorites have usually used the varietal nomenclature of Hey (1954), as for example in the work by Bevins and Rowbotham (1983), who reported the presence of brunsvigite, ripidolite and diabantite in low-grade metamorphosed igneous rocks from various parts of Wales. These correspond respectively to magnesian chamosite, magnesian aluminian chamosite (or iron aluminian clinochlore) and magnesian siliconian chamosite, following the classification of trioctahedral chlorites by Bayliss (1975).

Chamosite has been identified recently occurring in carbonaceous shales of Carboniferous age from Fforchaman Colliery, Cwmaman, near Aberdare, Mid Glamorgan. (National Museum of Wales X-ray No. 773).

Figure 56. Chalcopyrite tetrahedra from Caerau Colliery, Maesteg, Mid Glamorgan. Crystals reach up to 0.5 mm across. NMW specimen 73.9G.M55.1, *ex* J.N.M. Firth Collection.

Chloritoid
Monoclinic and triclinic
$(Fe^{+2},Mg,Mn)_2Al_4Si_2O_{10}(OH)_4$
An iron magnesium manganese aluminium silicate hydroxide which forms a series with carboirite. Chloritoid is developed typically in low and medium grade metamorphosed mudstones.

Chloritoid occurs widely in Snowdonia, being first reported from that region in Ordovician rhyolitic lavas by Harker (1889). More recently, chloritoid has been reported from Ordovician slates in the aureole of the Aber-Drosgl Intrusion (Evans, 1968) and also from exposures near Rhyd-ddu, as small (30-100 μm long, 6-20 μm wide) tabular porphyroblasts (Brearley, 1988). Analyses of the latter showed that they are Mn-rich chloritoids, with up to 8 wt% MnO. In addition, Roberts *et al.* (1989) noted that chloritoid occurs widely in Snowdonia in Ordovician mudstones belonging to the upper anchizone and epizone grades of metamorphism, for example in the Cwm Pennant area (see also Smith, 1988).

Chromite
Cubic
$Fe^{+2}Cr_2O_4$
An iron chromium oxide, belonging to the spinel group. It is dimorphous with donathite, and forms two series, with magnesiochromite and with hercynite. Chromite is

generally found associated with serpentinites or other ultramafic rocks.

Greenly (1919) reported chromite from various localities in chlorite-chromite-magnetite schists, talc schists, marbles and serpentinites of the Mona Complex, on Anglesey. Maltman (1977) confirmed this, describing chromite from the Mona Complex occurring in serpentinites in association with magnetite, minor picotite, leucoxenized ilmenite, and zircon. In South Wales, Boulton (1911) identified chromite in magnesian peridotite nodules in the Great House diatreme, near Usk, Gwent.

Chrysocolla
Monoclinic
$(Cu,Al)_2H_2Si_2O_5(OH)_4.nH_2O$
A copper aluminium silicate hydroxide which occurs in the oxidized zone of copper-bearing ore bodies.

Chrysocolla is of relatively restricted occurrence in Wales. Jones and Moreton (1977) reported the presence of botryoidal crusts of chrysocolla at Dylife Mine, and of earthy chrysocolla at Esgairfraith Mine, in the Central Wales Mining District. Elsewhere in the region chrysocolla as crusts have been recorded from Esgair Hir by Rust and Mason (1988), Gwaithyrafon (*British Micromount Society Newsletter*, No. 22), Llechweddhelyg (Jones, 1987), Llettyhen (NMW collections), and as infilling to voids in mudstone breccia at Mynyddgorddu (Clark and Rust, 1993). The last three occurrences have all been confirmed by X-ray diffraction at the National Museum of Wales. In addition, chrysocolla has been reported from Frongoch Mine (J.S. Mason, *personal communication*).

Records of chrysocolla from North Wales are few. A specimen in the collections of the National Museum of Wales is chrysocolla from Dinorwic Quarry (confirmed by X-ray diffraction), while Saich and Rust (1987) described chrysocolla from a trial level near Bontddu, in southern Snowdonia.

Chrysotile
Monoclinic
$Mg_3Si_2O_5(OH)_4$
A magnesium silicate hydroxide belonging to the kaolinite-serpentine group. Chrysotile generally develops as a result of alteration of mafic and ultramafic igneous rocks.

Greenly (1919) described the occurrence of chrysotile in a small quarry formerly worked for asbestos at Mynachdy, on Anglesey. The quarry exploited a small intrusion of serpentine, ophicalcite and altered dolerite.

A mineral from the Dulais Seam, at Cefn Coed Colliery, West Glamorgan, has been identified as 'amesite or chrysotile' (Natural History Museum X-ray no. x2724).

Cinnabar
Trigonal
HgS
Mercury sulphide, trimorphous with metacinnabar and hypercinnabar. Cinnabar typically forms in near-surface veins, or as impregnations associated with recent volcanic activity.

The only published account of cinnabar in Wales is that by Braithwaite (1982b) who identified the mineral forming brick-red powdery spots at Bwlchglas Mine, near Talybont, in the Central Wales Mining District. Cinnabar is also known from Machen Quarry, Mid Glamorgan, with specimens in the Mineral Collection of the National Museum of Wales. Identification was confirmed by qualitative energy dispersive analysis (T.F. Bridges, *personal communication*).

Clinochlore   Monoclinic
$(Mg,Fe^{+2})_5Al(Si_3Al)O_{10}(OH)_8$
A magnesium iron aluminium silicate hydroxide belonging to the chlorite group and forming a series with chamosite. Such chlorites are generally of secondary origin and develop in altered basic igneous rocks.

Following the nomenclature for the trioctahedral chlorites of Bayliss (1975), clinochlore is widely developed in Wales, being particularly abundant in altered basic igneous rocks. It pseudomorphs primary mafic minerals, such as olivine or pyroxene, infills veins or vesicles, or replaces groundmass. Bevins and Rowbotham (1983) identified chlorite as an important phase in altered basic igneous rocks throughout Wales and reported the presence of the varieties pycnochlorite and ripidolite (according to the classification of Hey, 1954), which correspond to iron clinochlore and iron aluminian clinochlore (following the chlorite nomenclature of Bayliss, 1975).

Clinoclase   Monoclinic
$Cu_3(AsO_4)(OH)_3$
A rare copper arsenate hydroxide, found in the oxidized zone of copper- and arsenic-bearing ore bodies.

Specimens in the National Museum of Wales with a bright blue friable coating on slate are labelled as clinoclase from the Ogwen Valley, Gwynedd. These most probably came from the site of the Tan-y-garth Mine, on the east side of the Ogwen Valley, near Bethesda, which formerly worked arsenopyrite. The ore is complex, also containing pyrite, chalcopyrite and pyrrhotite. X-ray diffraction investigation of supposed clinoclase from these specimens failed to confirm its identification, yielding only a very diffuse pattern. More recently clinoclase has been reported from the Great Orme mines, at Llandudno (Jenkins and Johnson, 1993).

Clinozoisite   Monoclinic
$Ca_2Al_3(SiO_4)_3(OH)$
Clinozoisite is a calcium aluminium silicate hydroxide of the epidote group. It forms a continuous series with epidote and is generally accepted as possessing less than 15 mol% $Ca_2FeAl_2Si_3O_{12}$ component. Clinozoisite develops typically in low-grade metabasic rocks.

Many early descriptions of altered basic igneous rocks from Wales referred to the presence of epidote. Roberts (1981), however, reported the occurrence of clinozoisite in such rocks from central Snowdonia and parts of Llŷn, while many so-called epidotes in metabasites from the Mynydd Preseli region of Dyfed are, in fact, clinozoisites (author's unpublished electron microprobe data).

Clinozoisite is probably, therefore, of greater abundance in Wales than has been recognised previously.

Clintonite (syn. xanthophyllite)   Monoclinic
$Ca(Mg,Al)_3(Al_3Si)O_{10}(OH)_2$
A calcium magnesium aluminium silicate hydroxide belonging to the mica group. Clintonite occurs in metamorphic rocks, in particular metamorphosed limestones.

Greenly (1919) described a strongly pleochroic (ruddy-brown to dull olivine-green) partly chloritised mica, which he considered to be clintonite, from two tectonic units on Anglesey. Firstly, Greenly reported its occurrence in hornfelses associated with the Coedana Granite, as for example *c.* 400 metres N of Bryn-ala and also in the vicinity of Llanfaelog Church, and secondly in graphite-schists of the Penmynydd Zone, exposed on the coast to the southwest of Llanfaelog. These occurrences represent the first record of clintonite in the British Isles but both however are dubious, and have not been verified in the course of recent studies in the area (J.M. Horák, *personal communication*).

Cobaltite   Cubic
$CoAsS$
A cobalt arsenic sulphide belonging to the cobaltite group of minerals. Cobaltite most commonly occurs in high temperature mineral deposits, associated with various cobalt and nickel sulphides.

Cobaltite is present in the Dolgellau Gold Belt region, being most abundantly developed in the southwestern extremity (Gilbey, 1968), especially at the Panorama and Vigra Mines. Gilbey (1968) also noted that it is found at the Wnion, Ffridd-goch, Afon Gain, Cefndeuddwr, Cefn Coch, and Clogau mines and trials. It forms cubes or pyritohedra up to 0.4 mm along their edge, included in chalcopyrite, pyrite, galena, sphalerite and pyrrhotite. At Clogau Mine cobaltite is associated with arsenopyrite and pyrrhotite crystals, the former often zoning from arsenopyrite cores to cobaltite rims (Naden, 1988).

Raybould (1976) reported the presence of small (20-30 μm), idiomorphic crystals of cobaltite enclosed by arsenopyrite at Hyddgen Mine, near Nant-y-moch Reservoir, in the Central Wales Mining District, although this has been re-interpreted as being cobaltian pyrite (J.S. Mason, *personal communication*).

Cobalt pentlandite   Cubic
Co_9S_8
A cobalt sulphide mineral belonging to the pentlandite group, and which forms a series with pentlandite. The mineral is relatively widespread as a replacement of siegenite.

Rust and Mason (1988) reported the presence of cobalt pentlandite at Esgair Hir Mine, in the Central Wales Mining District, occurring as a lamellar network in 'thiospinel'. This record represented the first description of cobalt pentlandite in the British Isles. Cobalt pentlandite has also been identified occurring as lamellae in siegenite and sometimes in chalcopyrite from a number of other mines in the Central Wales Mining

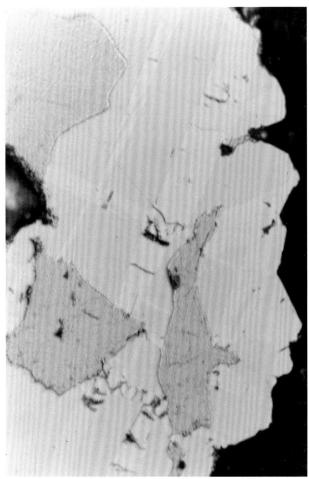

Figure 57. Lamellae of cobalt pentlandite (pale yellow) in siegenite (pale pink) from Erglodd Mine, in the Central Wales Mining District. Reflected light photomicrograph. Field of view is 150 μm across. *Ex* J.S. Mason Collection, now in the collection of the National Museum of Wales.

District, in particular Erglodd and Loveden, near Aberystwyth (J.S. Mason, *personal communication*).

Collophane
A massive fine grained member of the apatite group, usually carbonate-fluorapatite or carbonate-hydroxylapatite.

Woodland (1939b) described the presence of cryptocrystalline collophane intergrown with chlorite and associated with calcite in dark greenish-black, vitreous nodules set in a lighter matrix at the Benallt manganese mine, near Rhiw, Llŷn. This represented the first description of collophane from the British Isles. Groves (in Campbell Smith *et al.,* 1944b) noted that actually a small amount of collophane is present in virtually all manganese ore from the Benallt Mine, and reported that the largest and palest nodules in the No. 1 ore-body consist entirely of collophane. Collophane is also reported as being a minor component in the manganese ores of Cambrian age exposed in the Harlech Dome region in southern Snowdonia, forming nodules up to 0.5 mm in diameter in the Gamlan Flags (de Béthune, 1972).

Trythall (1988) recorded that the phosphate in nodules of the Ordovician ironstones exposed across North Wales

is commonly considered to be collophane, although X-ray diffraction of this material shows it to be carbonate-hydroxylapatite.

Connellite   Hexagonal
$Cu_{19}Cl_4(SO_4)(OH)_{32}.3H_2O$
A rare complex copper chloride sulphate hydroxide hydrate mineral found in the oxidized zone of certain base metal orebodies.

Connellite is very rare in Wales. It occurs as a crust of flattened blue needles associated with malachite forming a crust overlying masses of georgeite on Sneyd's Level, Britannia Mine, in central Snowdonia (Pollard *et al.,* 1989). Individual crystals reach up to 3 mm in length. Infrared spectroscopy shows the presence of CO_3^{2-} ions and the material was therefore identified as the new variety carbonatian connellite. Connellite has also been

Figure 58. Scanning electron micrograph of carbonatian connellite from Britannia Mine, Snowdonia, Gwynedd. NMW specimen 89.17G.M2. Reproduced with permission from the *Journal of the Russell Society.*

recorded from Gwaithyrafon Mine, near Cwmsymlog, Dyfed (Natural History Museum X-ray no. 8546F), and from Geufron Mine, near Llanidloes, Powys (*British Micromount Society Newsletter,* No. 33), possibly from Llettyhen Mine, near Talybont (*British Micromount Society Newsletter*, No. 36), and also recently from Lodge Park copper trial, near Tre'r-ddol (J.S. Mason, *personal communication*).

Cookeite   Monoclinic
$LiAl_4(Si_3Al)O_{10}(OH)_8$
A hydrous lithium aluminium silicate; a member of the chlorite group. Cookeite is a rare mineral, most often encountered in granite pegmatites.

The first record of cookeite in the British Isles was by Brammall *et al.* (1937) from Ogofau, near Pumsaint, Dyfed. It was found initially on the third (420-foot) level, occurring in small cavities along shear and fracture planes traversing both the ore-body and host shale. Subsequently it was found in drill cores at horizons below the 420-foot level. It forms patchy films or encrustations on other lode minerals.

Figure 59. Radiating connellite needles encrusting minute cuprite crystals (up to 0.2 mm across), from Lodge Park copper trial, Tre'r-ddol, in the Central Wales Mining District. Specimen JMLP515, from the J.S. Mason Collection.

Copiapite   Triclinic
$Fe^{+2}Fe^{3+}_4(SO_4)_6(OH)_2.20H_2O$
An iron sulphate hydroxide hydrate mineral belonging to the copiapite group of minerals, which typically develops in the oxidation zones of sulphide ore bodies and in post-mining environments.

Rare copiapite is developed on the floor of Cae Coch Mine, at Trefriw, Gwynedd, occurring in association with copious mounds of fibroferrite and jarosite (Johnson et al., 1979).

Copper   Cubic
Cu
Native copper. The most renowned occurrences of native copper are from altered basic lavas, such as the Keweenaw lavas in northern Michigan, U.S.A. It is also found, however, in the zone of enrichment in altered copper-bearing ore bodies.

In Wales, native copper is found infrequently in the enriched zones of ore bodies in the Central Wales Mining District. Jones and Moreton (1977) reported the presence of native copper at a small number of mines, namely Nantycagl (Eaglebrook), Dylife, and Cwmsymlog, although the latter occurrence has never been verified. Mason and Hughes (1990) and Mason

(1992) described its presence at Geufron Mine, while a further report in this district is from the Glogfawr Mine (*British Micromount Society Newsletter,* No. 16). In addition, it has also been recognised at the Ystrad Einion and Dolwen Mines (J.S. Mason, *personal communication*).

In southern Snowdonia, native copper has been recorded from the Dolgellau Gold Belt by Readwin (1888). In this area it is also known to be a constituent of the so-called 'Turf Copper', near Coed-y-Brenin (Allen and Jackson, 1985), which in fact is a copper-impregnated peat deposit that was exploited commercially in the early part of the 19th century.

Figure 60. Dendritic copper from Rhôs-mynach Mine, Anglesey. Field of view is 20 mm in the maximum dimension. NMW specimen 83.41G.M14, formerly K148 in the R.J. King Mineral Collection, *ex* Leicestershire Museums.

Greenly (1919) reported the presence of native copper forming leaf-like and moss-like aggregates at Parys Mountain, in gossan associated with the Great Lode. Elsewhere on Anglesey, native copper is also found at the Rhôs-mynach Mine, where it forms arborescent masses up to 6 cm in length (specimens in the National Museum of Wales from the R.J. King Collection).

A detailed account of arborescent native copper in Wales was provided by Vivian (1859), describing its presence at the Llandudno Mine, on the Great Ormes Head, in Gwynedd.

Cordierite   Orthorhombic
$Mg_2Al_4Si_5O_{18}$
A magnesium aluminium silicate, forming a series with sekaninaite and dimorphous with indialite. Cordierite forms as a result of contact metamorphism of mudstones and siltstones.

Bromley (1969) described ovoid, light to dark spots, usually between 1 mm and 5 mm in diameter composed of radial, concentric or sectoral aggregates of sericitic mica and chlorite, in sedimentary rocks surrounding the Tan-y-Grisiau microgranite, which he attributed to the replacement of cordierite and andalusite, stating that after a 'thorough search' cordierite was found at a few localities, although no specific sites are provided. Similarly Roach (1969) reported ovoid chlorite-rich pseudomorphs after cordierite in sedimentary rocks adjacent to the St. David's Head Intrusion in Dyfed.

Heard (1922) identified colourless grains of cordierite, partly altered to chlorite and containing inclusions of magnetite and zircon, as detrital grains in sandstones of the Pennant Series of Carboniferous age exposed to the east of the River Taff, in South Wales.

Corrensite
A clay mineral, with a 1:1 regular interstratification of trioctahedral chlorite with either trioctahedral vermiculite or trioctahedral smectite. Corrensite is a component of many mudstones and shales.

Merriman and Roberts (1985) described the occurrence of corrensite in rocks of Arenig and Llanvirn (Ordovician) age from Snowdonia and Llŷn, in mudstones close to intrusions and which had been affected by contact metamorphism prior to regional metamorphism. On Llŷn, chlorite/vermiculite is associated with basic intrusions of the Rhiw area, and chlorite/smectite is associated with intrusions in the Llanbedrog and Yr Eifl areas. More recently, Roberts and Merriman (1990) have identified corrensite as a component of metabentonites of Middle Cambrian age from the St. Tudwal's Peninsula, also on Llŷn.

Corundum   Trigonal
Al_2O_3
An aluminium oxide and a member of the hematite group of minerals. Corundum occurs in pegmatites, as well as in contact metamorphic zones.

Corundum has been identified in altered rhyolitic lavas and rhyolitic tuffs from a borehole near Treffgarne, Dyfed by Brown *et al.* (1987), although previously Heard (1922) had reported the presence of prismatic royal-blue corundum crystals in sandstones and shales of the Pennant Series of Carboniferous age exposed to the east of the River Taff, South Wales.

Covellite   Hexagonal
CuS
A copper sulphide which typically occurs as a secondary mineral in the oxidized and enriched zones of copper deposits.

Covellite is probably a comparatively common mineral in Wales, occurring as a replacement mineral after chalcopyrite, although literature records are few.

Bowler and Kingston (1971) identified thin covellite coatings on chalcopyrite at Llantrisant, Mid Glamorgan, formed during the oxidation and replacement of chalcopyrite by limonite.

Figure 61. Covellite (blue) associated with shattered pyrite (pale yellow), recemented by chalcopyrite (rich yellow) and galena (pale blue - white). Photographed in reflected light. This is typical ore from Parys Mountain, Anglesey. Field of view is 600 μm across. From the R.A. Ixer Collection.

In Central Wales covellite is common. It has been reported from Nantycagl (Eaglebrook) Mine (Jones and Moreton, 1977), from Esgair Hir Mine, where it forms rare platey hexagonal crystals up to 0.1 mm, and aggregates up to 2 mm (Rust and Mason, 1988), Dylife Mine (Rust and Rust, 1987), Bwlchrennaid Mine (*British Micromount Society Newsletter*, No. 18), Llechweddhelyg Mine (J.S. Mason, *personal communication*), and from South Nantycar Mine, near Rhayader, in Powys, forming iridescent coatings to chalcopyrite (*British Micromount Society Newsletter*, No. 34).

In North Wales Pointon and Ixer (1980) found covellite to be a relatively common replacement mineral after chalcopyrite at Parys Mountain, on Anglesey.

Gilbey (1968) reported covellite at numerous localities in the Dolgellau Gold Belt, such as Caegwian Mine; subsequently its presence was confirmed from Clogau Mine by Naden (1988), who reported its occurrence as a supergene alteration mineral surrounding galena.

Crossite   Monoclinic
$Na_2(Mg,Fe^{+2})_3(Al,Fe^{+3})_2Si_8O_{22}(OH)_2$
A sodium magnesium iron aluminium silicate hydroxide of the amphibole group which typically occurs in metamorphic rocks.

Holgate (1951) separated and analysed by wet-chemical methods blue amphiboles from schists of the Mona Complex exposed below the Marquis of Anglesey's Monument near Llanfairpwllgwyngyll, on Anglesey, and concluded that they were crossites, which represented the first description of the mineral from the British Isles. Subsequently Horák and Gibbons (1986) and Gibbons and Gyopari (1986) provided electron microprobe analyses of these amphiboles, and identified that in fact the green cores fall in the barroisite-ferrobarroisite-winchite range, while the blue rims plot in the crossite-glaucophane-ferroglaucophane fields. Although Holgate's original identification was therefore correct there are substantial differences between the wet-chemical and electron microprobe results, and it is doubtful that all of the green amphibole was effectively separated out during Holgate's investigations. Gibbons and Gyopari (1986) have also identified crossite in schists of similar age in a temporary roadcutting exposure during construction of the Llanfairpwllgwyngyll bypass.

Cubanite   Orthorhombic
CuFe$_2$S$_3$
A copper iron sulphide which is found in high temperature mineral deposits, often intimately associated with chalcopyrite.

Cubanite has been identified as forming oriented inclusions in chalcopyrite at Hendreforion Mine, in the Dolgellau Gold Belt (Gilbey, 1968).

Cuprite   Cubic
Cu$_2$O
Copper oxide. Cuprite is found most typically in the oxidized zone of copper deposits.

Records of cuprite in Wales are few, although it is

Figure 62. Cuprite cubes up to 0.2 mm scattered on a mudstone matrix from Lodge Park copper trial, near Tre'r-ddol, in the Central Wales Mining District. Specimen JMLP529, from the J.S. Mason Collection.

probably quite widely developed in the various copper deposits.

Figure 63. Close-up of cuprite cubes of Fig. 62, from Lodge Park copper trial, near Tre'r-ddol, in the Central Wales Mining District. Sample details as for Fig. 62.

In the Central Wales Mining District cuprite is recorded by Jones and Moreton (1977) from the Snowbrook, Geufron, and Nantycagl (Eaglebrook) Mines. The occurrence at Geufron was also noted by Mason and Hughes (1990), and by Mason (1992). Rust and Mason (1988) described the presence of cuprite at Esgair Hir Mine, associated with chalcocite, possible tenorite, and malachite. Elsewhere in the area cuprite has been identified from Dolwen, Ystrad Einion, Frongoch, Camdwrbach, Lodge Park copper trial, near Tre'r-ddol (J.S. Mason, *personal communication*), and Glogfawr (*British Micromount Society Newsletter*, No. 16). Generally in Central Wales, cuprite is poorly formed and at best finely crystalline.

In North Wales, cuprite has been reported from the mines at Great Ormes Head, Llandudno, Gwynedd (R.A. Ixer, *personal communication*), while Williams (1927) recorded acicular cuprite in association with biotite in vesicles in so-called 'copper dolerites' (pillow lavas) at Cwm Tregalan, in central Snowdonia. On Anglesey, cuprite occurs at Parys Mountain (Greenly, 1919), although no specific details are recorded.

Cymrite   Monoclinic
$BaAl_2Si_2(O,OH)_8.H_2O$
A rare barium aluminium silicate hydroxide hydrate.
Cymrite was first described from Wales, and takes its
name from the Welsh for Wales (Cymru).

Cymrite was first identified from Benallt Mine, near
Rhiw, Llŷn (Campbell Smith *et al.*, 1949), and so far this
is the only known Welsh locality for the mineral. Two
occurrences in the mine were described: firstly, on the
60-foot level in the no. 1 ore-body, forming colourless
plates up to 7 mm across and about 0.5 mm thick
(Natural History Museum specimen B.M. 1944, 48); and
secondly from the no. 5 ore-body as white crystals up to
1 mm in length closely associated with ganophyllite
(B.M. 1944, 36).

Descloizite   Orthorhombic
$PbZn(VO_4)(OH)$
A lead zinc vanadate hydroxide, belonging to the
descloizite group, and forming a series with mottramite.
It occurs typically in the oxidized zone of lead- and zinc-
bearing ore bodies.

Descloizite has been identified occurring in association with brochantite at Esgair Hir Mine, Dyfed
(Natural History Museum X-ray no. 6669F).

Figure 64. A spray (up to 0.75 mm across) of radiating, acicular
devilline crystals from a trial level near Bontddu, Gwynedd.
Specimen 331 from the S.A. Rust Collection.

Devilline   Monoclinic
$CaCu_4(SO_4)_2(OH)_6.3H_2O$
A calcium copper sulphate hydroxide hydrate found in
the oxidized zone of copper-bearing ore bodies.

Devilline is relatively rare in Wales. At Nantycagl
(Eaglebrook) Mine, in the Central Wales Mining District,
Jones and Moreton (1977) identified devilline in the
gossan, as rare blue-green interlaced crusts. This occurrence was subsequently confirmed by Braithwaite
(1982a), who described green blades of devilline up to
about 2 mm, coating fracture surfaces in massive
dolomite. Devilline is now known to occur at a small
number of other mines in the Central Wales Mining
District, such as Dylife where it forms green botryoidal
masses (Rust and Rust, 1987). In addition it has been
recorded from an old trial near Bontddu, in Gwynedd,
forming light blue-green to rich blue-green, lath-like
divergent crystals, tufted crystals on joints, and lattice-
like crystal crusts (Saich and Rust, 1987).

Diaspore   Orthorhombic
$AlO(OH)$
An aluminium oxide hydroxide, dimorphous with
böhmite. Diaspore typically develops as a weathering
product of aluminium-bearing rocks.

Griffiths and Stuart (1940) described the presence of
diaspore, along with other detrital minerals, in sandy
boulder clay at Ludchurch, Dyfed. The assemblage of
detrital minerals identified was considered by Griffiths
and Stuart (1940) as being typical of the Irish Sea Drift
of this area. The diaspore forms colourless plates up to
0.4 mm across.

Dickite   Monoclinic
$Al_2Si_2O_5(OH)_4$
An aluminium silicate hydroxide, polymorphous with
halloysite, kaolinite and nacrite, belonging to the
kaolinite-serpentine group. Dickite is a clay mineral
found in hydrothermal vein deposits, as well as forming
a cement in certain sedimentary rocks.

Until dickite was established as a new mineral species
by Ross and Kerr (1930), with its type locality of
Anglesey, there had been considerable confusion in the
literature. Kaolinite, nacrite and dickite were all
described under the name kaolinite and it became
essential, in view of their obvious differences, to
establish them as three discrete species. Dickite was so
named after Allan B. Dick, who had previously provided
extremely detailed descriptions (Dick, 1888, 1908) of the
mineral from Trwyn-Bychan, on Anglesey. At the type
locality dickite forms colourless to white hexagonal
plates or stacks of plates up to 0.1 mm across, on quartz
and dolomite.

Elsewhere in North Wales dickite is found as a rock
forming mineral, occurring in spaces between quartz
grains in sandstones of Carboniferous age (Brown and
Smithson, 1953; Smithson, 1954; Smithson and Brown,
1957). In Mid Wales it has been found at Dylife Mine,
near Staylittle, Powys (Natural History Museum X-ray
no. 7056F). In South Wales it is present in clay ironstone
nodules found in the Coal Measures (Firth, 1971), as

Figure 65. Dickite, from the type locality at Trwyn-Bychan, near Amlwch, Anglesey. The specimen measures 11 cm x 8.75 cm. NMW specimen 78.85G.M9.

Diopside is present in various ultrabasic and basic igneous rocks in Wales. For example, it is found in the Rhiw Intrusion, Llŷn (Hawkins, 1970), occurring in the Lower Ultrabasic Zone and the Lower Gabbro Zone (Cattermole, 1976), while Kokelaar (1977, 1986) reported the presence of diopside in cumulo-phyric lavas of the Rhobell Volcanic Complex, exposed in the Rhobell Fawr area, near Dolgellau, Gwynedd. In the Great House diatreme near Usk, Gwent, emerald-green chrome diopside occurs in magnesian peridotite xenoliths (D.T. Moffat, *personal communication*). In addition, many of the titanium-rich 'salite' pyroxenes from the Fishguard Volcanic Complex (Bevins, 1982), are diopsides according to the classification of Morimoto (1988), as are those described by Merriman *et al.* (1986) from the Tal y Fan Intrusion, Gwynedd.

Figure 66. Thin section of diopside phenocryst (4 mm across) showing slight compositional zoning, from a basanite dyke exposed at Golden Valley, near Chepstow, Gwent. NMW specimen 66.391.GR42b.

well as occurring in association with nacrite in the Aberfan borehole, Mid Glamorgan (Natural History Museum X-ray no. 1901F).

Digenite   Cubic
Cu_9S_5

A copper sulphide mineral which is typically developed in zones of supergene enrichment associated with copper-bearing ore bodies.

The only published record of digenite in Wales is by Bowler and Kingston (1971), who reported an intimate mixture of digenite and chalcocite replacing galena along its margins and along cleavage planes from the Llantrisant district, in Mid Glamorgan. Digenite has also been identified visually forming blue, isotropic rims up to 60 μm wide to chalcopyrite from mines at the Great Ormes Head, Llandudno, Gwynedd (R.A. Ixer, *personal communication*).

Diopside   Monoclinic
$CaMgSi_2O_6$

A calcium magnesium silicate belonging to the pyroxene group, and forming two series with hedenbergite and with johannsenite. Diopside is a primary mineral in ultra-basic and basic igneous rocks; in addition it forms as a result of high-grade metamorphism of calcareous rocks.

Greenly (1919) reported the presence of diopside in calc-silicate rocks of the Mona Complex, exposed in the Nebo Inlier, on Anglesey, forming colourless, anhedral crystals. Gibbons and Horák (unpublished field guide) confirmed this occurrence, describing the presence of diopside- and grossular-bearing assemblages from the Bryn Fuches and Rhôs-mynach areas of northeast Anglesey. Elsewhere on Anglesey, diopside was identified by Greenly (1919) in ophicalcite exposed near Cerig-moelion, on Holy Island, while Maltman (1977) reported diopside-bearing altered gabbros near Mynachdy.

Djurleite   Monoclinic
$Cu_{31}S_{16}$

Djurleite is a copper sulphide mineral which occurs as a supergene phase in the enriched zone of copper ore bodies.

Only two occurrences of djurleite are known from Wales, firstly from Porth Ysgo, near Aberdaron, Llŷn, Gwynedd, confirmed by X-ray diffraction (Natural History Museum X-ray no. 4674F), and secondly from the Great Orme, Llandudno, also in Gwynedd, where it has been identified optically as a pale blue isotropic phase forming areas up to 80 by 20 μm within limonite (R.A. Ixer, *personal communication*).

Dolomite   Trigonal
$CaMg(CO_3)_2$

A calcium magnesium carbonate mineral of the dolomite group which forms two series, with ankerite, and with kutnohorite. It occurs in limestones either as a direct precipitate or as a replacement of original calcite. Dolomite may also occur as a gangue mineral in hydrothermal vein deposits.

In Wales dolomite is widespread in the limestones of Carboniferous age, occurring as a result of replacement of original calcite. Many of the Carboniferous Limestone units of South Wales, for example, are dolomitized and, as a result of volume reduction, are cavernous. Well-formed, typically curved dolomite crystals are found in such rocks (North, 1916), such as at Machen Quarry, Mid Glamorgan. Dolomite is also found in clay ironstone nodules in the South Wales area; well formed dolomite crystals from the Fforchaman Colliery, Aberdare are in the Mineral Collection of the National Museum of Wales.

In North Wales well-formed dolomite crystals are found at Great Ormes Head, near Llandudno, Gwynedd, associated with chalcopyrite, azurite and malachite. It is also present as well formed rhombohedral crystals at Pant-y-Gaseg mine, near Amlwch, Anglesey.

Dolomite is a constituent of many mineral veins in Wales, particularly those from the Central Wales Mining District, where it is typically ferroan. Only rarely in this area is it well formed, although attractive rhombs, 5-10 mm across, are known from Hafan Mine (J.S. Mason, *personal communication*).

Dundasite   Orthorhombic
$PbAl_2(CO_3)_2(OH)_4.H_2O$

Dundasite is a comparatively rare lead aluminium carbonate hydroxyl hydrate found in the oxidized zone of lead-bearing ore deposits.

Prior (1906) recorded dundasite forming small (up to 1 mm diameter) white, spherical aggregates or tufts composed of radiating silky needles associated with glassy spherules of allophane and cerussite from the 23-

Figure 67. Minute spherical dundasite crystals (up to 0.5 mm across), associated with cerussite from Cyffty Mine, near Llanrwst, Gwynedd. NMW specimen 27.111.GR410, *ex* G.J. Williams Collection.

foot level on the Francis lode, at Welsh Foxdale (New Pandora) Mine, near Trefriw, Gwynedd. This original description was based on specimens passed on to him by H.F. Collins, but which were collected originally by G.J. Williams, former H.M. Inspector of Mines for North Wales. The account represented the first occurrence of the mineral in the British Isles. Subsequently, Russell (1944) reported two further occurrences of dundasite, both in the neighbourhood of the Welsh Foxdale Mine, namely at Cyffty Mine and Gorlan Mine. Cyffty specimens show snow-white spheres of dundasite associated with cerussite, while those from Gorlan have snow-white downy crusts of small silky needles of dundasite on gum-like brownish-yellow allophane, associated with cerussite, quartz and anglesite on galena, sphalerite, marcasite and quartz. Both of these two further occurrences were based also on specimens collected by G.J. Williams.

More recently, dundasite has been identified from Nantycagl (Eaglebrook) Mine, in the Central Wales Mining District, forming balls of radiating acicular crystals up to 0.5 mm in diameter, varying in colour from very pale blue at their centres to white at their terminations (Natural History Museum X-ray no. 6081F).

Electrum   Cubic
(Au,Ag)

An alloy of gold and silver, containing more than 20 wt% silver. Electrum is usually found associated with gold in mineral veins.

Forbes (1867) reported the occurrence of an alloy of gold and silver in quartz lodes from Clogau Mine, near Dolgellau, which represented the first occurrence of the mineral in the British Isles, while the presence of electrum in the Dolgellau area was mentioned subsequently by Readwin (1888) and Andrew (1910). Readwin (1888) in fact stated that gold from the Dolgellau area 'nearly answers to Pliny's "Electrum", containing 10 to 15 per cent of combined silver', while Andrew (1910) reported an analysis of gold from the Cefncoch lode as containing 22.70 wt% silver. Gilbey (1968) was not able to confirm the presence of electrum and indeed recent analyses of gold from Clogau Mine show a maximum Ag content of 15 wt% (J. Naden, *personal communication*). Electrum *sensu stricto* (with Ag >20 wt%) has, however, been confirmed recently from the northern part of the Dolgellau Gold Belt (J. Naden, *personal communication*).

Electrum is also found in trace amounts in the Central Wales Mining District; a single grain is known from Nantycagl (Eaglebrook), associated with galena and tucekite (J.S. Mason, *personal communication*).

Elyite   Monoclinic
$Pb_4Cu(SO_4)(OH)_8$

A rare lead copper sulphate hydroxide which forms in the oxidized zone of lead- and copper-bearing ore bodies.

Elyite was first identified in Wales in 1984 from Esgair Hir Mine, in the Central Wales Mining District, forming violet, fan-like sprays of crystals up to 2 mm in length in a cavity in altered galena, and associated with

Figure 68. Thin blades of elyite (purple), up to 0.75 mm long, from Llechweddhelyg Mine, in the Central Wales Mining District. Specimen 1244, in the S.A. Rust Collection.

covellite, anglesite, caledonite and hydrocerussite (S.A. Rust, *personal communication*). More recently, Rust and Mason (1988) recorded violet, radiating, lath-like elyite crystals up to 0.4 mm in length associated with an unknown pale blue mineral and covellite, also from Esgair Hir Mine. Both records are probably of post-mining age. Elyite has also been identified visually from Frongoch and Llechweddhelyg (J.S. Mason, *personal communication*).

Enargite   Orthorhombic
Cu_3AsS_4
A copper arsenic sulphide, dimorphous with luzonite. Enargite occurs in medium and low temperature hydrothermal veins.

Enargite has been found associated with other copper sulphide minerals in old copper mines at the Great Ormes Head, Llandudno, Gwynedd (R.A. Ixer, *personal communication*).

Endellite   Monoclinic
$Al_2Si_2O_5(OH)_4.2H_2O$
An aluminium silicate hydroxide hydrate belonging to the kaolinite-serpentine group. Endellite is also known as halloysite (10Å) in European literature.

Endellite forms creamy-white opaque masses filling

voids between crystals of brookite, albite and quartz at Fron Oleu (Fronolen), near Prenteg, Gwynedd, on a specimen collected in 1972 (G. Ryback, *personal communication*).

Enstatite   Orthorhombic
$Mg_2Si_2O_6$
An iron magnesium silicate belonging to the pyroxene group, forming a series with ferrosilite and dimorphous with clinoenstatite. Enstatite is a rock-forming mineral, occurring in ultrabasic, basic and intermediate igneous rocks. The classification used here follows that established by the IMA (see Morimoto, 1988).

Teall (1888) illustrated 'enstatite-diorite' from Penmaenmawr, Gwynedd, in his classic book *'British Petrography'*. Subsequently this enstatite was considered by Harker (1889) and by Sargent (1915) to be bronzite (a variety of enstatite), although in a subsequent, more detailed petrological description Sargent (1924) referred to the orthopyroxene mineral as indeed being enstatite. Later, Croudace (1982) reported the presence of enstatite in microtonalites from the Inner Garnfor Intrusion and the Penrhyn Bodeilias Intrusion, on Llŷn, with an average composition of $Ca_4Mg_{60}Fe_{36}$ for phenocrysts and $Ca_4Mg_{48}Fe_{48}$ for groundmass crystals.

In South Wales enstatite occurs in magnesian peridotite xenoliths from the Great House diatreme, near Usk, Gwent (D.T. Moffat, *personal communication*). Also, enstatite is present in laminated olivine gabbros from the St. David's Head Intrusion, Dyfed (author's unpublished data), although generally the orthopyroxenes in this intrusion are pseudomorphed by chlorite (Roach, 1969).

Epidote   Monoclinic
$Ca_2(Al,Fe^{+3})_3(SiO_4)_3(OH)$
A calcium aluminium iron silicate hydroxide which develops typically in low-grade metamorphic rocks. Epidote also occurs in contact metasomatic and hydrothermally altered rocks.

Epidote is widely developed in Wales, particularly in the groundmass of altered volcanic rocks of basic composition of Precambrian and Lower Palaeozoic age or in cross-cutting veins associated with quartz (see, for example, Greenly, 1919). Electron microprobe chemical analyses of epidote are presented in Bevins and Rowbotham (1983) and Bevins and Merriman (1988); minor chemical zoning of Fe and Al is evident in epidotes from various areas, such as Mynydd Preseli, in Dyfed.

Generally epidote in Wales is found only on the microscopic scale, although excellent crystalline epidote occurs at Marloes Bay, in Dyfed (National Museum of Wales specimen NMW 86.82G.M3), at Daran Belydr, Ganllwyd, north of Dolgellau (specimens NMW 27.111.GR302 and 27.111.GR303), and at Dinorwic Quarry, Gwynedd (specimens NMW 27.111.GR57 and 27.111.GR295).

Epsomite   Orthorhombic
$MgSO_4.7H_2O$
A magnesium sulphate hydrate, commonly occurring as
encrustations, efflorescences or stalactitic masses on
mine walls.

The only known occurrences of epsomite in Wales are
as stalactitic masses from Treharris, Mid Glamorgan, on
National Museum of Wales specimen NMW
27.128.GR2, and also on a specimen in the private
mineral collection of R.S.W. Braithwaite (specimen
number RSWB 68-347). Identification of epsomite on
specimen NMW 27.128.GR2 was confirmed by X-ray
diffraction (NMW X-282), which also indicated the
presence of hexahydrite, although the latter is most likely
to be a result of dehydration of epsomite in the museum
environment.

Erythrite   Monoclinic
$Co_3(AsO_4)_2.8H_2O$
A cobalt arsenate hydrate belonging to the vivianite
group of minerals which forms two series, one with
annabergite, the other with hoernesite. Known also as
'cobalt bloom', erythrite typically forms pale mauve to
pink earthy masses and crusts in the oxidized zones of
cobalt-bearing ore bodies.

Figure 69. Erythrite encrustations on quartz from Vigra Mine,
in the Dolgellau Gold Belt. The field of view is 7.5 cm across.
NMW specimen 83.41G.M8092, ex R.J. King Collection
specimen K8790-81.

In Wales, erythrite occurs at various localities in the
Dolgellau Gold Belt, including the Panorama, Clogau
and Vigra Mines (Dewey and Eastwood, 1925; Gilbey,
1968), being common at the last named mine on
cobaltite-bearing vein material. More recently Saich and
Rust (1987) have described erythrite forming pink to
deep reddish-pink drusy botryoidal crusts and scattered
balls up to 0.6 mm at a trial level 1.5 km NW of
Bontddu, near Dolgellau, Gwynedd, while further south,
in Dyfed, filmy pink coatings of erythrite are known
from Darren Mine, in the Central Wales Mining District
(Mason and Hughes, 1990; J.S. Mason, *personal communication*). Erythrite has also been recorded from mines at
the Great Ormes Head, Llandudno, in Gwynedd (Jenkins
and Johnson, 1993).

Ferro-actinolite   Monoclinic
$Ca_2(Fe^{+2},Mg)_5Si_8O_{22}(OH)_2$
A calcium magnesium iron silicate hydroxide mineral, a
member of the amphibole group which forms a series
with tremolite and actinolite. A rock-forming mineral
which develops typically in low-grade metamorphic
rocks of basic composition.

Ferro-actinolite occurs as colourless to pale green,
pleochroic needle-like crystals in the Tal y Fan Intrusion,
Gwynedd, rimming clinopyroxene, and resulting from
the effects of low-grade metamorphism. Identification
was confirmed by electron microprobe analysis (Bevins
and Merriman, 1988). This appears to be the first verified
record of ferro-actinolite in the British Isles.

Ferrobarroisite   Monoclinic
$NaCa(Fe^{+2},Mg)_3Al_2(Si_7Al)O_{22}(OH)_2$
A sodium calcium iron magnesium aluminium silicate
hydroxide of the amphibole group which forms a series
with barrosite. Ferrobarroisite is a rock-forming mineral
occurring in metamorphic rocks.

Greenly (1919) reported that blue amphiboles in mica
schists of the Mona Complex exposed beneath the
Marquis of Anglesey's Monument near
Llanfairpwllgwyngyll, on Anglesey, possess green
hornblende cores. Electron microprobe analyses by
Gibbons and Gyopari (1986) demonstrated, however,
that these green amphiboles fall in the range barroisite-
ferrobarroisite-winchite. Further occurrences of these
amphiboles were reported by Gibbons and Gyopari
(1986) from temporary roadcutting exposures related to
construction of the nearby Llanfairpwllgwyngyll bypass.
This appears to be the first record of ferrobarroisite in the
British Isles.

Ferroglaucophane   Monoclinic
$Na_2(Fe^{+2},Mg)_3Al_2Si_8O_{22}(OH)_2$
A sodium iron magnesium aluminium silicate hydroxide
of the amphibole group which forms a series with
glaucophane. It typically develops in high pressure, low
temperature metamorphic rocks.

Electron microprobe analyses by Gibbons and
Gyopari (1986) showed that blue amphiboles from the
classic locality beneath the Marquis of Anglesey's
Column east of Llanfairpwllgwyngyll, on Anglesey, first

described by Blake (1888), and from temporary exposures on the Llanfairpwllgwyngyll bypass, in fact straddle the compositional fields of glaucophane, crossite and ferroglaucophane. This appears to be the first record of ferroglaucophane in the British Isles.

Ferrohornblende   Monoclinic
$Ca_2(Fe^{+2},Mg)_4Al(Si_7Al)O_{22}(OH,F)_2$
A calcium magnesium iron aluminium silicate hydroxide mineral belonging to the amphibole group, and forming a series with magnesiohornblende. Ferrohornblende is a rock-forming mineral.

Ferrohornblende is recorded from altered gabbros of the Tal y Fan Intrusion, Gwynedd, with identification confirmed by electron microprobe analysis (Bevins and Merriman, 1988).

Fibroferrite   Monoclinic
$Fe^{3+}(SO_4)(OH).5H_2O$
An iron sulphate hydroxide hydrate, typically developed in the altered portions of sulphide ore bodies.

Fibroferrite forms copious mounds with jarosite and, more rarely, copiapite on the floor of Cae Coch Mine, at Trefriw, Gwynedd (Johnson *et al.*, 1979). This description, on the basis of X-ray diffraction and wet chemical analysis, represented the first identification of fibroferrite in the British Isles.

Florencite   Trigonal
$(La,Ce,Nd)Al_3(PO_4)_2(OH)_6$
A light rare earth aluminium phosphate hydroxide belonging to the crandallite group. Florencite occurs in carbonatitic and pegmatitic igneous rocks, as well as a detrital mineral in various sedimentary rocks.

Florencite has been identified by energy dispersive analysis in mudstones of Ordovician age from the Corris district of Gwynedd (A.T. Kearsley, *personal communication*). Qualitative analysis suggests that the mineral is florencite-(Ce). This identification represented the first reported occurrence of florencite in the British Isles.

Fluorapatite   Hexagonal
$Ca_5(PO_4)_3F$
A calcium phosphate fluoride belonging to the apatite group. Fluorapatite is found in a wide variety of environments. In particular it is a minor phase in igneous rocks, especially those of alkaline affinity, as well as occurring as a component of hydrothermal, and in particular Alpine-type, mineral veins.

Analyses of apatite group minerals from Wales are generally wanting, and hence the particular species is commonly not known. However, Matthews and Scoon (1964) reported the presence of apatite in stilpnomelane-bearing veins from Tyllau Mwn Mine, in the vicinity of Drws-y-nant, near Dolgellau, analyses of which indicate that its composition lies close to ideal fluorapatite. More recently Starkey and Robinson (1992) reported that apatites from the brookite-bearing quartz veins near Prenteg, Gwynedd, are also fluorapatites.

In South Wales, fluorapatite has been identified on the basis of electron microprobe analysis in altered gabbros of the Pen Caer area, near Fishguard, Dyfed (R. Metcalfe, *personal communication*).

Fluorite   Cubic
CaF_2
A calcium fluoride mineral, typically developed in hydrothermal veins, associated with lead and zinc ores.

Fluorite is relatively rare in Wales, being identified from only a few areas. The presence of fluorite in the Halkyn mining district in Clwyd has been known since the days of Thomas Pennant (1726-1798) (see Campbell Smith, 1913), where it occurs in association with calcite, sphalerite, galena and chalcopyrite, in strata of Carboniferous age. Particularly fine crystals have been collected in this area from the Bryn-gwiog, Halkyn, and Rhosesmor Mines (Carruthers *et al.*, 1916). In addition, fluorite is found at other localities along the outcrop of the Carboniferous strata in Clwyd, for example at Maes-y-safn Mine, near Mold and further south, at Llanarmon-yn-Ial, where it occurs in a quarry near Tan-y-graig Mine (Strahan, 1890). It has also been identified from Llandudno Mine, at Llandudno (R.S.W. Braithwaite, *personal communication*). Smith (1973) provided an account of fluid inclusions in fluorites from the North Wales ore field.

In Gwynedd fluorite has been reported from the contact aureole of the Bwlch y Cywion Intrusion, on the shoulder of Y Llymllwyd, where it is developed in slates, associated with almandine garnet (Williams, 1927). In addition, fluorite is present in the riebeckite-bearing Mynydd Mawr Microgranite Intrusion, forming small inclusions in riebeckite crystals (R.S. Thorpe, *personal communication*). A further report of fluorite in Gwynedd is from near the cromlech [SH 513 819], at Benllech, on Anglesey (R.S.W. Braithwaite, *personal communication*).

In Mid Wales, Jones and Moreton (1977) reported the presence of fluorite at Alltycrib Mine near Talybont, in the Central Wales Mining District, although there are no known specimens to verify this occurrence and its presence is highly dubious.

In South Wales colourless fluorite is present in thin, mineralized veins in Carboniferous Limestone, immediately below the unconformity with overlying Mercian Mudstones of Triassic age, on Sully Island, South Glamorgan. Individual cubes up to 3 mm in size have been collected. Elsewhere in South Glamorgan, Storrie (1895) recorded the presence of small pale cubes of fluorite, along with grains of gold, in a boring for water in Working Street, Cardiff.

In Mid Glamorgan, Howard (1899) noted that fluorite occurs in lead-bearing veins cutting the Carboniferous Limestone at Risca, while purple fluorite, in cubes reaching up to 25 mm in size, occurs in cavities associated with hydrocarbon material in Carboniferous Limestone at Vaynor Quarry, in Merthyr Tydfil.

Further west, fluorite is recorded from Bryn-Ambor, at Llandewi Brefi, in Dyfed (Hall, 1971), although this report is dubious.

Figure 70. Fluorite from the Carboniferous Limestone at Vaynor Quarry, Merthyr Tydfil, showing a colourless rim and purple core. The cube is 17 mm x 12 mm. Collected December 1991. I. Jones Collection.

Forsterite Orthorhombic
Mg_2SiO_4
A magnesium silicate which forms a series with fayalite and which is trimorphous with ringwoodite and wadsleyite. Forsterite, a member of the olivine group, is a rock-forming mineral which develops in ultrabasic and basic igneous rocks, as well as in carbonate rocks affected by contact metamorphism.

Greenly (1919) identified forsterite in crystalline limestones of the Mona Complex exposed in the Nebo Inlier, near Brynfuches, on Anglesey. Recent detailed studies in this area, including a re-examination of Greenly's original thin sections, however, have failed to confirm its presence (Horák, 1993).

Forsterite does occur, however, in the Rhiw Intrusion, on Llŷn, occurring throughout many of the layered units. Hawkins (1970) recorded compositions in the range Fo_{85} to Fo_{79}, while Cattermole (1976) indicated compositions between Fo_{86} and Fo_{80}. In other basic intrusions in Wales olivine is typically replaced by chlorite.

Elsewhere, forsterite has been identified in magnesian peridotite nodules in the Great House diatreme, near Usk, Gwent, with compositions around Fo_{90} being typical (D.T. Moffat, *personal communication*).

Fraipontite Monoclinic
$(Zn,Al)_3(Si,Al)_2O_5(OH)_4$
A zinc aluminium silicate hydroxide mineral belonging to the kaolinite-serpentine group. Fraipontite is a rare mineral, occurring in the oxidized zone of zinc-bearing mineral deposits.

X-ray diffraction analysis (NMW X-850, NMW X-851) of a pale grey-green to white mineral with a waxy lustre and soapy feel, associated with hydrozincite on galena from Machen Quarry, Mid Glamorgan, suggests the presence of fraipontite. However, the X-ray patterns were poor, with faint and diffuse lines, and hence the identification requires verification.

Freibergite Cubic
$(Ag,Cu,Fe)_{12}(Sb,As)_4S_3$
A silver copper iron antimony arsenic sulphide which forms two series with tetrahedrite and with argentotennantite. Freibergite is a member of the tetrahedrite group which most typically occurs in silver-bearing mineral veins.

Forbes (1868) reported the occurrence of 'polytelite' disseminated in lead ore at Tyddyn Gwladys Mine, near Dolgellau, Gwynedd. However, in view of the fact that it only contained 11.25 wt% Ag, it is more likely that it was argentian tetrahedrite. Gilbey (1968), however, recorded freibergite containing up to 23.7 wt% Ag associated with pyrargyrite as irregular inclusions in galena from the same mine. More recently, Mason and Hughes (1990) recorded silver-copper-antimony sulphide minerals from the Darren mines, in the Central Wales Mining District, containing up to 18 wt% of silver; hence these are probably also freibergites.

Galena   Cubic
PbS

Galena is a lead sulphide mineral, and is the principal ore of lead. It forms a series with clausthalite. Galena occurs most typically in low-temperature mineral veins in association with other sulphides, in particular chalcopyrite and sphalerite.

Galena is of widespread occurrence in Wales, being known from every county. It was the principal mineral exploited during the heyday of Welsh mining, although sphalerite is often equally abundant in the Central Wales Mining District. The history of exploitation of lead in Wales certainly goes back to Roman times. A comprehensive review of lead mining in Wales is provided by Lewis (1967), while extensive geological details are provided by Smith (1921), Dewey and Smith (1922) and Jones (1922).

In Gwynedd galena occurs in the mineral veins of Snowdonia associated with chalcopyrite and sphalerite. The principal lead mines were in the Llanrwst district of Gwynedd, and especially fine specimens from this area came from the Trecastell Mine. At Parys Mountain, on Anglesey, galena is one of the component sulphides of the massive 'bluestone' ore; sphalerite and chalcopyrite are the other important phases (Greenly, 1919; Pointon and Ixer, 1980).

In Clwyd galena is a common mineral, occurring associated with sphalerite in veins cutting the Carboniferous Limestone. Old lead mines are located along the whole length of the outcrop of the limestone, from the Minera district in the south, through the highly productive Halkyn region, to Abergele in the north. This area was the most important producer of lead in Wales, with some 658,000 tons of lead concentrate being produced from 245 mines between 1845 and 1938 - some 13% of Britain's lead ore at that time.

Another important lead-producing district was the Central Wales Mining District in the old counties of Cardiganshire and Montgomeryshire (now largely in Dyfed but partly also in Powys), covering over 1000 sq. km, with over 130 mines (see Bick, 1974, 1975, 1976, 1977, 1978, 1991). Galena, along with comparatively minor amounts of chalcopyrite and sphalerite, occurs in a series of veins commonly associated with steeply dipping ENE-WSW trending faults cutting Ordovician and Silurian sedimentary rocks. Particularly fine specimens from this area come from mines in the Ysbyty Ystwyth area.

Slightly further south galena-bearing veins were exploited from various veins in an isolated region around Rhandirmwyn, in Powys, while to the east numerous trials for lead are found in the area between Builth Wells and Llandrindod Wells, although these do not appear to have been successful.

Galena is not so common in South Wales, although once again galena-bearing veins cut the Carboniferous Limestone, this time exposed on the north and south crops of the South Wales Coalfield. Old lead mines in

Figure 71. Galena on millerite from Wyndham Colliery, Ogmore Vale, Mid Glamorgan. The galena crystal is 2 mm across. NMW specimen 83.42G.M20, from the collection of Mr C.T. and the late Mrs I. Taylor.

this region are found at Machen in the east across to Mynydd-y-Garreg in the west. Galena is also found in clay ironstone nodules of the South Wales Coalfield, occurring in association with millerite, chalcopyrite, sphalerite and siegenite (Firth, 1971). Thin galena-bearing veins also occur in the Jurassic rocks of the Vale of Glamorgan; such veins were exploited, for example, at Llangan near Cowbridge. Similar veins are also exposed on the coast at Ogmore-by-Sea and Porthcawl (Fletcher, 1988).

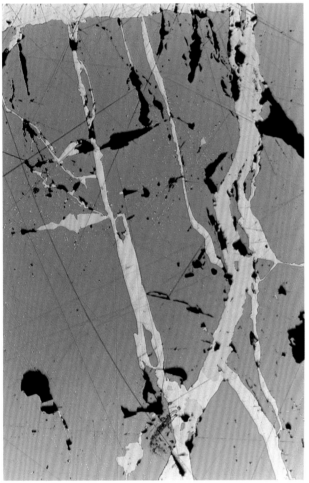

Figure 72. Galena and chalcopyrite veining sphalerite, from Erglodd Mine, in the Central Wales Mining District. Field of view is 1.4 mm across. *Ex* J.S. Mason Collection, now National Museum of Wales specimen 93.90G.M34.

Further west galena-bearing veins occur in the Carmarthen area and were exploited, for example, at the Vale of Towy (Nant) Mine to the east of the town. In the old county of Pembrokeshire, however, galena is only known to have been produced in any quantity from old mines in the vicinity of Llanfyrnach.

Galenobismutite   Orthorhombic
$PbBi_2S_4$
A lead bismuth sulphide occurring as a relatively rare component of hydrothermal assemblages, and generally associated with other bismuth minerals and galena.

Galenobismutite has been reported from the lead-zinc-copper ores of Parys Mountain, on Anglesey by Sivaprakash (1977) and Pointon and Ixer (1980). It

occurs as fine grained (5-20 μm) intergrowths associated with bismuthinite, bournonite, native bismuth and kobellite as contact rims around chalcopyrite, galena, and tetrahedrite group minerals, as inclusions within sphalerite, and as a cement to framboidal pyrite. Electron microprobe analyses are presented by Sivaprakash (1977). This account represented the first description of the mineral in the British Isles.

Ganophyllite   Monoclinic
$(K,Na)_2(Mn,Al,Mg)_8(Si,Al)_{12}O_{29}(OH)_7.8-9H_2O$
A rare sodium potassium manganese aluminium magnesium silicate hydroxide hydrate occurring in manganese deposits.

Ganophyllite was first collected in Wales in 1911 at the Nant Mine, on Llŷn by the late Sir Arthur Russell, although mention of this occurrence was not made until the very brief report by Russell (1946), which represented the first occurrence of the mineral in the British Isles. A more complete description of ganophyllite was subsequently presented by Campbell Smith (1948), although this was from the nearby Benallt Mine, relating to specimens collected in 1945 by Campbell Smith in the company of A.W. Groves. At Benallt Mine, ganophyllite occurs as six-sided cinnamon-brown flakes up to 4 mm across, possessing a perfect basal cleavage. Some of the ganophyllite from Benallt Mine was later identified as the new mineral bannisterite (Smith and Frondel, 1968), named in honour of Dr F.A. Bannister, former Keeper of Mineralogy at the Natural History Museum. Further data on ganophyllite, including chemical analyses of the mineral, were provided by Dunn *et al.* (1983).

Georgeite   Amorphous
$Cu_2(CO_3)(OH)_2.6H_2O$
A rare copper carbonate hydroxide hydrate which occurs in oxidation assemblages in certain base metal ore bodies.

Pollard *et al.* (1989) have identified the presence of amorphous pale blue georgeite overlain by carbonatian connellite and malachite on Sneyd's Level, at Britannia Mine, in Snowdonia, Gwynedd. This report represented the first occurrence of the mineral in the British Isles and only the second known occurrence of georgeite world-wide.

Gersdorffite   Cubic
NiAsS
A nickel arsenic sulphide mineral belonging to the cobaltite group.

Gersdorffite occurs as coatings on fractures associated with annabergite within hydrocarbon on Great Ormes Head, at Llandudno, Gwynedd (P. Eakin, *personal communication*). In addition, arsenic-bearing gersdorffite has been recorded from Gwaithyrafon Mine, in the Central Wales Mining District, an identification confirmed by electron probe microanalysis (author's unpublished data).

Gibbsite   Monoclinic
Al(OH)$_3$

An aluminium hydroxide, polymorphous with bayerite, doyleite, and nordstrandite. Gibbsite is a secondary mineral which develops as a result of weathering of aluminium minerals.

Ball (1964) identified gibbsite as the only crystalline component in the clay fraction of a < 25 cm thick soil horizon developed over the Bwlch y Cywion Granite, on Y Llymllwyd, near Nant Ffrancon, in Snowdonia. In addition, gibbsite has been found in the mine dumps at Glasdir, near Dolgellau, Gwynedd, forming white globules (0.2 mm diameter) on clear, glassy, colourless to pale blue allophane (G. Ryback, *personal communication*).

Glauconite   Monoclinic
(K,Na)(Fe^{+3},Al,Mg)$_2$(Si,Al)$_4$O$_{10}$(OH)$_2$

A potassium sodium iron aluminium magnesium silicate hydroxide belonging to the mica group. It is found in sedimentary rocks which accumulated in shallow marine environments.

The only record of glauconite in Wales was provided by North (1916) in describing its presence in the Sutton Stone of the Bridgend area, Mid Glamorgan.

Glaucophane   Monoclinic
Na$_2$(Mg,Fe^{+2})$_3$Al$_2$Si$_8$O$_{22}$(OH)$_2$

A sodium magnesium iron aluminium silicate hydroxide belonging to the amphibole group which forms a series with ferroglaucophane. It occurs typically in metamorphic rocks and in particular is indicative of high pressures and low temperatures of metamorphism. It is blue in colour, and is responsible for the colour of so-called "blueschists".

Figure 73. Thin section of glaucophane (blue) crystal 450 μm across in a blueschist from Llanfairpwllgwyngyll, Anglesey. The green core to the zoned rhombic crystal in the centre of the image is barroisite. Reproduced from Gibbons and Gyopari (1986), with permission of the authors.

Blake (1888) provided the first description of glaucophane from the British Isles, reporting its occurrence in rocks of the Mona Complex exposed in a quarry near the 'Anglesey Monument' (the Marquis of Anglesey's

Figure 74. Inclusion of goethite in quartz from Mwyndy Mine, Llantrisant, Mid Glamorgan. The crystal is 8 mm across. NMW specimen 85.124, donated to the Cardiff Museum by S. Vivian towards the end of the last century.

Column) at Llanfairpwllgwyngyll, on Anglesey; Blake's identification was on the basis of optical determinations. Greenly (1919) confirmed the presence of 'true glaucophane' but recorded the fact that some of the crystals were zoned, possessing green 'hornblende' cores passing outwards to blue rims. The first chemical analysis of these amphiboles was undertaken by Holgate (1951), who separated out the blue amphibole, apparently removing the green amphibole cores; on this basis Holgate suggested that the blue amphiboles were crossite. Macpherson (1983) recalculated Holgate's analysis and noted that according to the IMA amphibole classification (see Leake, 1978) they are magnesio-arfvedsonites. Much more reliable data, however, have been presented by Horák and Gibbons (1986), and Gibbons and Gyopari (1986). These authors presented electron microprobe analyses which showed that the green cores are in fact barroisite (not hornblende), while the rims span the crossite-glaucophane-ferroglaucophane fields. Gibbons and Gyopari (1986) also described a further occurrence of blue amphibole-bearing schists in temporary exposures related to construction of a bypass for the village of Llanfairpwllgwyngyll, near to the site of the original description.

Goethite   Orthorhombic
α-Fe^{+3}O(OH)

An iron oxide hydroxide, trimorphous with feroxyhyte and lepidocrocite. One of the most common iron oxides, which forms as a result of alteration of other iron minerals, particularly iron-bearing carbonates and sulphides.

In Wales, goethite is extremely common; hence only a few more notable occurrences are described here.

Figure 75. Goethite pseudomorphs after pyrite from Blaengwynlais Quarry, near Rhiwbina, South Glamorgan. The pseudomorphs reach up to 18 mm across. NMW specimens 87.73G.M132 (right) and 87.73G.M60 (left), both *ex* A. Dean Collection.

Goethite is an important component in the various limestone-hosted iron ore deposits exposed across the southern crop of the South Wales Coalfield, occurring in association with hematite. It occurs as inclusions in quartz (Vivian, 1876, 1877). The dominant ore at Llanharry, Mid Glamorgan (Gayer and Criddle, 1969; Rankin and Criddle, 1985) however consists of layers (1 mm to 1 m thick) of colloform and crystalline goethite.

Figure 76. Goethite needles up to 4 mm in length, collected by R.W. Barstow from the Deep Adit Level of the Chidlaw lode at Gwynfynydd Mine, in the Dolgellau Gold Belt, Gwynedd. NMW specimen 85.70G.M23, *ex* R.W. Barstow Collection.

Cavernous areas are typically filled with finely stalactitic goethite and euhedral crystals of goethite, hematite, calcite and quartz, while spheroidal goethite is also found in calcite scalenohedra. Goethite also occurs associated with hematite at the Garth Iron Mine, near Taff's Well, Mid Glamorgan (Rankin and Criddle, 1985), as well as forming pseudomorphs after pyrite at a number of localities in the same district (e.g. in quarries at Blaengwynlais, Machen, and Miskin). At Tŷ Coch, near Porthcawl, also in Mid Glamorgan, goethite is found as botryforms or compound crystallites interlayered with romanèchite in manganese ore (Criddle and Symes, 1977).

Figure 77. Goethite stalactites collected from the old tips at Llanharry Mine, Mid Glamorgan. The tallest stalactite illustrated is 7 mm. NMW specimen 89.4G.M67, *ex* A. Dean Collection.

In the Central Wales Mining District, an interesting occurrence of goethite is at Aberdaunant Mine, where it coats galena in layers 2-3 mm thick, associated with cerussite and pyromophite (J.S. Mason, *personal communication*).

In North Wales spectacular rosettes of goethite crystals up to 5 mm in length occur associated with marcasite at Gwynfynydd Mine, near Dolgellau, Gwynedd. It is also present at Great Ormes Head, near Llandudno, Gwynedd, forming pseudomorphs after cuprite.

Gold   Cubic
Au

Native gold, which forms a series with silver, occurs chiefly in quartz-bearing hydrothermal veins. It is also hosted by black shale sequences and is a constituent in placer deposits.

Wales is renowned for its gold deposits, which occur at surface in three principal areas. The first, and best known, is the so-called Dolgellau Gold Belt, which occurs in southern Snowdonia. Gold was first reported in this area from Cwmheisian lead mine by Arthur Dean, in a presentation to the British Association in 1844 (Dean, 1845). However, this report was to spark considerable controversy, with Robert Roberts reporting in the pages of the *Mining Journal* for the year 1844 that in fact he had identified gold in the region in 1836. The situation is further complicated by a water colour painting, now housed in the Welsh Industrial and Maritime Museum, entitled 'Panning gold: Mawddach', by John Glover (1767-1849), and dated *c.* 1795; critically John Glover emigrated to Australia in 1831, where he lived out the rest of his life.

Figure 78. Gold in quartz from the St. David's Mine, in the Dolgellau Gold Belt. The specimen measures 4 cm x 5.5 cm. NMW specimen 27.111.GR475, *ex* G.J. Williams Collection.

The Dolgellau Gold Belt extends from Barmouth in the southwest to Cwm Prysor near Trawsfynydd in the northeast, and flanks the southern, southeastern and

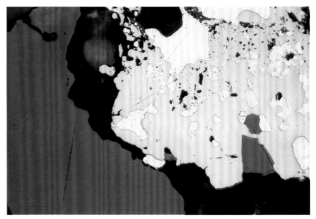

Figure 79. Gold in pyrite, from Dolgellau, Gwynedd, photographed in reflected light under oil immersion. Field of view is 600 µm across. Specimen GM077R44 in the Natural History Museum Collection.

eastern flanks of the major structure known as the Harlech Dome. Early reviews of the gold mineralization in this area are presented by Calvert (1853), Ramsay (1854), Readwin (1860, 1862), Smyth (1862), Forbes (1867, 1868), Readwin (1888), and Andrew (1910). The most recent perspectives are provided by Gilbey (1968), Allen and Jackson (1985), Bottrell (1986), Bottrell and Spiro (1988), Bottrell *et al.* (1988), Naden (1988), and Bottrell *et al.* (1990). In this region gold has been worked at one time or another from more than 30 mines, from a series of typically steeply-dipping NE-SW oriented, anastomosing quartz veins, which reach up to 6 m wide. The veins tend to be of two kinds, dominated respectively by pyrite-chalcopyrite-pyrrhotite-arsenopyrite/cobaltite in the southwest, and pyrite-sphalerite-galena in the northeast. The gold is typically dispersed in quartz or associated with sulphides, in particular sphalerite; sometimes, however, it occurs as a replacement or exsolution of pyrite or arsenopyrite on the micro scale. Interestingly, the gold mineralization is locally associated with a range of tellurium minerals (Gilbey, 1968; Naden, 1988; Bevins and Stanley, 1990), in particular from the Clogau Mine. The gold-bearing veins occur at all stratigraphic horizons from the Rhinog Formation upwards, but were concentrated at the level of the black mudstones of the Clogau Formation (Allen and Jackson, 1985). In a recent review of the mineralization of the Dolgellau Gold Belt, Shepherd and Bottrell (1993) reported that the ores are thought to relate to dewatering of the Precambrian and earlier Cambrian sediments during uplift. Concentration of the ore in the Clogau Formation was due to the interaction of the ore-forming fluids and the graphitic shales, leading to methane and nitrogen enrichment in the fluid and precipitation of the gold.

Many fine specimens of gold have been recovered from this region, and an excellent collection is in the National Museum of Wales. Particularly fine specimens of gold with sphalerite were recovered from the Gwynfynydd Mine in 1984, during the last serious period of mining. A specimen of particular note in the National Museum of Wales is a leaf gold aggregate measuring 4 cm x 2 cm, reputedly from Gwynfynydd Mine.

Because of its high density, gold eroded from exposed

mineral veins tends to be concentrated in gravels of the adjacent river systems. The gravels of the Afon Mawddach are no exception, and have long been panned for alluvial gold. Even today small gold nuggets can be collected, while a number of years ago planning permission was filed for dredging of the sediments of the Mawddach Estuary.

More general accounts of the mines and mining history of the Dolgellau area are provided by Hall (1975) and Morrison (1975).

To the northeast of the Dolgellau Gold Belt, a minor occurrence of gold mineralization occurs in quartz veins cutting Ordovician black shales and volcanic tuffs at Castell Carn Dochan, 8 km SW of Bala. The first record of this occurrence was by Readwin (1864) in a presentation to the British Association meeting at Newcastle. At Castell Carn Dochan, gold is visible to the naked eye, individual grains typically being scattered in quartz. There is little further literature record of this occurrence.

Figure 80. Leaf gold, from Gwynfynydd Mine, in the Dolgellau Gold Belt. The specimen measures 40 mm x 20 mm. NMW specimen 72.33G.M7.

Further north, gold has been recovered from a small mine at Rhôs-mynach-fawr, on Anglesey (Greenly, 1919), where it occurs in quartz veins which also contain chalcopyrite, pyrite, arsenopyrite, bismuthinite and tetradymite. Greenly (1919) also recorded the presence of gold at Parys Mountain, on Anglesey.

In South Wales, gold is present at Ogofau, in the Pumsaint district of Dyfed, from where it has been exploited since Roman times. Only very rarely, however, is this gold visible; usually it occurs as grains up to 200 μm (but typically 15-30 μm in diameter), in pyrite or arsenopyrite. A specimen from this locality in the Mineral Collection of the National Museum of Wales, however, is a single grain of visible gold. At Ogofau the gold is found in thinly bedded turbiditic shales and sandstones of Upper Ordovician to Lower Silurian age, with the gold deposit found on the western flank of a north-east trending anticline. The principal deposit occurs in a saddle reef structure termed the 'Roman Lode' (Hughes, 1959; Jones and Lewis, 1971; Steed et al., 1976). A recent review of the gold mineralization at Ogofau is provided by Annels and Roberts (1989).

Elsewhere in Dyfed, gold is a minor constituent of certain mineral veins in the Central Wales Mining District; for example, Jones and Moreton (1977) reported its occurrence at Caegynon Mine (of dubious validity) and Copa Hill, Cwmystwyth, while Mason and Hughes (1990) noted its presence in mines of the Darren district. Other occurrences are known from Erglodd, Nantycagl (Eaglebrook) and Llechweddhelyg (J.S. Mason, personal communication).

Further south, grains of gold associated with fluorite were recorded from a borehole in Triassic rocks at Working Street, Cardiff by Storrie (1895). More recently, Gayer and Rickard (1993) reported the presence of collomorphic gold, 2-10 μm across, in bed-normal fractures in Middle Coal Measures strata from the western anthracite zone of the South Wales Coalfield.

Unsubstantiated reports of gold in Wales are known from many districts not listed above. For example, old Ordnance Survey topographical maps of the Moel Fammau area, in Clwyd, indicate old trials for gold. Investigation of these trials, however, has failed to determine the presence of gold (D.H.M. Alderton, personal communication). Another example is the legend of gold in the North Pembrokeshire region (Davies, 1948).

Goslarite   Orthorhombic
$ZnSO_4.7H_2O$
A zinc sulphate hydrate which develops typically as a result of alteration of sphalerite, and grows in old mine workings.

Sowerby (1811) illustrated 'sulphate of zinc' from Holywell, Clwyd, describing it occurring on a red earthy oxide of iron, and being distinguished from iron or copper sulphate by its white colour. This was presumably the source of reference for the goslarite entry by Hall (1868), although no further reference to this mineral in Wales is known.

Graphite   Hexagonal and trigonal
C
Native carbon, also known as plumbago. Carbon is a constituent of many sedimentary rocks and also of low to high grade metamorphic rocks, forming by the alteration of carbonaceous material, or by the reaction of carbon

compounds with circulating hydrothermal or magmatic fluids.

In Wales graphite is a common constituent of many of the sedimentary rocks of Lower Palaeozoic age, although it does not form large masses. The most notable occurrence of graphite in Wales is from Nant Mine, on Llŷn, with specimens from this locality in the Mineral Collection of the National Museum of Wales.

Greenockite   Hexagonal
CdS
Cadmium sulphide, dimorphous with hawleyite, with which it is commonly confused. Greenockite is a relatively rare mineral, typically found as a coating on sphalerite.

Jones and Moreton (1977) and Moreton (1982) reported that greenockite occurs at Dylife Mine, in the Central Wales Mining District, forming canary yellow globular coatings in cavities in sphalerite, and also yellow powdery coatings on hemimorphite. Greenockite has also been found at the nearby Bwlchglas Mine, as thin, bright yellow films on sphalerite (Braithwaite, 1982b), and from the Cwmystwyth and Frongoch Mines (J.S. Mason, *personal communication*). It has also been reported from the Pen-y-Bryn Shaft, at Halkyn, Clwyd (R.S.W. Braithwaite, *personal communication*).

Grossular   Cubic
$Ca_3Al_2(SiO_4)_3$
A calcium aluminium silicate belonging to the garnet group which forms three series, with andradite, with hibschite and katoite, and with uvarovite. Most typically grossular develops as a result of contact metamorphism of calcareous rocks.

Henslow (1822) described well formed, small (up to 'seven-tenths of an inch in diameter'), olive-brown crystals with 'rhomboidal dodecahedron' forms from altered calcareous shales adjacent to the Plas Newydd Dyke, on Anglesey; these were identified as being garnets. Harker (1887) gave further account of these garnets, based on examination of Henslow's specimens preserved in the Sedgwick Museum in Cambridge, while Greenly (1919) stated that the Plas Newydd exposures were no longer available for inspection and thus merely re-iterated the findings of Henslow and Harker. Subsequent X-ray diffraction investigations on specimens in the Mineral Collection of the Natural History Museum confirm the garnet as being grossular (X-ray numbers 2501F-1979 P71, and 2499F-1979 P741).

Grossular has also been described from two other areas on Anglesey, with identifications confirmed by electron microprobe analysis. Maltman (1977) identified grossular occurring in altered gabbros, some of which are rodingites, from a number of localities on Holy Island (eg. 80 m NW of Dinas-bach), and also from near Mynachdy in NW Anglesey. In addition, Horák (1993) and Gibbons and Horák (unpublished field guide) reported the presence of grossular in meta-limestones and meta-calc-pelites from the Nebo Gneisses exposed in scattered exposures around Bryn Fuches and Rhôs-mynach in NE Anglesey.

"Grovesite"   Monoclinic
$(Mn,Mg,Al)_3(Si,Al)_2(O,OH)_9$
A rare manganese magnesium aluminium silicate hydroxide.

Grovesite was described as a new mineral from the No. 5 ore-body at Benallt Mine, on Llŷn, by Bannister *et al.* (1955), who considered that it represented a member of the cronstedtite-berthierine-amesite group. Subsequent analysis of this material suggests, in fact, that it is a one-layer polytype manganese trioctahedral chlorite which is chemically similar to the two-layer polytype manganese trioctahedral chlorite pennantite (Peacor *et al.*, 1974). Thus grovesite is discredited as a valid mineral species.

Gypsum   Monoclinic
$CaSO_4.2H_2O$
Calcium sulphate hydrate. Gypsum most commonly occurs as an evaporite mineral, due to evaporation of lakes in arid regions.

White to pale pink gypsum occurs as nodules and forms beds of nodules in the undivided 'red mudstones' and the Blue Anchor Formation of the Mercia Mudstone Group of Triassic age exposed in the South Wales area, for example on the coast between Barry and Penarth (North, 1916; Waters and Lawrence, 1987). Individual nodules up to 0.63 m have been recorded. Fibrous gypsum ('satin spar') also occurs, forming thin veins in the 'red mudstones'. Locally the gypsum is fine grained and granular, and is the variety alabaster, which was quarried in the Penarth area for ornamental purposes.

Selenite crystals are found forming thin films on black shales of Ordovician age at Abereiddi, in North Pembrokeshire, Dyfed, most probably resulting from the breakdown of pyrite in the shales. Elsewhere in South Wales, selenite crystals are found on the walls of caves in the Carboniferous Limestone, for example at Ogof Agen Alwedd, and Ogof Daren Cilau, in the Llangattwg area of Gwent.

Delicate crystals of the variety selenite are commonly found on old mine walls and spoil heaps in Wales, relating to the breakdown of the sulphide-rich ores. Examples are known from the Britannia Mine, Snowdon, Cae Coch Mine, near Trefriw, and Castell Carn Dochan, in North Wales, Dylife, Cwmrheidol and Goginan, in the Central Wales Mining District, and Ogofau, in south Central Wales.

Halotrichite   Monoclinic
$Fe^{+2}Al_2(SO_4)_4.22H_2O$
An iron aluminium sulphate hydrate which forms a series with pickeringite and is a member of the halotrichite group. Halotrichite typically develops as a result of alteration of pyrite, and is found growing on mine walls, along with other sulphate minerals.

Halotrichite has been collected from Gwynfynydd Mine, near Dolgellau, and from Trwyn Cae Iago, near Porthmadog, both in Gwynedd, preserved on specimens NMW 83.41G.M9093 and NMW 79.10G.M2 respectively in the Mineral Collection of the National Museum of Wales. It is also known to form encrustations at Parys Mountain, Anglesey (D.A. Jenkins, *personal communication*). In addition, various specimens, formerly labelled as alunogen, in the Mineral Collection of the National Museum of Wales, from Cymmer Colliery, Porth, and Deep Navigation Colliery, near Treharris, both in Mid Glamorgan, and from Parys Mountain, Anglesey, have all subsequently been proved, on the basis of X-ray diffraction analysis, to be halotrichite.

Harmotome   Monoclinic
$(Ba,K)_{1-2}(Si,Al)_8O_{16}.6H_2O$
A barium potassium aluminium silicate hydrate belonging to the zeolite group. Harmotome occurs typically as a secondary mineral in altered basic igneous rocks.

Campbell Smith *et al.* (1944a) described harmotome from the no. 2 ore body of the Benallt Mine, Llŷn, as crystals up to 0.03 mm across, associated with barite coating banalsite. A second occurrence of harmotome was described subsequently by Campbell Smith (1945), this time from the no. 5 ore-body at Benallt Mine, and again coating banalsite.

Harmotome is also found as small crystals forming a thin film coating mudstones at Cwm Orog Mine, near Llangynog, Powys, as on specimens NMW 27.111.GR442 and NMW 78.85G.M19, from the Mineral Collection in the National Museum of Wales. Details of this occurrence are mentioned in unpublished Russell manuscripts currently housed in the Natural History Museum. Harmotome has also been collected from Craig Rhiwarth Mine (R. Starkey, *personal communication*)

Further south, in the Central Wales Mining District, harmotome has been identified at Pen-y-Clun Mine, near Llanidloes, Powys, where it occurs with barite and witherite (Morgan and Starkey, 1991), and also from the nearby Gorn Mine (N. Hubbard, *personal communication*).

Hastingsite   Monoclinic
$NaCa_2(Fe^{+2},Mg)_4Fe^{+3}(Si_6Al_2)O_{22}(OH)_2$
A sodium calcium iron magnesium aluminium silicate hydroxide belonging to the amphibole group which forms a series with magnesiohastingsite. Hastingsite is a rock-forming mineral, occurring in basic igneous rocks.

Titanium-rich hastingsite occurs along with titanium-rich pargasite and titanium-rich biotite in gabbros of the St. David's Head Intrusion, Dyfed, forming either rims to clinopyroxene crystals or euhedral crystals in the groundmass, with identification confirmed by electron microprobe analysis (author's unpublished data). Hastingsite is also a component of the Rhiw Intrusion, Llŷn (author's unpublished data).

Bromley (1969) reported the occurrence of ferrohastingsite in the Tan-y-Grisiau microgranite, although no analytical data were presented.

Hatchettite
A hydrocarbon mineral; a kind of paraffin wax with a composition near $C_{38}H_{78}$.

Hatchettite was first described by Conybeare (1821) from clay ironstone nodules in the Merthyr Tydfil district (Mid Glamorgan), who proposed the name hatchettine in honour of the eminent English chemist Charles Hatchett (1765-1847). The name hatchettine was adopted initially, but subsequently modified to hatchettite by Dana (1868). An early analysis of hatchettite by Johnston (1838) gave C 85.91% and H 14.62%.

Hatchettite is soft, yellowish to deep-orange, translucent and waxy when fresh, but becomes darker and opaque when exposed to air. It is known from various localities in the eastern part of the South Wales Coalfield, including Newbridge, Bedwellty, Ogmore Vale and Porth (North and Howarth, 1928). Firth (1971) and Firth and Eglinton (1971) provided a detailed account of hatchettite from the South Wales Coalfield, describing its occurrence at many localities in Mid Glamorgan, including: Llanwynno Tips, Tylorstown; Great Western Colliery, Pontypridd; Cymmer Colliery, Porth; Standard Colliery, Ynyshir; Hirwaun Common East Opencast; Cwm Colliery, Beddau; Coed Ely Colliery, near Llantrisant; St. John's Colliery, Maesteg; Tylorstown Colliery, Rhondda Fach; Big Colliery, Blaenavon; and Wern Tarw Colliery, Pencoed. Small orange/red, translucent spheres, noted by North and Howarth (1928) at Bedwellty, were originally thought to be related to hatchettite but Firth (1971) and Firth and Eglinton (1971) noted that they are amorphous, with a composition C 87.36%, H 10.40% and therefore that they are not hatchettite. Firth (1971) described in particular such spheres from Parc Colliery, at Cwm Parc, Mid Glamorgan.

Hausmannite   Tetragonal
$Mn^{+2}Mn_2^{+3}O_4$
A manganese oxide mineral found in manganese ore deposits.

Hausmannite has been identified in manganese ore from a disused manganese mine at Tŷ Coch, Mid Glamorgan (Criddle and Symes, 1977), where it forms: i) euhedral to subhedral grains intimately associated with braunite, and interstitial and vug-filling calcite, manganocalcite, ferroan calcite, dolomite, barite, minor pyrobelonite and vanadinite; and ii) euhedral crystal clusters associated with brown calcite interlayered with goethite and romanèchite.

Hausmannite is also found in manganese ores at Benallt Mine, near Rhiw, Llŷn, where it occurs as brown, iridescent plates associated with altered pyrochroite (on Natural History Museum specimen B.M. 1945, 133).

Hedenbergite   Monoclinic
$CaFe^{+2}Si_2O_6$
A calcium iron silicate belonging to the pyroxene group and forming two series, one with diopside, the other with johannsenite. Hedenbergite is a rock-forming mineral which is found in fractionated tholeiitic igneous rocks, as well as a component of high grade metamor-

phosed calcareous rocks, such as limestones.

In Wales hedenbergite is rare. Horák (1993) reported the presence of hedenbergite in Precambrian calc-silicate marbles and clinopyroxene-feldspar gneisses of the Coedana Complex, exposed in the Nebo Inlier on Anglesey, with identification confirmed by electron microprobe analysis.

Hedleyite   Trigonal
Bi_7Te_3

A rare bismuth telluride which occurs in sulphide mineral veins, and also in skarn deposits.

Naden (1988) reported the identification of hedleyite as small (20 μm) inclusions in galena in a specimen from Clogau Mine, near Dolgellau, Gwynedd, currently in the Kingsbury Collection (K3), Natural History Museum. This appears to be the first record of hedleyite in the British Isles.

Hematite   Trigonal
α-Fe_2O_3

An iron oxide, dimorphous with maghemite, and a member of the hematite group. A common mineral, occurring in a wide variety of settings, for example in mineral veins, in sandstones, and in igneous and metamorphic rocks.

Hematite is widely developed in Wales, typically occurring in pockets in limestones of Carboniferous age in North and South Wales. In South Wales, hematite-bearing iron ore deposits are particularly abundant across the south crop of the South Wales Coalfield, where hematite occurs associated principally with goethite, along with crystalline quartz. Important deposits occur in Mid Glamorgan, at the Llanharry, Mwyndy, Bute, and Trecastle Mines, near Llantrisant, and Garth Mine, near Pentyrch (Vivian, 1885; Rankin and Criddle, 1985). One especially interesting occurrence in this area is the presence of hematite replacing crinoids, bryozoa and other fossils in limestone exposed at Rhiwbina, South Glamorgan (Strahan, 1899). Minor hematite is also present in ore from a disused manganese mine at Tŷ Coch, near Porthcawl, occurring with various manganese minerals (Criddle and Symes, 1977).

In North Wales, hematite is less abundant. In Clwyd it occurs in Carboniferous Limestone associated with nickel and cobalt minerals at Moel Hiraddug, and at the nearby Cwm Iron Mine, near Tyddyn-y-cyll, and Henfryn Mine, near Dyserth (Le Neve Foster, 1882; Strahan, 1885; Warren et al., 1984), as well as at the Bodfari Mine, located in a small faulted outlier of Carboniferous Limestone ca. 7 km NE of Denbigh (Warren et al., 1984). Hematite is also a minor component in oolitic iron ores of Ordovician age exposed at Llandegai, near Bangor, Gwynedd (Pulfrey, 1933). In Snowdonia, large hematite crystals, up to 30 mm across, are found in veins associated with quartz and chlorite, cutting slates at the Penrhyn Quarry, near Bethesda. Elsewhere in Snowdonia, hematite is a constituent of the manganese deposits of Cambrian age exposed in the Harlech Dome region (Bennett, 1987b), being responsible for the colouration in the red laminated

Figure 81. Hexagonal platey hematite crystal from Penrhyn Quarry, Bethesda, Gwynedd. The crystal measures 10 mm across. NMW specimen 85.70G.M28, *ex* R.W. Barstow Collection.

horizons. On Llŷn, hematite is an important component in manganese ores formerly mined at Nant-y-Gadwen and Mynydd Rhiw (Woodland, 1939b).

Hemimorphite   Orthorhombic
$Zn_4Si_2O_7(OH)_2.H_2O$

A zinc silicate hydroxide hydrate which develops in the oxidized zone of zinc-bearing ore bodies.

In Wales hemimorphite is widely developed in the Central Wales Mining District, being recorded from numerous mines in the area. Jones and Moreton (1977) noted its presence at the Dylife and Nantycagl (Eaglebrook) Mines, while Braithwaite (1982a and b) recorded colourless radiating aggregates of hemimorphite from the Nantycagl (Eaglebrook) and Bwlchglas Mines. Radiating spherical aggregates (up to 2.5 mm in diameter) of acicular hemimorphite crystals have been collected from the Cwmystwyth Mine, now preserved as National Museum of Wales specimen NMW 87.21G.M10 (*ex* T.F. Bridges Collection) and NMW 87.43G.M38. Hemimorphite specimens from this locality are also in the Natural History Museum, as are specimens from Nantycreiau, Nantycreiau West, and Esgairlle West. Elsewhere in the Central Wales Mining District hemimorphite has been recorded from

Mynyddgorddu Mine, as flat crystals on joints in sphalerite (*British Micromount Society Newsletter*, No. 15; Clark and Rust, 1993), Henfwlch Mine, forming sprays 2-3 mm across on sphalerite and ferroan dolomite (J.S. Mason, *personal communication*), and colourless crystals lining vugs in gossan (*British Micromount Society Newsletter*, No. 15), Bwlchrhennaid Mine, as white crystalline crusts on veinstone (*British Micromount Society Newsletter*, No. 18) and associated with wulfenite (Mason, 1992), Brynyrafr (*British Micromount Society Newsletter*, No. 35),Ystrad Einion (S.A. Rust, *personal communication*), and from Esgair Hir Mine, occurring as white crusts of drusy, bladed crystals on botryoidal green to brown hemimorphite (Rust and Mason, 1988). Some of the most attractive hemimorphites from Central Wales are from Llettyhen Mine, as white to pale blue botryoids up to 5 cm across and 1 cm thick.

Figure 82. Hemimorphite crystal aggregates up to 1 mm across, scattered on quartz collected in 1980 from Level Fawr, Cwmystwyth Mine, in the Central Wales Mining District. NMW specimen 87.43G.M38, *ex* A. Dean Collection.

In Powys, hemimorphite is known from two mines in the Llangynog district, namely Llangynog Mine and Craig Rhiwarth Mine (*British Micromount Society Newsletter*, No. 22 and also Williams, 1985).

In South Wales, hemimorphite is relatively abundant in lead-bearing veins cutting Carboniferous Limestone in Machen Quarry and in the Draethen area, in Mid

Glamorgan, for example at Cwmleyshon Quarry, where it forms radiating aggregates of colourless acicular crystals up to 5 mm in length, and also at Hendy Quarry, Miskin (*British Micromount Society Newsletter*, No.35).

In Clwyd, hemimorphite occurs in the Halkyn district, for example on National Museum of Wales specimen NMW 68.378.GR24, and also in the Minera district, as 3-5 mm brown sheaves on quartz and calcite (J.S. Mason, *personal communication*).

Hessite   Monoclinic
Ag$_2$Te
A rare silver telluride mineral.

Gilbey (1968) identified discrete, anhedral crystals of hessite in tellurobismuthite associated with tetradymite, galena, altaite and native gold at the Clogau Mine, near Dolgellau, Gwynedd. This account represented the first

Figure 83. A row of hessite grains (grey) in tellurobismuthite from the Clogau Mine, in the Dolgellau Gold Belt. Field of view is 600 μm across. Specimen JN4, R.A. Ixer Collection.

description of the mineral in the British Isles. More recently hessite has been confirmed by electron microprobe studies from the same mine as small (30-40 μm) grains in galena ("silver glance") occurring in tellurobismuthite-bearing assemblages in an ore shoot on the 4th level of the Llechfraith section (Naden, 1988).

Heulandite   Monoclinic
(Na,Ca)$_{2-3}$Al$_3$(Al,Si)$_2$Si$_{13}$O$_{36}$.12H$_2$O
A sodium calcium aluminium silicate hydrate belonging to the zeolite group.

Although there are no verified occurrences of heulandite in Wales, there is a reference in *Mineralogical Magazine* (volume 17, p.27) to specimens of 'heulandite and prehnite from Wales' being exhibited by Sir Arthur Russell at a General Meeting of the Mineralogical Society held on March 17, 1914.

Hexahydrite   Monoclinic
MgSO$_4$.6H$_2$O
A magnesium sulphate hydrate, belonging to the hexahydrite group. It occurs typically as a dehydration product of epsomite.

Certain specimens labelled 'epsomite' from Treharris, Mid Glamorgan, in the Mineral Collection of the National Museum of Wales, revealed the presence also of hexahydrite on the basis of X-ray diffraction (e.g. NMW X-282). However, the presence of hexahydrite is most likely the result of dehydration of epsomite in the museum environment.

Hollandite   Monoclinic
$Ba(Mn^{+4},Mn^{+2})_8O_{16}$
A barium manganese oxide belonging to the cryptomelane group.

So-called psilomelane and pyrolusite associated with minor N-S vertical faults on Mochowgryn and in the vicinity of Nant yr Helfa, in the Migneint area of Gwynedd, were shown by Lynas (1973) to be hollandite, on the basis of chemical analysis, X-ray powder photography and oscillation photographs. This account represented the first description of hollandite in the British Isles.

Hydrobiotite   Monoclinic
A potassium iron aluminium silicate hydroxide, being a 1:1 regular interstratification of biotite and vermiculite. Hydrobiotite develops as an alteration product of igneous rocks as a result of hydrothermal activity.

Rice and Sharp (1976) described the presence of hydrobiotite along with illite and chlorite in highly fractured phyllitic rock associated with the Coed-y-Brenin copper mineralization, NNE of Dolgellau, Gwynedd.

Hydrocerussite   Trigonal
$Pb_3(CO_3)_2(OH)_2$
A lead carbonate hydroxide. An uncommon mineral which develops as a result of alteration of lead-bearing minerals.

A specimen in the Natural History Museum, B.M. 1913, 69, from the mineral collection of Thomas Pennant (1726-1798), the Welsh mineralogist, traveller and zoologist, is labelled hydrocerussite and is 'said to be from Halkin, Flintshire (but undoubtedly Mendip Hills, Somersetshire; LJS 1913)'. The qualifying statement was by L.J. Spencer, the former Keeper of Mineralogy at the Natural History Museum.

More recently hydrocerussite has been confirmed by X-ray diffraction on specimens from Dylife (Rust and Rust, 1987), Frongoch (forming pearly crusts up to several cm across of crystals up to 1mm), Darren, Llechweddhelyg and Esgair Hir Mines, in the Central Wales Mining District. At Darren Mine, an *in situ* occurrence was noted during temporary exposure of the lode when a stope just above Francis' shaft was being prepared for capping. Pearly crusts of hydrocerussite were observed, associated with leadhillite, linarite, and malachite (J.S. Mason, *personal communication*). At Esgair Hir Mine four distinct forms have been identified, *viz:* i) white to greenish divergent crystal sprays up to 0.4 mm in length; ii) pearly white, creamy to blue and green stained coatings or encrustations up to several millimetres across; iii) flattened hexagonal crystals up to 0.4 mm with shallow pyramid faces and; iv) zoned colourless to white prismatic crystals with triangular cross-section, sometimes showing concave prismatic faces (Rust and Mason, 1988).

Hydronium jarosite   Trigonal
$(H_3O)Fe_3^{3+}(SO_4)_2(OH)_6$
A hydronium iron sulphate hydroxide, and a member of the alunite group. Hydronium jarosite results from the oxidation of pyrite-bearing ore bodies, and is typically developed in old mine workings.

'Carphosiderite' occurs abundantly in underground mine workings at Parys Mountain, Anglesey (D.A. Jenkins, *personal communication*). Carphosiderite is now a discredited species, but whether this record corresponds directly with hydronium jarosite has not been ascertained. If verified, this would represent the first record of the mineral in the British Isles.

Hydroxylapatite   Hexagonal
$Ca_5(PO_4)_3(OH)$
A calcium phosphate hydroxide belonging to the apatite group.

Baqri and Hodson (1979) reported that coal partings or 'dirt bands' in the Lower Hornlo (Red Vein) seam in the neighbourhood of Brynamman, West Glamorgan, contained up to 40% of hydroxylapatite. This appears to be the first record of hydroxylapatite in the British Isles, although the identification requires confirmation.

Hydrozincite   Monoclinic
$Zn_5(CO_3)_2(OH)_6$
A zinc carbonate hydroxide which develops as a secondary mineral in the oxidized zone of zinc-bearing ore bodies.

Hydrozincite is relatively abundant in Wales, occurring as a result of alteration of sphalerite-bearing veins. It typically forms white, earthy coatings on sphalerite or rock matrix. Some of the most spectacular specimens of hydrozincite from Wales have been collected from Van Mine, near Llanidloes, in the Central Wales Mining District, forming thick coatings, often showing a rippled surface. Hydrozincite has also been

Figure 84. Hydrozincite, showing ripple structures related to growth from solutions flowing down the walls of old workings above No. 3 Level, Parc Mine, Llanrwst, Gwynedd. Collected July 1978. The specimen measures 11.5 cm across. NMW specimen 85.70G.M29, *ex* R.W. Barstow Collection.

collected from numerous other mines elsewhere in the Central Wales Mining District, such as Dylife, Esgair Hir, Frongoch, Castell, and Cwmystwyth, to name but a few.

In Gwynedd, hydrozincite specimens from mines near Llanrwst, including Aberllyn, Trecastell, Llanrwst, and Parc are all present in the Mineral Collection of the National Museum of Wales. At Parc Mine hydrozincite forming a pale apple-green cement (up 1 mm in thickness) to rubble on the No. 2 level has been shown to be a nickeloan hydrozincite, containing up to approximately 4 wt% Ni (Alwan and Williams, 1979). Further investigations by Bevins, O'Brien and others (1982) identified the presence of nickeloan hydrozincite also on the No. 3 level. Hydrozincite is also recorded from Castell Carn Dochan Mine, near Bala (J.S. Mason, *personal communication*).

In South Wales hydrozincite has been collected from Llanfyrnach Mine, in Dyfed, and is also known from Cwmleyshon Quarry, near Draethen, Mid Glamorgan and at the nearby Machen Quarry (*British Micromount Society Newsletter*, No. 36).

Ilmenite   Trigonal
$Fe^{+2}TiO_3$

An iron titanium oxide of the ilmenite group of minerals which forms two series, one with geikielite and the other with pyrophanite. Ilmenite is a common accessory mineral in basic igneous rocks.

Ilmenite is widely developed in Wales, being present in many basic igneous rocks. In those rocks which have been heavily altered, however, ilmenite may be replaced by leucoxene, titanite or a TiO_2 polymorph mineral. Ilmenite is present, for example, in the centre of the Tal y Fan Intrusion, Gwynedd, although towards the margins of the intrusion it is replaced by titanite (Merriman *et al.*, 1986). Ilmenite also occurs in the St. David's Head Intrusion, Dyfed, in which it forms up to 12% of the mode in the laminated quartz ferrogabbros (author's unpublished data). Ilmenite-plagioclase-mesocumulates are present in the Rhiw Intrusion, on Llŷn (Cattermole, 1976), although once again the ilmenite is largely replaced.

Spectacular ilmenite-bearing tuffs of Ordovician age are developed in Central Snowdonia, occurring in the Lower Rhyolitic Tuff Formation exposed near Beddgelert, and in the Bedded Pyroclastic Formation at a variety of locations, including Cwm Meirch, in the vicinity of Lliwedd, in the crags of Gallt-y-llyn and Coed Pant Agored, and also near Snowdon summit (Williams, 1927). These ilmenite crystals are platey, reach up to 0.3 mm in length and 0.1 mm in width, and are manganese-rich (MnO reaches over 10 wt%; R.J. Merriman, unpublished data).

Iridium   Cubic
Ir

Native iridium. A rare mineral, found sparingly in placer deposits.

Andrew (1910) recorded that Readwin had described platiniridium (= platian iridium) from the Dolgellau Gold Belt, Gwynedd, although he was not specific as to the paper in which the reference was made. This represented the first occurrence of iridium in the British Isles, although it requires verification.

Jacobsite   Cubic
$(Mn^{+2},Fe^{+2},Mg)(Fe^{+3},Mn^{+3})_2O_4$

A manganese iron magnesium oxide belonging to the spinel group. It forms a series with magnetite and is dimorphous with iwakiite. Jacobsite is a constituent mineral in many manganese ore deposits.

The first recorded British occurrence of jacobsite was from the Benallt manganese mine, on Llŷn, by Campbell Smith *et al.* (1944a). It is present as black, angular, magnetic patches, up to 1 cm in length, in various white minerals (calcite, barite, tephroite and alleghanyite) forming thin veins cutting the manganese ore, and was found on the 'footwall side of no. 1 ore-body by no. 1 Chute, 50-60 feet west of the main shaft, and some 10-20 feet above the 130-foot level'.

Jamborite   Hexagonal
$(Ni^{+2},Ni^{+3},Fe)(OH)_2(OH,S,H_2O)(?)$

A nickel iron hydroxide hydrate, which typically forms as an alteration product of primary nickel sulphide minerals.

Natural History Museum specimen B.M. 1971, 363 from Bedwas Colliery, Mid Glamorgan, is labelled ?jamborite on millerite. Jamborite has also been found at Cymmer Colliery, at Porth, Mid Glamorgan (R.S.W. Braithwaite, *personal communication*). This represents the first occurrence of the mineral in the British Isles.

Firth (1971) considered that green secondary coatings on millerite from South Wales are morenosite, although X-ray analysis of such coatings on specimens in the Mineral Collection of the National Museum of Wales have so far failed to provide a distinctive pattern.

Jamesonite   Monoclinic
$Pb_4FeSb_6S_{14}$

A lead iron antimony sulphide, dimorphous with parajamesonite and forming a series with benavidesite. Jamesonite occurs with other lead antimony sulphosalt minerals and stibnite in antimony ore deposits.

Russell (1944) reported the presence of 'minute hair-like filaments of a grey metallic mineral either stibnite or jamesonite (plumosite)' occurring between semseyite crystals on specimens from Bwlch Mine, at Deganwy, Gwynedd. More recent investigations by Bevins *et al.* (1988) have confirmed the presence of jamesonite as capillary crystals associated with quartz and other sulphosalt minerals at Bwlch Mine, on the basis of optical, X-ray diffraction and electron microprobe investigations.

Jarosite   Trigonal
$KFe_3^{+3}(SO_4)_2(OH)_6$

A potassium iron sulphate hydroxide belonging to the alunite group. Jarosite develops in the oxidized zone of sulphide-bearing mineral deposits.

Jarosite is most probably widespread in Wales, occurring on mine walls as a result of oxidation of sulphide minerals although specific records are few. Johnson *et al.* (1979) reported the presence of yellow jarosite along with fibroferrite and rarer copiapite on the floor of Cae Coch Mine, Trefriw, Gwynedd. It is also present at Parys Mountain, on Anglesey (D.A. Jenkins, *personal communication*).

Jordanite   Monoclinic

$Pb_{14}(As,Sb)_6S_{23}$

A rare lead arsenic antimony sulphide which forms a series with geocronite, and is typically developed with other rare sulphosalt minerals, in association with galena and sphalerite in hydrothermal deposits.

Sivaprakash (1977) reported the presence of a rare lead sulpharsenide mineral from the Parys Mountain mineral deposit, on Anglesey. Electron microprobe analyses recalculated closest to the mineral jordanite.

Kaersutite   Monoclinic

$NaCa_2(Mg,Fe^{+2})_4Ti(Si_6Al_2)O_{22}(OH)_2$

A sodium calcium magnesium iron titanium aluminium silicate hydroxide of the amphibole group which forms a series with ferrokaersutite. Kaersutite is a rock-forming mineral usually found in alkaline igneous rocks.

Kaersutite forms small strongly pleochroic crystals in the central zone of the Tal y Fan Intrusion, Gwynedd. Merriman *et al.* (1986) presented an electron microprobe analysis of kaersutite from this locality. In addition kaersutite occurs as a minor component in Ordovician doleritic and gabbroic intrusions in Dyfed, such as the Llanwnda Intrusion exposed to the west of Fishguard (Bevins, 1979); in these intrusions it is associated with chlorite and is probably of late magmatic origin.

Kaolinite   Triclinic

$Al_2Si_2O_5(OH)_4$

A clay mineral, polymorphous with dickite, halloysite, and nacrite; a member of the kaolinite-serpentine group. Kaolinite is widely distributed in sedimentary rocks.

North (1916) noted that kaolinite is present in Carboniferous rocks in the South Wales Coalfield, especially in fault zones, such as at Cwm Fforch-wen, in the Garw Valley, Mid Glamorgan. Detailed X-ray diffraction investigations by Gill *et al.* (1977) revealed that kaolinite is in fact relatively widespread in the clay mineral fraction of these strata as a rock-forming mineral, while Robinson *et al.* (1980) reported the presence of kaolinite in some of the Carboniferous rocks they examined from southwest Dyfed. Elsewhere in Dyfed kaolinite is reported from heavily altered rhyolitic lavas and tuffs in a borehole near Treffgarne (Brown *et al.*, 1987).

Kermesite   Triclinic

Sb_2S_2O

Kermesite is an antimony sulphur oxide, commonly developed as an alteration product of stibnite.

Cherry-red coatings on stibnite from Bwlch Mine, near Deganwy, Gwynedd may well be kermesite, although this has yet to be substantiated (Bevins *et al.*, 1988). In addition a specimen of stibnite in the Mineral Collection of the National Museum of Wales (NMW 27.111.GR283), reputedly collected from the coast between Rhôs-mynach Mine and Dulas, on Anglesey has a cherry-red secondary mineral coating its surface, which may also be kermesite. However the validity of the provenance of this specimen is questionable as no other antimony-bearing minerals are known from this part of Anglesey.

Kobellite   Orthorhombic

$Pb_{22}Cu_4(Bi,Sb)_{30}S_{69}$

A rare lead copper bismuth antimony sulphide which forms a series with tintinaite. Kobellite is usually found in copper-bearing ore deposits.

Kobellite has been reported from the Parys Mountain lead-zinc-copper mineral deposit on Anglesey, by Sivaprakash (1977) and Pointon and Ixer (1980). It occurs as fine grained intergrowths (5-20 μm) associated with bismuthinite, galenobismuthite, bournonite, and native bismuth, forming contact rims around chalcopyrite, galena and tetrahedrite group minerals, as inclusions within sphalerite, and as a cement to framboidal pyrite. The results of electron microprobe analyses are presented in Sivaprakash (1977), which represented the first occurrence of the mineral in the British Isles.

Ktenasite   Monoclinic

$(Cu,Zn)_5(SO_4)_2(OH)_6.6H_2O$

A copper zinc sulphate hydroxide hydrate which occurs in the oxidized zone of copper and zinc bearing ore deposits.

Ktenasite has been recorded forming greenish-blue prisms in dolomite at the Ystrad Einion Mine, near Furnace, in the Central Wales Mining District (S.A. Rust, *personal communication*), confirmed by X-ray diffraction at the Natural History Museum.

Kutnohorite   Trigonal

$Ca(Mn,Mg,Fe^{+2})(CO_3)_2$

A calcium manganese magnesium iron carbonate which forms two series, one with dolomite and one with ankerite and which is a member of the dolomite group. Kutnohorite is found associated with manganese ore minerals.

Bennett (1987a and b) identified kutnohorite in various manganese-rich horizons in the Hafotty Formation of Cambrian age from the Harlech Dome region of Gwynedd. In particular it is found in the red, layered parts of the manganese ore horizon, and in the pyritic mudstones. Identification was confirmed by electron microprobe analyses, which showed that some of the carbonates contain between 30 and 50 mol% $MnCO_3$, and hence are parakutnohorites following the classification of Mottana (1986). Also Bennett (1987a) identified kutnohorite from a concentrically zoned 'object' in a thick bedded, fine grained altered tuff from the Cared Formation, at Porth Ceiriad, on the St. Tudwal's Peninsula, Llŷn, Gwynedd. More recently, kutnohorite has been identified by Roberts and Merriman (1990) as a component in metabentonites on the St. Tudwal's Peninsula, also on Llŷn. The identifications by Bennett (1987a and b) represented the first verified occurrence of kutnohorite in the British Isles.

Kyanite Triclinic
Al_2SiO_5
An aluminium silicate, trimorphous with andalusite and sillimanite. Kyanite develops in pelitic rocks which have been affected by high-grade metamorphism.

No record of *in situ* kyanite in Wales is known, although it has been recorded as a detrital mineral in glacial sands. For example, Strahan *et al.* (1909) identified kyanite in glacial sands exposed south of Castell-tôch, near Pendine, in Dyfed, while Griffiths and Stuart (1940) reported kyanite as a component of glacial sands at Ludchurch, also in Dyfed.

Labradorite Triclinic
$(Ca,Na)Al(Al,Si)_3O_8$
A calcium aluminium silicate belonging to the feldspar group. It forms part of the plagioclase series, with An_{50-70}. Labradorite forms one of the major rock-forming minerals in igneous rocks of basic composition.

Labradorite is widely distributed throughout Wales in basic igneous rocks. In many cases, however, original labradorite has been replaced by a lower temperature feldspar (usually albite) as a result of low-grade metamorphism. However, fresh labradorite compositions have been determined by electron microprobe analysis from the Tal y Fan Intrusion, Gwynedd (Merriman *et al.*, 1986), from the Llanwnda Intrusion, Dyfed (Bevins, 1982), and from the St. David's Head Intrusion, also in Dyfed (author's unpublished data).

Langite Monoclinic
$Cu_4(SO_4)(OH)_6.2H_2O$
A copper sulphate hydroxide hydrate, found in the oxidized zones of copper-bearing ore bodies.

Langite is found quite widely on mine dumps in the Central Wales Mining District. Jones and Moreton (1977) recorded the presence of langite at the Frongoch and Esgairfraith Mines, while later Rust and Mason (1988) identified it from Esgair Hir. Occurrences at Frongoch, Cwmystwyth, Eaglebrook and Llechweddhelyg have been confirmed by X-ray diffraction at the Natural History Museum. Other reported occurrences include Glogfawr (*British Micromount Society Newsletter*, No. 16), Dylife (Rust and Rust, 1987), a small trial level near Loveden Mine, Tre'r-ddol (J.S. Mason, *personal communication*), and Geufron (*British Micromount Society Newsletter*, No. 36), while specimens in the National Museum of Wales are from Gwaithyrafon and Dylife.

In southern Snowdonia langite was identified from a trial level near Bontddu (Saich and Rust, 1987), while a specimen in the National Museum of Wales is from 'Simmdle Dallhuan' (presumably Simmde Dylluan), in the Nantlle Valley, in central Snowdonia.

Figure 85. Langite crystals up to 1 mm in length from Lodge Park copper trial, near Tre'r-ddol, in the Central Wales Mining District. J.S. Mason Collection, specimen JMLP005.

Lanthanite-(Ce) Orthorhombic
$(Ce,La,Nd)_2(CO_3)_3.8H_2O$
A cerium lanthanum neodymium carbonate hydrate which occurs as a secondary mineral deriving from weathering of primary rare earth element-bearing rocks.

Lanthanite-(Ce) is found as colourless, transparent plates covered by radiating tufts of malachite, and associated with brochantite, posnjakite and chalcoalumite occurring on the walls and the back of the adit on Sneyd's Level of Britannia Mine, in Central Snowdonia (Bevins *et al.*, 1985). This represented the first description of this new mineral, and the type specimen is housed in the National Museum of Wales (specimen NMW 84.6G.M1).

Laumontite Monoclinic
$CaAl_2Si_4O_{12}.4H_2O$
A calcium aluminium silicate hydrate belonging to the zeolite group. Laumontite is found with other zeolite group minerals in cavities and veins in altered igneous rocks.

In Wales laumontite has only been identified in thin calcite-bearing veins (*c.* 20-30 mm thick) cutting altered basic lavas of Ordovician age exposed in Llanelwedd Quarry, at Builth Wells, Powys (Bevins and Horák,

Figure 86. Scanning electron micrograph of platey crystals of lanthanite-(Ce), with radiating tufts of malachite from the type locality at Britannia Mine, in Snowdonia, Gwynedd. NMW specimen 84.6G.M1. Reproduced from Bevins *et al.* (1985), with permission of the American Mineralogical Society.

1985). In these veins the laumontite is pale pink in colour and massive. Identification was confirmed by X-ray diffraction (National Museum of Wales X-ray no. NMW-X149), from National Museum of Wales specimen NMW 83.47G.M1. This report has subsequently been confirmed by Metcalfe (1990).

Lautenthalite   Monoclinic
$PbCu_4[(OH)_6/(SO_4)_2].3H_2O$
A rare lead copper hydroxide sulphate hydrate which is the lead analogue of develline. Lautenthalite occurs as a secondary mineral after primary lead and copper sulphide minerals.

Lautenthalite was recently described as a new mineral from the Harz Mountains (Medenbach and Gebert, 1993). In Wales, it has been identified as emerald green tabular crystals at Hendrefelen Mine, in the Central Wales Mining District (S.A. Rust, *personal communication*).

Lawsonite   Orthorhombic
$CaAl_2Si_2O_7(OH)_2.H_2O$
A calcium aluminium silicate hydroxide hydrate, dimorphous with partheite. Lawsonite is a characteristic mineral of metamorphic rocks which have been affected by moderate to high pressures at low temperatures.

Figure 87. Thin section of tabular lawsonite crystals up to 800 μm long in blueschists from from Hendrefor, Anglesey.

Lawsonite forms idioblastic, tabular crystals (generally 0.4 x 0.2 mm, although some are greater than 1 mm long) in narrow bands (less than 1 m thick) interleaved with crossite-bearing basic schists and muscovite-quartz schists of the Aethwy Unit, on Anglesey (Gibbons and Mann, 1983). The first reported occurrence of lawsonite in the British Isles was in fact by Nataraj (1967) from north of Hendrefor, also on Anglesey (SH 548 773). This occurrence was confirmed subsequently by Gibbons and Mann (1983), who also located several other occurrences of lawsonite on the northern shore of the Menai Straits (in the vicinity of SH 552 719), with identification on the basis of optical characteristics and electron microprobe analyses.

Lead   Cubic
Pb
Native lead. A very rare mineral, occurring typically in the oxidized zone of lead-bearing mineral deposits.

Sowerby (1817) described the presence of native lead from Golch Rake, near Holywell, Clwyd, on a specimen collected in 1811 by R. Jones, and subsequently presented to the Geological Society. In addition, Forbes (1867) noted that Readwin had reported the occurrence of native lead in association with gold in the Dolgellau Gold Belt, Gwynedd. Both occurrences are extremely dubious and require confirmation before the presence of native lead in Wales is verified.

Leadhillite   Monoclinic
$Pb_4(SO_4)(CO_3)_2(OH)_2$
A lead sulphate carbonate hydroxide which develops typically in the oxidized zone of lead-bearing ore bodies. It is named after the Scottish locality of Leadhills.

Leadhillite has been identified from numerous localities in the Central Wales Mining District. Braithwaite (1982a) described the presence of microscopic, hexagonal-shaped colourless tablets at Nantycagl (Eaglebrook) Mine, and has also identified the mineral at the Esgair Hir, Frongoch, Llettyhen and Cwmystwyth Mines (R.S.W. Braithwaite, *personal communication*). At Esgair Hir Mine leadhillite forms tabular, pseudo-hexagonal crystals up to 1 mm and very rare prismatic crystals up to 0.4 mm, in vughs and along joints (Rust and Mason, 1988). Leadhillite has also been identified from Darren Mine (J.S. Mason, *personal communication*), Dylife (Rust and Rust, 1987), and tentatively reported from Glogfawr (*British Micromount Society Newsletter,* No. 16) and Bwlchrhennaid (*British Micromount Society Newsletter,* No. 15).

Lepidocrocite   Orthorhombic
γ-$Fe^{+3}O(OH)$
An iron oxide hydroxide, trimorphous with feroxyhyte, and goethite. Lepidocrocite is a secondary mineral, commonly associated with goethite, which results from the oxidation of primary iron minerals.

Probably lepidocrocite is very widely developed in Wales, being an important component of gleyed soils, although actual records are few. Brown (1953) identified lepidocrocite in certain Anglesey soils, while Adams and

Kassim (1984) reported that lepidocrocite is abundant and widespread in the soils of Mid Wales, in particular in brown earths of the Denbigh Soil Series.

Lepidolite   Monoclinic
$K(Li,Al)_3(Si,Al)_4O_{10}(F,OH)_2$

A potassium lithium aluminium silicate fluoride hydroxide, belonging to the mica group. Lepidolite is a relatively rare mineral, occurring in certain granites, aplites and granitic pegmatites.

The only reference to lepidolite in Wales is that by Griffiths (1939), occurring as pale blue to pink pleochroic crystals, forming a component in glacial deposits exposed in the area between the River Neath and the River Tywi, in South Wales.

Linarite   Monoclinic
$PbCu(SO_4)(OH)_2$

A lead copper sulphate hydroxide which develops in the oxidized zone of lead- and copper-bearing ore bodies.

Linarite is relatively widespread in mine dumps in the Central Wales Mining District. Jones and Moreton (1977) reported deep azure-blue linarite, typically occurring as single prismatic crystals, from numerous localities, including the Geufron, Glogfawr, Esgairfraith, Frongoch, Dylife, Dyfngwm and Eaglebrook Mines.

Figure 88. Sprays of linarite crystals up to 3 mm across from the Esgair Hir Mine in the Central Wales Mining District. S.A. Rust Collection specimen 721.

Braithwaite (1982a) described the presence of blue blades of linarite up to 2 mm in length, commonly in radiating bunches, from Eaglebrook Mine. More recently, Rust and Mason (1988) gave account of bladed prismatic (up to 2 mm) linarite from Esgair Hir Mine, while it has also been reported from Bwlchrhennaid Mine, occurring either as rare euhedral crystals on malachite or more commonly as a crystalline crust (*British Micromount Society Newsletter,* No. 18), and Brynyrafr Mine (*British Micromount Society Newsletter,* No. 35). In addition blue spherules up to 1 mm on quartz from Llechweddhelyg Mine have been shown to have a composition midway in the series linarite-schmiederite (Rust, 1990b). Other occurrences include the Penrhiw and Dolwen-Mynach Vale Mines (J.S. Mason, *personal communication*).

In south Dyfed, linarite is present as rare, very small crystals with cerussite and brochantite on galena in dump material from Bonville's shaft at the Vale of Towy (Nant) Mine, near Carmarthen (G. Ryback, *personal communication*).

Linnaeite   Cubic
$Co^{+2}Co_2^{+3}S_4$

A cobalt sulphide which forms a series with polydymite, belonging to the linnaeite group of minerals. Linnaeite occurs along with other sulphide minerals in cobalt-bearing hydrothermal veins.

Small (0.25-0.75 mm diameter), silvery-white octahedral crystals with a brilliant metallic lustre, on a specimen from 'Rhonda Valley, Glamorganshire', belonging to 'Mr. Terrill of Swansea', were identified by Des Cloizeaux (1880) as linnaeite. North (1916) referred to this earlier description of linnaeite, although he thought that the original specimen had not been preserved, while North and Howarth (1928) added a further occurrence, from the No. 1 Pit, at Ferndale, Mid Glamorgan, the latter crystals forming isolated octahedral crystals between 0.2 to 0.4 mm across. North (1916) did, however, question the true identity of this mineral, in view of the fact that an analysis by Des Cloizeaux showed the presence of nickel also. Further descriptions of so-called linnaeite were subsequently provided by Howarth (1928) and Howarth (1954); in the latter paper Howarth noted that the original specimen described by Des Cloizeaux had in fact been transferred subsequently to the National Museum of Wales (now as NMW 37.239.GR1) when it acquired by donation in 1937 a large collection of minerals from Mrs Terrill. Subsequent analysis of this specimen, along with one from Wyndham Colliery, at Ogmore Vale, also in Mid Glamorgan, showed that this so-called linnaeite was, in fact, the nickel-cobalt sulphide mineral siegenite (Bevins and Horák, 1985).

A specimen in the Mineral Collection of the National Museum of Wales (NMW 83.41G.M1489; *ex* King Collection K4554; previously *ex* Harwood Collection 2881, collected in 1967) is labelled as linnaeite from Great Ormes Head, Llandudno (Gwynedd), with discrete metallic grey cubo-octahedral crystals up to 4 mm across.

Litharge   Tetragonal
PbO
A lead oxide mineral, dimorphous with massicot. Litharge forms alteration crusts on lead-bearing minerals, in particular galena.

Litharge has been identified as scattered blebs and occasional octahedra at Frongoch Mine, in the Central Wales Mining District, confirmed by X-ray diffraction at the Natural History Museum. This occurrence is thought to have been formed by reaction between lime from collapsed masonry and cerussite or galena (J.S. Mason, *personal communication*).

Lizardite   Trigonal and hexagonal
$Mg_3Si_2O_5(OH)_4$
A magnesium silicate hydroxide of the kaolinite-serpentine group which is polymorphous with antigorite, clinochrysotile, orthochrysotile and parachrysotile, and forms a series with nepouite. Lizardite typically results from the alteration of ultrabasic rocks.

Lizardite occurs associated with antigorite in serpentinized peridotites of the Mona Complex, on Anglesey (Maltman, 1977), replacing primary olivine and orthopyroxene. Lizardite has also been identified from the Rhiw Intrusion, on Llŷn, from Trwyn Talfarach (Natural History Museum X-ray no. 5920F).

Mackinawite   Tetragonal
$(Fe,Ni)_9S_8$
An iron nickel sulphide which occurs both as a primary mineral in ultrabasic and basic igneous rocks and in sulphide ore bodies.

Although potentially mackinawite might be dispersed quite widely in ultrabasic and basic igneous rocks in Wales, studies of the opaque minerals in these rocks are few. However Ixer (in Thorpe *et al.*, 1991) reported the presence of mixed pyrrhotite-chalcopyrite-mackinawite grains in an altered basic intrusion from Carn Menyn, in the Mynydd Preseli, Dyfed.

Mackinawite has been identified from the Dolgellau Gold Belt, in Gwynedd (Gilbey, 1968), occurring as oriented inclusions in chalcopyrite and as vermiculoid, irregular inclusions in chalcopyrite associated with pyrrhotite. It has been found at Cefndeuddwr Mine, and also from a lode in the Foel Ispri area.

Magnesiohornblende   Monoclinic
$Ca_2(Mg,Fe^{+2})_4Al(Si_7Al)O_{22}(OH,F)_2$
A calcium magnesium iron aluminium hydroxide belonging to the amphibole group and forming a series with ferrohornblende. Magnesiohornblende is a rock-forming mineral occurring in basic igneous rocks.

Magnesiohornblende occurs in the Llech Dafad Intrusion, of Ordovician age, exposed to the northeast of Aberbach, Dyfed. It forms green, pleochroic needle-like crystals overprinting clinopyroxene and replacing groundmass in the intrusion, with identification confirmed by electron microprobe analysis (Bevins, 1979). Magnesiohornblende is also present in gabbros of the St. David's Head Intrusion, exposed to the NW of St.

David's, also in Dyfed (author's unpublished data).

In North Wales, magnesiohornblende occurs in basic rocks of the Sarn Complex, on Llŷn, with identification confirmed by electron microprobe analysis (Horák, 1993).

Magnesite   Trigonal
$MgCO_3$
Magnesium carbonate, a member of the calcite group, which forms two series, with gaspéite and with siderite. Magnesite is found associated with talc in serpentinized ultramafic rocks, and may also replace dolomite in contact metamorphosed limestones.

Henry (1830) described as magnesite a greenish-white, foliated mineral, soapy to the touch, in narrow veins cutting serpentine from a 'low hill' located 'S.W. and within a mile' of Parys Mountain, on Anglesey; this account requires substantiation, however. Greenly (1919) suggested that some of the carbonates in serpentinites and calc-silicate rocks of the Mona Complex on Anglesey may be magnesite, although these records also require verification. Magnesite has been identified occurring with smithsonite and barite from 'Ochr-Chwith, Glamorgan' (? = Ochrwyth, near Risca, Gwent); Natural History Museum X-ray no. x14629.

Magnetite   Cubic
$Fe^{+2}Fe_2^{+3}O_4$
An iron oxide mineral which forms two series, with jacobsite and with magnesioferrite. Magnetite belongs to the spinel group of minerals. It is widespread, occurring as an accessory mineral in igneous rocks, as a component of metamorphic rocks, and in many sedimentary rocks also. Magnetite is widely developed in Wales, particularly in igneous rocks; hence only a few of the more notable occurrences are described.

Spectacular octahedral magnetite crystals up to 5 mm across, associated with chromite, occur in chlorite schists of the Mona Complex exposed near Rhoscolyn, on Anglesey, as described by Greenly (1919) and Maltman (1977). Fine grained magnetite is a minor component of oolitic and pisolitic iron ores of Ordovician age exposed across Anglesey and Snowdonia. Hallimond (1924) reported the presence of magnetite-bearing oolitic chamosite mudstones at Pen-yr-allt, near Llanfrothen, while Pulfrey (1933) described magnetite-chlorite oolites at Cross Foxes, Pen-yr-allt and Betws Garmon. More recently Matthews and Scoon (1964) described magnetite-bearing chamosite pisolitic mudstones at Tyllau Mwn, to the northeast of Dolgellau, containing magnetite octahedra up to 0.1 mm across, while Trythall (1988) noted that magnetite-bearing oolitic ironstones of Ordovician age are present at a number of localities in Snowdonia, namely Bwlch y Cywion, Llanberis Valley, Betws Garmon, Tremadog, Rhyd, Cadair Idris and Tyllau Mwn.

Near Nant Peris, in Snowdonia, a thin horizon of spessartine-magnetite 'schist' of Ordovician age crops out at Tan-yr-allt (Williams, 1927; Williams, 1930). Individual crystals average 0.5 mm across. Elsewhere in Snowdonia, magnetite occurs in a mineral vein cutting volcanic rocks of the Snowdon Volcanic Group in Cwm Tregalan; the vein also contains quartz, hematite, pyrite and rare grains of cassiterite (Reedman *et al.*, 1985). It is also present as a detrital concentrate in certain sandstones in central Snowdonia, thought to be the cause of an aeromagnetic anomaly over the area (see Howells *et al.*, 1991)

On Llŷn, magnetite is found in abundance in the Rhiw Intrusion (Hawkins, 1970; Cattermole, 1976), while in the Harlech Dome it occurs as a detrital mineral in sedimentary rocks, as for example in the Harlech Grits Group (Woodland, 1938b and c).

Malachite   Monoclinic
$Cu_2(CO_3)(OH)_2$
A copper carbonate hydroxide mineral which is a common secondary mineral found in the oxidized zone of copper-bearing ore bodies.

Malachite is widely developed in Wales, being found quite commonly in the alteration zones of copper-bearing veins across the whole of the Principality.

Jones and Moreton (1977) reported that malachite is widespread in the Central Wales Mining District, forming thin coatings, stains or botryoidal crusts, for example at Penrhiw, Darren, Llettyhen (Vaughan),

Figure 89. Malachite pseudomorphs after chalcopyrite from former copper mines at Great Ormes Head, Llandudno. The specimen measures 11 cm x 9cm. NMW specimen 83.41G.M4713.

Snowbrook, Copa Hill, Dylife, Mynyddgorddu, Esgairfraith, Geufron and Eaglebrook. Some of the most impressive specimens, however, have been collected from Llechweddhelyg Mine. At Geufron, massive malachite occurs associated with cuprite and native copper. Malachite has also been confirmed by X-ray diffraction from Gwaithyrafon Mine (S.A. Rust, *personal communication*). In addition, specimens in the National Museum of Wales collections are from Llettyhen, Frongoch and Bwlchrhennaid.

In South Wales, malachite is found at various localities in the vicinity of Cardiff where the Carboniferous Limestone is cut by thin chalcopyrite-bearing veins, for example at Goldsland Wood (Wenvoe), Creigiau Quarry, Machen Quarry, Cwmleyshon Quarry, and Cwrt-yr-Ala Park (Michaelston-le-Pit). At Penarth, malachite is commonly found in association with gypsum in Triassic strata, with identification confirmed by X-ray diffraction in the National Museum of Wales (NMW X-67). In the Llantrisant area, Fletcher and Young (1988) described zincian malachite associated with rosasite and aurichalcite in Carboniferous Limestone at Bute Quarry, while a specimen of malachite in the Mineral Collection at the National Museum of Wales is from the roadcuts along the A4119 to the east of Bute Quarry. Malachite has also been recorded from the adjacent Hendy Quarry (*British Micromount Society Newsletter*, No.35). Fletcher and Young (1988) also reported a similar assemblage of malachite, rosasite and aurichalcite from a borehole through Carboniferous Limestone at Locks Common, Porthcawl. Minor amounts of malachite are known from ironstone nodules of the South Wales Coalfield, including Tirpentwys Colliery, and Llanwynno Tips, at Tylorstown.

Further west, malachite is recorded from exposures of Carboniferous Limestone in the vicinity of Mynydd-y-Garreg, near Cross Hands, in Dyfed (Strahan *et al.*, 1909), while elsewhere in Dyfed malachite is described along with azurite in sandstones of Devonian age from various localities in south Pembrokeshire (Dixon, 1921), and is also known from the Vale of Towy (Nant) Mine, near Carmarthen, with a specimen from the last locality in the collections of the National Museum of Wales.

In North Wales, malachite is of relatively restricted occurrence. Bevins *et al.* (1985) described malachite tufts on lanthanite-(Ce) from Britannia Mine, Snowdon, while a specimen of malachite in the National Museum of Wales is from Drws-y-Coed, near Nantlle.

Attractive malachite pseudomorphs after chalcopyrite occur at the Great Orme, Llandudno, in veins cutting the Carboniferous Limestone. On Anglesey, malachite and azurite are found at the Pant-y-Gaseg Mine, near Amlwch, and are also recorded from Parys Mountain (Greenly, 1919). Minor amounts of malachite are also known from old mines at Llanfair Talhaiarn, in Clwyd.

In the Welsh Borderlands region, malachite has been collected from mines in the vicinity of Llanymynech, Powys, while elsewhere in Powys attractive radiating acicular malachite is known from Old Radnor (see Hall, 1868).

Manganhumite   Orthorhombic

$(Mn,Mg)_7(SiO_4)_3(OH)_2$

A rare manganese magnesium silicate hydroxide belonging to the humite group. It occurs typically in skarn deposits.

Bennett (1987a) reported the presence of rare orange-yellow Mn-humite associated with barite in a microconcretion and in adjacent carbonate-rich red laminated ore in the manganese ore bed of the Hafotty Formation, of Cambrian age, exposed at Llŷn Dywarchen, near Moel Ysgyfarnogod, in the Harlech Dome area of Gwynedd (Bennett analysis 12457). This appears to represent the first record of manganhumite in the British Isles.

Manganite   Monoclinic

MnO(OH)

A manganese oxide hydroxide trimorphous with feitknechtite and groutite. Manganite is usually found occurring with other manganese minerals in low-temperature hydrothermal veins.

Hall (1868) recorded manganite from the Gower Peninsula, West Glamorgan, although no details of this occurrence are provided, and no further record of manganite in this region is known. Williams (1927) described the presence of manganite in tuffs of Ordovician age in the vicinity of Lliwedd, in Snowdonia, although again no further descriptions are available. However, specimens of manganite from Benallt Mine, on Llŷn, and from Gyrndu, near Clynog, both in Gwynedd, are preserved in the Mineral Collection of the Natural History Museum.

Manganosite   Cubic

MnO

Manganese oxide, a member of the periclase group. A relatively rare manganese mineral.

Manganosite has been confirmed from the Benallt Mine, Llŷn, associated with hausmannite and pyrochroite (Natural History Museum X-ray no. x3434).

Marcasite   Orthorhombic

FeS_2

Iron sulphide, dimorphous with pyrite and a member of the marcasite group. Marcasite is a common component of sulphide mineral veins, as well as forming in sedimentary rocks.

Marcasite is widely developed in Wales, and only a few occurrences are described here.

Excellent marcasite crystals associated with calcite are known from the Trecastell and Parc Mines, in the Llanrwst Mining District of Gwynedd; specimens from these localities are preserved in the Mineral Collection of the National Museum of Wales. Marcasite is also associated with ores at Cyffty, Hafna, Klondyke and Welsh Foxdale (= New Pandora) Mines, in the same area. Further to the south, crystalline cockscomb marcasite was collected from the railway tunnel between Blaenau Ffestiniog and Roman Bridge, again specimens being preserved in the National Museum of Wales.

Figure 90. Cog-wheel marcasite crystals up to 10 mm across associated with acicular goethite, collected by R.W. Barstow in May 1982 from Gwynfynydd Mine, in the Dolgellau Gold Belt, Gwynedd. NMW specimen 86.95G.M2.

Readwin (1888) recorded the presence of marcasite in the Dolgellau Gold Belt, although no specific locality details were provided. Gilbey (1968) also recorded marcasite in the Gold Belt, in particular in the southwestern part of the area, where it occurs in intimate association with pyrite. Attractive marcasite crystals, associated with needle-like goethite aggregates, are known from Gwynfynydd Mine, with specimens in the National Museum of Wales.

Marcasite is widely developed in the Central Wales Mining District. Jones and Moreton (1977) noted its presence at the Penrhiw, Ystumtuen, Eaglebrook and Clara Mines, while they noted that fine crystals had been collected from the Brynyrafr and Plynlimon Mines. Raybould (1976) also noted the presence of pale yellow marcasite in the ores at Ystumtuen, as well as at the Bwlchgwyn and Penrhiw Mines, all on the Castell mineral lode. It is the presence of abundant marcasite which is responsible for the pollution from the No. 9 Cwmrheidol adit, from which metal-laden waters emerge with a pH of around 2.6. Elsewhere in the area marcasite is known from the Esgair Hir, Esgairfraith, Alltycrib, Tan-yr-allt, and Blaenceulan Mines (specimens in the Mineral Collection at the National Museum of Wales).

Margarite   Monoclinic
$CaAl_2(Al_2Si_2)O_{10}(OH)_2$
A calcium aluminium silicate hydroxide belonging to the mica group. Margarite is typically developed in metamorphosed sedimentary rocks.

Greenly (1919) suggested that high Ca contents in certain quartzites, belonging to the Mona Complex, on Anglesey, might possibly be accounted for by the presence of margarite in these rocks. No evidence was provided, however, for a positive identification of this mineral.

Matildite   Hexagonal
$AgBiS_2$
A rare silver, bismuth sulphide mineral. Typically matildite occurs in medium to high temperature sulphide mineral veins.

To date only one small grain of matildite (30-40 μm in diameter) in galena has been identified in Wales, present in a complex tellurobismuthite-tetradymite-galena-chalcopyrite-pyrrhotite-hessite-altaite-gold-'wehrlite'-cobaltite-bismuth-matildite assemblage from the 4th level, below the main adit level at Clogau Mine, near Dolgellau, Gwynedd (Naden, 1988). This account represents the first occurrence of matildite in the British Isles.

Mattheddleite   Hexagonal
$Pb_{20}(SiO_4)_7(SO_4)_4Cl_4$
A lead silicate sulphate chloride, a secondary lead mineral which develops in the oxidized zone of lead-bearing ore bodies.

Mattheddleite has been identified from only a few localities in the Central Wales Mining District. At Esgair Hir Mine, it forms colourless, acicular crystals up to 0.2 mm in length, coating caledonite and associated with leadhillite (Rust and Mason, 1988); a specimen of mattheddleite from this locality is preserved in the Mineral Collection of the National Museum of Wales as specimen NMW 88.61G.M1 (donated by S.A. Rust). Mattheddleite has been identified also from the Darren, Frongoch and Llechweddhelyg Mines, with confirmation by X-ray diffraction (Rust, 1990a; S.A. Rust, *personal communication;* J.S. Mason, *personal communication*).

Melanterite   Monoclinic
$Fe^{+2}SO_4.7H_2O$
An iron sulphate hydrate of the melanterite group of minerals. Melanterite forms commonly as post-mining deposits in old coal and metalliferous mine workings as an oxidation product of pyrite.

Melanterite is probably of widespread distribution in Wales, although records are few. Hall (1868) and Greenly (1919) both recorded the presence of melanterite at Parys Mountain, on Anglesey, while Johnson *et al.* (1979) described seams of green melanterite at Cae Coch Mine, near Trefriw, Gwynedd. A specimen of melanterite from the latter locality is preserved in the Mineral Collection of the National Museum of Wales (registration number NMW 84.24G.M1).

Bor (1950) reported on the occurrence of pisanite (a cuprian variety of melanterite) as pale blue acicular crystals forming a 'fungus-like growth' in clefts and cavities in country rock at Parys Mountain, on Anglesey.

A specimen in the Mineral Collection of the Natural History Museum is labelled as melanterite, from Abertysswg Colliery, at Rhymney, Mid Glamorgan.

Microcline   Triclinic
$KAlSi_3O_8$
A potassium aluminium silicate dimorphous with ortho-clase and belonging to the feldspar group. Microcline is a widespread component of many of the acidic intrusive rocks, such as granites, pegmatites and aplites.

Microcline is probably present in many of the acidic intrusive rocks in Wales, although specific records are few; rather the vague term 'alkali feldspar' is used. Bloxam and Dirk (1988) did specifically record the presence of rare microcline in the St. David's granophyre, exposed in the vicinity of St. David's, in Dyfed. In addition, Horák (1993) recorded microcline from various units in the Precambrian of Anglesey and Llŷn, including granitic rocks of the Coedana Complex, and calc-silicate gneisses in the Nebo Inlier.

Millerite   Trigonal
NiS
A widespread nickel sulphide mineral, occurring in a variety of environments, in particular nickel-bearing sulphide veins.

The first description of millerite from Wales was by W.H. Miller, then Professor of Mineralogy at Cambridge, in his report on the presence of crystals of sulphide of nickel in the Coal Measures of South Wales (Miller, 1842). At that time the mineral was called 'hair pyrites' or 'capillary pyrites', only being named millerite, in honour of Miller, some years later (Haidinger, 1845). It is present as brassy-yellow tufts or radiating groups of needle-like or capillary crystals in clay ironstone nodules, in association with other sulphide minerals including galena, sphalerite, chalcopyrite and siegenite.

Subsequent brief reference to the occurrence of the mineral in the South Wales Coalfield is contained in (Rogers *et al.,*1861), and also in the work by Jordan (1876). A more complete account of the distribution of millerite in South Wales was presented by North and Howarth (1928), who reported 15 separate localities from which millerite had by then been collected (see Table 6 below), while Howarth (1928) made one addition, namely Powell Dyffryn Pit, Bargoed. More recently Firth (1971) added to the known localities, reporting some 23 occurrences (see Table 7 below). In addition to these localities (all of the Firth specimens are housed in the National Museum of Wales) additional or more precise localities for millerite in the South Wales Coalfield as represented by specimens in the National Museum of Wales are presented in Table 8.

Millerite is also known from various mines in the Central Wales Mining District, such as Eaglebrook

Figure 91. Twisted, acicular millerite crystals up to 4 cm long in a cavity in an ironstone nodule, associated with the Seven Feet Seam, Treharris, Mid Glamorgan. NMW specimen 52.385.GR3, donated by the Ocean Coal Company Ltd.

(Jones and Moreton, 1977), and Brynyrafr (crystals up to 1-2 cm on occasion), Henfwlch, Camdwrmawr, Erglodd, Brynarian, and Hyddgen (J.S. Mason, *personal communication*) and also Esgair Hir and Esgairfraith Mines (Rust and Mason, 1988). In Snowdonia, millerite has been identified from Drws-y-Coed Mine (N. Hubbard, *personal communication*, and National Museum of Wales specimen NMW 82.22G.M1).

Table 6. Localities from which North and Howarth (1928) and Howarth (1928) reported millerite from the South Wales Coalfield

Bedwellty Pits	Hopkinstown
Blaenavon	Llanbradach
Blaina	Nantyglo
Brynna Pits, Pencoed	Newbridge
Cymmer Colliery, Porth	Ogmore Vale
Dowlais	Treharris
Ebbw Vale	Ynysddu
Ferndale No. 1 Pit	

Table 7. Localities from which Firth (1971) reported millerite from the South Wales Coalfield

Avan Colliery, Abergwynfi	Marine Colliery, Ebbw Vale
Bedwas Colliery, Bedwas	Nine Mile Point Colliery, Wattsville
Beynon Colliery, Brynmawr	Parc Colliery, Cwm Parc
Big Colliery, Blaenavon	Penallta Colliery, Ystrad Mynach
Bryn Colliery, Maesteg	Royal Arms Opencast Site, Merthyr Tydfil
Coed Ely Colliery, Llantrisant	St. John's Colliery, Maesteg
Cwm Colliery, Llantrisant	Tirpentwys Colliery, Pontypool
Cwm Dare Colliery, Aberdare	Tylorstown Colliery, Llanwynno Tips
Cwm-felin-fach Colliery, Cwmfelinfach	Ty Trist, Tredegar
Deep Navigation Colliery, Treharris	Wern Tarw, Pencoed
Gwaunton Opencast site, Abercrave	Windsor Colliery, Abertridwr
Maerdy Colliery, Rhondda Fach	

Table 8. Additional (or more exact) localities for millerite in the South Wales Coalfield as represented by specimens in the National Museum of Wales

Blackwood Colliery, Blackwood	Ocean Deep Navigation Colliery, Treharris
Blaenrhondda	Pentre Colliery, Pentre
Celynen South Colliery, Newbridge	Scotch Colliery, Gilfach Goch
Cwm Cynon Colliery, Mountain Ash	Senghenydd Colliery, Senghenydd
Dowlais Cardiff Colliery, Abercynon	Tower Colliery, Hirwaun
Eagle Brickworks Quarry, Cwmavon, Port Talbot	Universal Colliery, Senghenydd
Ffaldau Colliery, Pontycymmer	Wern Fawr Colliery, North Gower (nr. Swansea)
Fforchaman Colliery, Cwmaman	Wyndham Colliery, Ogmore Vale
International Colliery, Blaengarw	
Lewis Merthyr Colliery, Trehafod	
Ocean Colliery, Ferndale	

Mimetite   Hexagonal
$Pb_5(AsO_4)_3Cl$
A lead arsenate chloride belonging to the apatite group of minerals, dimorphous with clinomimetite. Mimetite is a secondary mineral which develops as a result of the alteration of primary lead-bearing minerals.

Andrew (1910) reported that Readwin had noted the occurrence of mimetite from the Dolgellau Gold Belt, Gwynedd, although he was not specific in which paper this reference was made. Mimetite has also been confirmed at Dylife Mine, Powys, as almost colourless to golden yellow acicular crystals up to 0.75 mm in length, or, more rarely, forming divergent groups of crystals, and also from Hendrefelen Mine, Dyfed (S.A. Rust, *personal communication*, and Clark and Rust, 1993). Both occurrences have been confirmed by X-ray diffraction at the Natural History Museum, X-ray nos 7420F and 8501F, respectively. More recently, mimetite has been recorded from Gwaithyrafon Mine, near Cwmsymlog (J.S. Mason, *personal communication*) and from Darren Mine (S.A. Rust, *personal communication*).

Minium   Tetragonal
$Pb_2^{+2}Pb^{+4}O_4$

Lead oxide, resulting from the oxidation of lead-bearing minerals, in particular galena.

Greg and Lettsom (1858) listed the occurrence of minium from Anglesey, occurring in 'veins of clay-slate with galena', and also from 'Merionethshire'. Hall (1868) also recorded minium from Anglesey, giving the locality as 'Pary's mine', now known as Parys Mountain.

In South Wales minium has been described from lead-bearing veins cutting the Carboniferous Limestone exposed 'about a quarter of a mile west of the Rhymney tunnel' (Howard, 1899); this is the tunnel which lies to the north of Cefn Onn, South Glamorgan.

Molybdenite   Hexagonal
MoS_2

Molybdenum sulphide. Molybdenite occurs as a primary mineral in granites, or in late-stage quartz veins. It is also a constituent of porphyry copper deposits.

The earliest reference to molybdenite in Wales appears to be that by W. Williams (1802) referring to the mineral near Blaen-y-nant, in the Nant Ffrancon area of Gwynedd. Further reference to this occurrence is made by Smith and Carruthers (1925) on the basis of information supplied by G.J. Williams, and a specimen from this locality is preserved in the Mineral Collection in the National Museum of Wales from the G.J. Williams Collection (specimen no. NMW 27.111.GR288). Another specimen in the National Museum of Wales (NMW 27.111.GR287), also from the G.J. Williams Collection, is molybdenite from the Ffestiniog Granite Quarry, Cefn Bychan, near Ffestiniog, Gwynedd. Reference to the presence of molybdenite associated with allanite, pyrophyllite and quartz in pipes cutting the Tan-y-Grisiau Granite is provided by Roberts (1979).

Rice and Sharp (1976) reported molybdenite in the Coed-y-Brenin porphyry copper deposit in southern Snowdonia, forming thin smears on joint surfaces, and small blebs in microfractures and in quartz-calcite veinlets. Close by, molybdenite has also been identified in the Clogau Mine, near Dolgellau, as small isolated laths (10-20 μm) and clumps of crystals closely associated with galena (J. Naden, *personal communication*).

Finally, molybdenite is also present in the Cae Coch massive sulphide deposit near Trefriw, Gwynedd (Ball and Bland, 1985).

Monazite   Monoclinic
$(La,Ce,Nd)PO_4$

A group name for a suite of light rare earth element phosphate minerals. Monazite is found commonly as a placer mineral. It occurs also in pegmatites, Alpine-type veins, and metamorphic rocks.

Cooper *et al.* (1983) and Read *et al.* (1987) described the occurrence of grey, ellipsoidal nodular monazites, 0.05-2 mm in diameter, in Lower Palaeozoic sedimentary rocks from the Harlech Dome, the Berwyn Dome, Mynydd Preseli, and Central Wales. The nodules show pronounced rare earth element zoning and contain an inclusion fabric of low-grade metamorphic minerals. The inference from the fabric is that the monazite grew by *in situ* recrystallization and authigenic growth of detrital monazite.

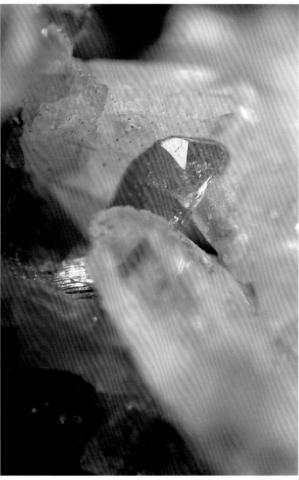

Figure 92. Orange monazite crystal (1 mm) associated with quartz from Fron Oleu, near Prenteg, Gwynedd. Collected May 1984. I. Jones Collection.

Primary igneous monazite has been identified from Ramsey Island, Dyfed, where it occurs in a rhyolitic ash-flow tuff of Ordovician age (author's unpublished data; identification by energy dispersive analysis).

Small euhedral monazite crystals have also been reported in rhyolites of Ordovician age at Gallt y Wenallt and Carneddau y Cribau, Gwynedd (A.T. Kearsely, *personal communication;* Howells *et al.*, 1991).

Pinkish to yellow rhombic monazite-(Ce) crystals up

to 0.5 mm occur in association with anatase and xenotime-(Y) in mineralized joints at Hendre Quarry, near Glyn Ceiriog, Clwyd (Starkey *et al.*, 1991), while undifferentiated, orange monazite crystals have also been collected from Fron Oleu, near Prenteg, Gwynedd (I. Jones, *personal communication*).

Monohydrocalcite   Hexagonal
$CaCO_3.H_2O$
A rare calcium carbonate hydrate, which typically occurs in association with calcite.

The first, and so far only published, account of monohydrocalcite from Wales was by Saich and Rust (1987) from a trial 1.5 km NW of Bontddu, Gwynedd. It occurs as minute, colourless pyramidal crystals in a chalcopyrite-quartz vein, associated with aragonite and calcite. Identification has been confirmed by X-ray diffraction (Natural History Museum X-ray no. 6257F).

Morenosite   Orthorhombic
$NiSO_4.7H_2O$
A nickel sulphate hydrate which occurs as an alteration product of nickel-bearing sulphides.

The presence of a 'yellow-green substance' occurring as partial coatings on millerite from the Elled Vein at Bedwellty, Gwent, was reported by North and Howarth

Figure 94. Radiating mass up to 25 mm across of probable morenosite coating millerite in a cavity in a clay ironstone nodule from Gelli Colliery, Mid Glamorgan. Collected July 1984. I. Jones Collection.

(1928) as being probable morenosite. More recently Firth (1971) described altered millerite from Tylorstown Colliery, Mid Glamorgan, coated with exfoliations of morenosite resulting from oxidation. Neither of these reports, however, were based on definitive tests and the presence of morenosite awaits confirmation; so far all X-ray diffraction patterns of light green alteration coatings on millerite from the South Wales Coalfield determined by the National Museum of Wales have only given patterns for millerite.

Mottramite   Orthorhombic
$PbCu(VO_4)(OH)$
A lead copper zinc vanadate hydroxide, a member of the descloizite group which forms a series with descloizite. Mottramite develops in the oxidized zone of ore deposits, in association with descloizite, pyromorphite, mimetite and vanadinite.

An X-ray investigation by the Natural History Museum of a sample from 'Flintshire' was identified as 'mottramite or very near' (Natural History Museum X-ray no. 3008F).

Muscovite   Monoclinic
$KAl_2(Si_3Al)O_{10}(OH,F)_2$
A potassium aluminium silicate hydroxide, belonging to

Figure 93. Probable morenosite coating millerite, associated with galena, from Gelli Colliery, Mid Glamorgan. The crystal is 13 mm long. Collected July 1984. I. Jones Collection.

the mica group. A rock-forming mineral which is a constituent of granites and pegmatites, it occurs as a component in many pelitic metamorphic rocks, and is a detrital component in many sedimentary rocks.

Muscovite is very widespread in Wales, being a component in sedimentary, igneous and metamorphic rocks. Accordingly, only a few records are presented here.

Muscovite is a primary component of particular types of granites, although true granitic rocks are relatively rare in Wales. Horák (1993) noted the presence of muscovite in the Coedana Granite, of late Precambrian age, exposed on Anglesey. In many igneous rocks, however, sericitic muscovite is of secondary origin, being a low temperature alteration product, typically after an original high temperature feldspar. Analyses of such secondary white micas are presented in Bevins and Rowbotham (1983).

In sedimentary rocks, muscovite is of detrital origin. In cases where the percentage of detrital white mica is high the rocks, typically sandstones, assume a sheen, and become flaggy. In Wales, such sandstones are common and of diverse ages, including Upper Cambrian (see Cope, 1982), Devonian (Waters and Lawrence, 1987), and Carboniferous, in particular the 'Pennant' (see Woodland and Evans, 1964).

In metamorphosed rocks, varying types of muscovite are found, depending on the temperature of recrystallization. Typically the muscovite replaces original clay minerals, and hence muscovite is a major component of metamorphosed mudstones. Merriman and Roberts (1985) and Robinson and Bevins (1986) have described such occurrences from various parts of Wales. Horák (1993) also reported metamorphic muscovite from Anglesey and Llŷn, occurring for example as a component of hornfelses surrounding the Coedana Granite, and also in higher grade gneisses exposed in the Holland Arms area.

Nacrite   Monoclinic
$Al_2Si_2O_5(OH)_4$
A hydrous aluminium silicate belonging to the kaolinite-serpentine group and polymorphous with kaolinite, dickite and halloysite. Nacrite occurs typically as a minor phase in hydrothermal ore deposits.

Nacrite has been identified in strata of Middle Coal Measures age from Trimsaran Borehole No. 2, Kidwelly, Dyfed (on Natural History Museum specimen 1985 GM MI 29620), and associated with dickite from a depth of '380 to 382' feet in the Aberfan Borehole, Mid Glamorgan (on Natural History Museum specimen 1985 GM MI 33153); both identifications have been confirmed by X-ray diffraction at the Natural History Museum.

Nagyagite   ?Orthorhombic
$Pb_5Au(Te,Sb)_4S_{5-8}$
A lead gold tellurium antimony sulphide which occurs in ore veins commonly in association with gold and other telluride minerals.

Gilbey (1968) reported the presence of nagyagite at the contact between gold and telluride minerals in a tellurobismuthinite-tetradymite-galena-gold-nagyagite assemblage at Clogau Mine, Dolgellau, Gwynedd. This represented the first occurrence of nagyagite in the British Isles.

Namuwite   Hexagonal
$(Zn,Cu)_4SO_4(OH)_6.4H_2O$
A rare zinc copper sulphate hydroxide hydrate which occurs in the oxidized zone of zinc- and copper-bearing ore bodies.

Namuwite is present as a pale sea-green encrustation, amorphous to the naked eye, 1.5 x 5.0 cm in area and up to 0.5 cm in thickness on hydrozincite which coats sphalerite on a specimen from Aberllyn Mine, Betws-y-coed, Gwynedd (Bevins *et al.*, 1982). The original description of the mineral species was based on specimen NMW 27.111.GR414, purchased by the National Museum of Wales as part of the G.J. Williams Collection. This specimen, still housed in the National Museum of Wales, represents the type specimen for namuwite. It was labelled originally as 'Hydrozincite (coloured by malachite) ...'. Scanning electron microscopy reveals the presence of near perfect hexagonal plates up to 60 μm across. Namuwite has more recently been identified from the Dylife Mine in the Central Wales Mining District, where it occurs as

Figure 95. Scanning electron micrograph of namuwite crystals from the type locality at Aberllyn Mine, near Betws-y-coed, Gwynedd. NMW specimen 27.111.GR414, *ex* G.J. Williams Collection.

translucent platey, blue-green hexagonal crystals on altered sphalerite associated with schulenbergite. This occurrence has been confirmed by X-ray diffraction at the Natural History Museum, X-ray nos. 7529F and 7029F, respectively. Namuwite has also been recorded from the Frongoch and Llywernog Mines (*British Micromount Society Newsletter*, No. 35). Namuwite is named in honour of the <u>Na</u>tional <u>Mu</u>seum of <u>W</u>ales.

Natrolite   Orthorhombic
$Na_2Al_2Si_3O_{10}.2H_2O$
A sodium aluminium silicate hydrate belonging to the zeolite group, dimorphous with tetranatrolite. Natrolite is commonly found in vugs or cavities in basic igneous rocks, resulting from low-temperature alteration.

One of the earliest records of natrolite in Wales was by Harrison (1894) from Gimlet Quarry, at Pwllheli, Gwynedd, occurring as radiating spherical groups 'from 1/4 to 1/2 inch in diameter', associated with calcite and quartz in cavities in altered dolerite. A brief mention of this occurrence is also provided by Harrison (1897), in a report on the presence of prehnite at Gimlet Quarry.

Boulton (1911) considered that a fibrous, colourless, faintly birefringent zeolite mineral forming radiating aggregates in the groundmass of a monchiquitic basanite in the Great House diatreme, near Usk, Gwent was probably natrolite, an identification also made by Haslett (1992) for a similar mineral in a monchiquite dyke exposed at nearby Glen Court.

On Anglesey, Greenly (1919) reported that a zeolite mineral (identified by H.H. Thomas as natrolite) occurs in a basic mass in gneisses of the Mona Complex exposed west of the farmhouse of Henblâs.

Williams (1930) identified natrolite, associated with thomsonite in olivine-dolerite dykes of probable Tertiary age cutting Ordovician volcanic and sedimentary rocks in central Snowdonia, in the tract of country between Nant Peris and Nant Ffrancon. It occurs in amygdales up to 2 cm in diameter, although identification is only possible in thin section.

Probably the most spectacular natrolite crystals known from Wales were collected in 1911 by the late Sir Arthur Russell, from Benallt Mine, on Llŷn. Discrete crystals up to 3.5 cm in length and 0.4 cm square, as well as non-terminated crystal fragments up to 5 cm in length and 1 cm square were recovered. Apparently when they were first collected the crystals were clear but they rapidly became white to opaque unless kept in a closed tube. These crystals were subsequently described in detail by Hey (1932) in his study of zeolite minerals. Dewey and Bromehead (1915) remarked that brecciated manganese ore at Benallt was sometimes cemented by massive, crystalline natrolite. A further account of natrolite from Benallt Mine is provided by Campbell Smith *et al.* (1944b), who described it present in small interstices and minute veins cutting manganese ore from the footwall side of the no. 1 ore body by no. 1 chute, '50-60 feet west of the main shaft and some 10-20 feet above the 130-foot level'.

Neotocite   ?
$(Mn,Fe^{+2})SiO_3.H_2O$
An inadequately described manganese iron silicate hydrate, which typically occurs in manganese deposits of volcanogenic-sedimentary origin.

Dark brown to black, vitreous neotocite, with a conchoidal fracture, occurs at the Nant Mine, on Llŷn (National Museum of Wales specimen NMW 27.111.GR444, from the G.J. Williams Collection, with identification confirmed by L.J. Spencer). Clark *et al.* (1978) described a neotocite specimen from no. 2 level at Nant Mine, one of four originally collected by Sir Arthur Russell in 1911, as being massive, black and resinous, giving dark olive-green to brown translucent fragments.

Nickeline   Hexagonal
NiAs
Nickel arsenide, a member of the nickeline group. A relatively uncommon mineral which usually occurs as a primary mineral in hydrothermal veins associated with basic igneous rocks.

Parnell (1988) reported the presence of cobaltian nickeline, with an average composition $(Ni_{0.82}Co_{0.18})_{0.95}As$, occurring in association with uraninite-bearing hydrocarbons from the Ty Gwyn Mine, Great Ormes Head, Llandudno, Gwynedd.

Oligoclase   Triclinic
$(Na,Ca)Al(Al,Si)_3O_8$
A sodium calcium aluminium silicate belonging to the feldspar group. Oligoclase belongs to the plagioclase series, with An_{10-30}. Oligoclase is a primary mineral in igneous rocks of intermediate composition but also develops as a result of alteration of originally more calcic plagioclase feldspars as a result of low-temperature metamorphism.

Electron microprobe analyses of oligoclase feldspars have been presented by Bevins (1982) from a basalt lava in the Fishguard Volcanic Group, Dyfed, by Bevins and Rowbotham (1983) from dolerites from the Mynydd Preseli district of Dyfed and from the Cadair Idris area of Gwynedd, and by Merriman *et al.* (1986) from the Tal y Fan Intrusion, Gwynedd.

Olivenite   Orthorhombic
$Cu_2(AsO_4)(OH)$
Copper arsenate hydroxide, which forms a series with adamite. A secondary copper mineral which develops in the alteration zone of copper-bearing ore bodies.

The only verified occurrence of olivenite from Wales is from Gwaithyrafon Mine, near Cwmsymlog, Dyfed (confirmed by X-ray diffraction, Natural History Museum X-ray no. 8545F). Olivenite has been reported from the mines at Great Ormes Head, Llandudno (F.P. Jowett, *personal communication*), although this report requires verification.

Orpiment   Monoclinic
As_2S_3
Arsenic sulphide, which typically forms in low-temperature hydrothermal veins, or in hot spring environments.

Andrew (1910) noted that Readwin had recorded the presence of orpiment in the Dolgellau Gold Belt, Gwynedd, although he was not specific as to the paper in which this report appeared. This report requires verification.

Orthoclase — Monoclinic
$KAlSi_3O_8$

A potassium aluminium silicate, and a member of the feldspar group, dimorphous with microcline, and which forms a series with celsian and hyalophane. Orthoclase is a major component of granites and pegmatites. It also occurs in mineral veins.

Orthoclase is probably very widely developed in Wales, although particular references are relatively few; commonly reference is made to the presence of 'alkali feldspar'. It is known from Station Quarry at Arenig, Gwynedd (Natural History Museum specimen B.M. 1946, 38; X-ray no. x10843), while Bloxam and Dirk (1988) refer to the presence of rare anhedral orthoclase in the St. David's granophyre, exposed near St. David's, in Dyfed.

Osmium — Hexagonal
(Os,Ir)

Osmium iridium which is most commonly found in placer deposits in association with platinum.

Readwin (1888) reported the presence of detrital iridosmine (= osmium) from the Dolgellau Gold Belt, Gwynedd, occurring in the Afon Mawddach and Afon Gain, associated with gold and platinum. This represented the first occurrence of the mineral in the British Isles, although requires verification.

Ottrelite — Monoclinic and triclinic
$(Mn,Fe^{+2},Mg)_2Al_4Si_2O_{10}(OH)_4$

A manganese iron magnesium aluminium silicate hydroxide, similar to chloritoid but richer in manganese. Typically ottrelite develops in metamorphosed manganiferous sediments.

The only record of ottrelite in Wales is from 'Snowdon' by Hall (1868); similar minerals in this district have later been shown to be chloritoid, although they do contain up to 8 wt% MnO (see Brearley, 1988).

Palygorskite — Monoclinic and orthorhombic
$(Mg,Al)_2Si_4O_{10}(OH).4H_2O$

A magnesium aluminium silicate hydroxide hydrate. Palygorskite develops in a variety of environments, including mineral veins, and altered ultrabasic rocks (serpentinites).

Vivian (1887) reported the presence of mountain leather (generally considered to be a variety of palygorskite) associated with the hematite deposits of South Wales, but gave no specific locality details. North (1916) stated that mountain leather had been found with iron ore at the Mwyndy Mines (near Llantrisant, Mid Glamorgan), and that a small specimen had been added to the collections in the National Museum of Wales. X-ray examination of three specimens in the Mineral Collection of the National Museum of Wales, all labelled as mountain leather, confirm them to be palygorskite (see Criddle and Symes, 1977). Fibrous, white and grey palygorskite has been found subsequently coating shear surfaces in manganese ore from Tŷ Coch, near South Cornelly, Mid Glamorgan (Criddle and Symes, 1977).

Paracelsian — Monoclinic
$BaAl_2Si_2O_8$

A rare barium aluminium silicate belonging to the feldspar group, and dimorphous with celsian.

Russell (1911) reported the presence of celsian from North Wales on specimens passed to him by G.J. Williams, and suggested that a dimorphous form was also present. A full description of this material from the Benallt manganese mine, Llŷn, was not provided until that by Spencer (1942), which represented the first account of paracelsian in Britain. It forms white to milky white prismatic crystals up to 5 cm in length and 1 cm wide, with a vitreous lustre. Paracelsian, along with celsian, was found in a band in shales and sandstones of Ordovician age associated with lavas and tuffs, and beds of black manganese ore.

Figure 96. Paracelsian crystals up to 25 mm in length from Benallt Mine, Llŷn. NMW specimen 27.111.GR387, *ex* G.J. Williams Collection.

Paragonite — Monoclinic
$NaAl_2(Si_3Al)O_{10}(OH)_2$

A sodium aluminium silicate hydroxide belonging to the

mica group. A rock-forming mineral which develops in mudstones.

Greenly (1919) reported the occurrence of paragonite on Anglesey, present in both glaucophane-bearing schists, and in hornblende-schists exposed near Plasberw. This account represented the first record of paragonite in the British Isles.

Paragonite was later identified at Benallt Mine, on Llŷn, Gwynedd, from the Ty Canol incline, forming the main constituent of thin (0.5 mm), white and pink veins associated with analcime and rarer banalsite and pennantite (Campbell Smith et al., 1946).

More detailed studies of clay mineral assemblages in the Lower Palaeozoic pelites of Wales have shown paragonite to be widely developed (Merriman and Roberts, 1985). It is abundant, for example, in the slates of the Llanberis Slate Formation (of Cambrian age), such as the typical roofing slates of Bethesda and Nantlle (in Snowdonia). It is particularly abundant also in pelites of Arenig and Llanvirn age which are exposed in a broad tract of country extending across Gwynedd, from Aber in the northeast to St. Tudwal's in the southwest. It is particularly abundant in strongly cleaved rocks. In rocks of Caradoc age paragonite occurs in southern Snowdonia in the area between Cwm Pennant and Penmachno. In contrast, paragonite is largely absent from Silurian mudstones in North Wales.

A regular interlayered paragonite/muscovite mineral has been reported from pelites in North Wales (eg. in Tremadoc age slates; Merriman and Roberts, 1985) and elsewhere in Wales (Robinson and Bevins, 1986), conforming to the regular mixed-layer mineral first described by Frey (1969). More recently, however, the nature of this phase has been questioned by Jiang and Peacor (1993), who consider that it actually represents a distinct interlayering of a Na- and a K-mica.

Pargasite   Monoclinic
$NaCa_2(Mg,Fe^{+2})_4Al(Si_6Al_2)O_{22}(OH)_2$
A sodium calcium magnesium iron aluminium silicate hydroxide mineral belonging to the amphibole group, and forming a series with ferropargasite. Pargasite is a rock-forming silicate mineral which develops in igneous rocks of basic to intermediate composition.

Pargasite occurs in various igneous rocks of the Ordovician Rhobell Volcanic Complex, exposed near Dolgellau, Gwynedd (Kokelaar, 1977; Kokelaar, 1986). It is present in basalt lavas as dark green, subhedral to anhedral crystals up to 4 cm in length which are colourless to pale olive green or brown and which show both normal and oscillatory zoning in plane light. Typically it forms 1-5% of the mode and up to 47% in cumulo-phyric varieties. It is found also comprising cognate mesocumulate and adcumulate blocks up to 10 cm in diameter within the cumulo-phyric lavas. Representative electron microprobe analyses of pargasites from the Rhobell Volcanic Complex are presented in Kokelaar (1986).

Pargasite occurs in the St. David's Head Intrusion, forming anhedral to euhedral crystals replacing intercu-

mulus liquid, and as an alteration product rimming clinopyroxene and is also a component in the gabbros of the Rhiw Intrusion, Llŷn (author's unpublished data).

Parisite   Trigonal
$Ca(Ce,Nd,La)_2(CO_3)_3F_2$
A rare calcium light rare earth carbonate fluoride mineral, found in altered igneous rocks, as well as in pegmatitic pods and pipes in granitic rocks.

Howells et al. (1991) recorded parisite as one of a range of secondary minerals found in thin veins or forming rims to primary accessory minerals in altered Ordovician rhyolites in central Snowdonia. This account represented the first description of parisite in the British Isles.

Parnauite   Orthorhombic
$Cu_9(AsO_4)_2(SO_4)(OH)_{10}.7H_2O$
A rare copper arsenate sulphate hydroxide hydrate which develops in the oxidized zone of copper-bearing ore bodies.

Parnauite has been identified at Gwaithyrafon Mine in the Central Wales Mining District (S.A. Rust, personal communication), with identification confirmed by X-ray diffraction at the Natural History Museum.

Parsettensite   Monoclinic
$(K,Na,Ca)(Mn,Al)_7Si_8O_{20}(OH)_8.2H_2O$
A potassium sodium calcium manganese aluminium silicate hydroxide hydrate which occurs in manganese ore deposits.

Natural History Museum X-ray no. x19721 is parsettensite from a specimen from Cwm Nantcol, in the Harlech Dome area of Gwynedd. This is the first and only known record of parsettensite in the British Isles.

Pectolite   Triclinic
$NaCa_2Si_3O_8(OH)$
A sodium calcium silicate hydroxide which forms a series with serandite. It forms typically as a result of low temperature alteration of basic igneous rocks.

Pectolite is rare in Wales. Sargent (1925) reported the presence of pectolite in the Penmaenmawr Intrusion, Gwynedd, occurring as drusy clusters of brownish elongate crystals associated with axinite in veins in the Graig Lwyd area. X-ray examination of a specimen of so-called pectolite from the Penmaenmawr Intrusion in the Mineral Collection of the National Museum of Wales proved, however, to be prehnite (NMW-X59). Elsewhere in Gwynedd, pectolite has been identified at Gimlet Quarry near Pwllheli (National Museum of Wales specimens NMW 27.111.GR29-30 and Natural History Museum X-ray no. x5302, specimen B.M. 1944.3).

Pectolite is also known from Hendre Quarry, near Glyn Ceiriog, Clwyd (Wedd et al., 1929), forming radiating aggregates of crystals associated with prehnite and apophyllite. National Museum of Wales specimen NMW 27.111.GR254 from this locality is illustrated by Starkey et al. (1991).

Figure 97. Botryoidal pectolite crystals up to 15 mm long from Hendre Quarry, near Glyn Ceiriog, Clwyd. NMW specimen 27.111.GR252, *ex* G.J. Williams Collection.

Pennantite   Monoclinic
$Mn_5Al(Si_3Al)O_{10}(OH)_8$

A manganese aluminium silicate hydroxide belonging to the chlorite group which is found rarely in manganese ore bodies.

Pennantite is found associated with the manganese ores of Benallt Mine, near Rhiw, Llŷn, where it occurs as very poorly crystallized patches and small specks in the matrix. More rarely it is present as minute flakes in the ore or in thin veins which traverse the ore. In one vein small (0.5 mm) orange-brown flakes were recovered and formed the basis of the account presented by Campbell Smith *et al.* (1946). This represented the first description of the new mineral, named after Thomas Pennant (1726-1798), the Welsh traveller, zoologist and mineralogist.

So-called grovesite, described by Bannister *et al.* (1955) as forming dark brown rosettes up to 0.5 mm across from no. 5 ore-body at Benallt Mine, and considered by them to be a new mineral of the serpentine group, has been shown, in fact, to be pennantite (Peacor *et al.*, 1974). Natural History Museum X-ray no. x16695 is pennantite from Penrhyn Slate Quarry, at Bethesda, Gwynedd, although this occurrence requires verification.

More recently Bennett (1987b) has reported the occur-

rence of pennantite in the manganese ore bed of the Hafotty Formation of Cambrian age, exposed in the Harlech Dome area of Gwynedd.

Pentlandite   Cubic
$(Fe,Ni)_9S_8$

An iron nickel sulphide belonging to the pentlandite group of minerals, forming a series with cobalt pentlandite. Most commonly pentlandite is found in basic igneous rocks, and is usually associated with pyrrhotite.

Records of pentlandite in Wales are few. Gilbey (1968) recorded single, elongate lamellae of pentlandite in pyrrhotite at Cesailgwm and Clogau, in the Dolgellau Gold Belt, Gwynedd, while Ixer (in Thorpe *et al.*, 1991) noted the presence of rare pentlandite exsolution flames in pyrrhotite in a dolerite from Carn Menyn, in the Mynydd Preseli, Dyfed.

Perovskite   Orthorhombic
$CaTiO_3$

A calcium titanium oxide belonging to the perovskite group. Perovskite develops as an accessory mineral in igneous rocks.

Elsden (1904) noted that certain crystals replacing ilmenite in altered dolerite dykes of the Llŷn Padarn area of Gwynedd have the optical characteristics of perovskite, although he did state that a positive identification could not be based on optical determination alone. If verified, this would represent the first occurrence of perovskite in the British Isles.

Similarly, rather dubious descriptions of perovskite in altered pyroxenites and gabbros from the Mona Complex of Anglesey were provided by Greenly (1919). Williams (1927) noted that colourless perovskite occurs in association with chlorite in altered palagonite tuffs in the vicinity of Snowdon, such as near the head of the Afon Glaslyn at the head of Cwm Dyli. It is most likely that all of these descriptions in fact refer to titanite.

Pharmacosiderite   Cubic
$KFe_4^{+3}(AsO_4)_3(OH)_4.6-7H_2O$

A secondary potassium iron arsenate hydroxide hydrate which occurs as a result of alteration of arsenic-bearing minerals, particularily in the oxide zone of arsenic-bearing ore bodies.

Pharmacosiderite is currently known from only one locality in Wales, namely Gwaithyrafon Mine, near Cwmsymlog, in the Central Wales Mining District, occurring as small cubic crystals on quartz and chalcopyrite (S.A. Rust, *personal communication*) with confirmation by X-ray diffraction at the Natural History Museum.

Phlogopite   Monoclinic
$KMg_3Si_3AlO_{10}(F,OH)_2$

A potassium magnesium aluminosilicate hydroxide mineral of the mica group. It forms a continuous series with biotite, phlogopite having Mg:Fe > 2:1.

Strongly pleochroic pale-brown mica, associated with

chlorite in rutile-bearing tuffs of Ordovician age exposed on Lliwedd, Gwynedd, was considered by Williams (1927) most probably to be phlogopite. Elsewhere in Gwynedd, phlogopite occurs in association with calcite at Arenig Station Quarry (Natural History Museum specimens B.M. 1931, 483, B.M. 1931, 485 and B.M. 1931, 486, confirmed by X-ray diffraction). Pleochroic pale yellow to dark reddish-brown, Ti-rich phlogopite occurs in biotite-pyroxenite xenoliths from the Great House agglomeratic diatreme near Usk, Gwent (D.J. Moffat, *personal communication*). Recently, phlogopite has been reported from Esgair Hir Mine, Dyfed, associated with hydrocerussite (Rust and Mason, 1988).

Phosgenite   Tetragonal
$Pb_2(CO_3)Cl_2$
A secondary lead carbonate chloride mineral, developed in the oxidized zone of lead-bearing ore bodies.

Only two occurrences of phosgenite are known from Wales. A specimen from dumps at Pen-y-bryn shaft, Halkyn, Clwyd is in the R.S.W. Braithwaite Collection (no. 64-403), collected 15 November 1964. More recently pinkish-white striated prisms and colourless tabular crystals of phosgenite up to 1.5 mm in size have been collected from Penrhyn Du Mine, on Llŷn, Gwynedd (Hubbard, 1991).

Pickeringite   Monoclinic
$MgAl_2(SO_4)_4.22H_2O$
A magnesium aluminium sulphate hydrate. Pickeringite forms as a result of alteration of pyrite, and is commonly found on mine walls.

Pickeringite occurs on Natural History Museum specimen B.M. 1978, 453, from 'a 2/3" stringer associated with the north or 3rd load (*sic*) on the main level', at Gwynfynydd Mine, Dolgellau, Gwynedd. Pickeringite is also recorded on a specimen from Parys Mountain, on Anglesey, in the collections of the National Museums on Merseyside.

Piemontite   Monoclinic
$Ca_2(Al,Mn^{+3},Fe^{+3})_3(SiO_4)_3(OH)$
A calcium aluminium manganese iron silicate hydroxide belonging to the epidote group. Piemontite typically develops as a result of low-grade metamorphism of manganese-rich rocks.

The first record of piemontite in Wales was by Greenly (1919), who identified the mineral in a thin section of 'green-mica-schist' from the New Harbour Group (a part of the Mona Complex), collected in the vicinity of Holyhead, Anglesey. Subsequently Williams (1927) described the presence of granules of a rose-pink, strongly pleochroic epidote (presumably piemontite) in altered rhyolitic intrusions in the Llanberis Pass district, Gwynedd. Recently, piemontite has been identified from Benallt Mine, Llŷn, as small greenish-brown to reddish-brown prismatic crystals (N. Hubbard, *personal communication*).

Pilsenite   Trigonal
Bi_4Te_3
A rare bismuth telluride.

Naden (1988) reported the presence of 'werhlite' in galena-dominated gold-bearing veins at the Clogau Mine, in the Dolgellau Gold Belt, Gwynedd. 'Werhlite', however, is a mixture of pilsenite and hessite. This is the first record of pilsenite in the British Isles.

Plagionite   Monoclinic
$Pb_5Sb_8S_{17}$
A rare lead antimony sulphide mineral found in antimony-bearing mineral veins.

The first occurrence of plagionite in the British Isles was reported by Bevins *et al.* (1988) from Bwlch Mine, Deganwy, Gwynedd. It occurs in association with other lead antimony sulphosalt minerals and stibnite in altered, spherulitic, rhyolitic ash-flow tuff belonging to the Capel Curig Volcanic Formation. The sulphosalt minerals at Bwlch Mine typically occur in irregular patches and thin veins and stringers up to 2 cm (but more typically about 0.5 cm) in width, and are visually extremely similar, even in reflected light under the microscope. In addition their physical and structural properties are nearly identical. Consequently positive identification relies on X-ray and electron probe micro-analyses.

Platinum   Cubic
Pt
Native platinum. Platinum occurs chiefly in placer deposits, although it also is a constituent of certain basic and ultrabasic rocks.

Readwin (1888) recorded detrital platinum from the Dolgellau Gold Belt, Gwynedd, occurring in the Afon Mawddach and Afon Gain, associated with gold and iridosmine (= osmium). This requires confirmation.

Plumbojarosite   Trigonal
$PbFe_6^{3+}(SO_4)_4(OH)_{12}$
A lead iron sulphate hydroxide belonging to the alunite group of minerals. Plumbojarosite is a secondary mineral which is found in the oxidized zone of lead-bearing ore bodies.

Plumbojarosite has been tentatively identified occurring in association with beaverite at Ystrad Einion Mine, near Talybont, in the Central Wales Mining District (*British Micromount Society Newsletter*, No. 35).

Polybasite   Monoclinic
$(Ag,Cu)_{16}Sb_2S_{11}$
A silver copper antimony sulphide which forms a series with pearceite. Polybasite occurs in silver-bearing mineral veins.

Polybasite has been identified as inclusions in galena, associated with pyrargyrite (into which it passes with decreasing Cu content) and freibergite in the Dolgellau Gold Belt, Gwynedd (Gilbey, 1968). This account represented the first occurrence of the mineral in the British Isles.

Posnjakite   Monoclinic
$Cu_4(SO_4)(OH)_6.H_2O$
A copper sulphate hydroxide hydrate which forms in the oxidized zone of copper-bearing ore bodies.

Posnjakite occurs in stalactitic growths with brochantite in the second lowest accessible level at Britannia Mine, Snowdon, Gwynedd (National Museum of Wales specimen NMW 84.7G.M1), with identification confirmed by X-ray diffraction (Bevins et al., 1985).

Posnjakite has also been identified as blue tabular crystals associated with brochantite and galena from Copa Hill, Cwmystwyth, Dyfed, on specimen no. B.M. 1981, 461 in the Natural History Museum; identification by X-ray diffraction (analysis number 20730).

Prehnite   Orthorhombic
$Ca_2Al_2Si_3O_{10}(OH)_2$
A calcium aluminium silicate hydroxide. Prehnite is widely developed in basic igneous rocks affected by low temperature alteration.

Prehnite is widely developed in Wales, occurring as an alteration mineral in basic lavas and intrusions, principally of Ordovician age. It occurs in a variety of settings, generally replacing groundmass minerals, but also infilling vesicles, replacing phenocrysts, in cross-cutting veins or forming spherulitic 'spots'.

The first description of prehnite in Wales was by Harrison (1897), reporting its occurrence at Gimlet Rock, near Pwllheli, Gwynedd, where it occurs on joint planes in association with quartz, calcite, natrolite and brookite. Subsequently, Schaub (1905) and Sargent (1915, 1925) described prehnite-bearing vein assemblages and acid segregations from the Penmaenmawr Intrusion, Gwynedd. Greenly (1919) reported the presence of prehnite in the margins of certain hornblende-picrites from Anglesey, although was not specific concerning which particular intrusions. Elsewhere in North Wales, prehnite has been reported as being developed in abundance in the Tal y Fan Intrusion, in northern Snowdonia (Bevins and Merriman, 1988).

In Mid Wales, prehnite has been recorded in altered lavas at Llanelwedd Quarry, near Builth Wells, Powys (Nicholls, 1958; Metcalfe, 1990), as inclusions in plagioclase phenocrysts. It also occurs in associated tuffs at Llanelwedd, forming ovoid spots up to 2 cm in diameter and also pseudomorphing original lithic fragments.

Roach (1969) described prehnite from the St. Davids Head Intrusion, Dyfed, forming alteration patches in plagioclase feldspar and attributed its presence to deuteric alteration. It is also found in veins and pods associated with quartz. Bevins and Rowbotham (1983), however, suggested that the widespread occurrence of prehnite in altered basic igneous rocks of Wales is due to low-grade burial metamorphism. Electron microprobe analyses presented by Bevins and Rowbotham (1983) show considerable substitution of Fe^{3+} for Al^{3+} in the crystal structure. Elsewhere in Dyfed, prehnite 'spots' are present in acidic tuffs exposed east of Strumble Head, near Fishguard, and also in an altered dolerite at Porthgain Quarry, near St. David's. At the latter locality prehnite occurs in thin veins, some containing small well-formed crystals in cavities. At Garn Folch, west of Fishguard, prehnite and pumpellyite pods occur in altered dolerite (Bevins et al., 1993).

Pumpellyite   Monoclinic
$Ca_2(Mg,Fe)Al_2(SiO_4)(Si_2O_7)(OH)_2.H_2O$
A group name, comprising pumpellyite showing a range in Fe and Mg contents. Pumpellyite develops in basic igneous rocks affected by low grade metamorphism.

Pumpellyite is widely developed in Wales, occurring as a result of alteration of basic lavas and intrusions, principally of Lower Palaeozoic age. It typically forms small prismatic crystals in albitised plagioclase feldspar crystals, in association with chlorite, prehnite and epidote. The first description of pumpellyite in the British Isles was by Nicholls (1957), who reported it from altered basaltic lavas of Ordovician age from Llanelwedd Quarry, Builth Wells, Powys. This account was followed by a more complete description (Nicholls, 1958). More lately Bevins (1985) and Metcalfe (1990) attributed the presence of pumpellyite-rich domains in altered basic lavas at Llanelwedd Quarry to the effects of an Ordovician hydrothermal system.

Bevins (1978) described the widespread occurrence of pumpellyite in the Fishguard area and presented electron microprobe analyses. However, almost certainly the pleochroic sea-green to colourless mineral with high refractive index described from the Fishguard area by Reed (1895) as "anomalous chlorite" was pumpellyite, although pumpellyite itself was not formally described until 1925, from the Keweenaw Peninsula, Michigan, U.S.A. (Palache and Vassar, 1925). Spectacular pumpellyite-dominated pods are found in an altered dolerite at Garn Folch, near Fishguard, north Pembrokeshire (Bevins et al., 1993).

Jenkins and Ball (1964) identified pumpellyite in soils of the Conwy Valley district of Gwynedd, which they traced back to altered gabbros and dolerites in the vicinity of Bwlch y Ddeufaen. A comprehensive investigation of the occurrence of pumpellyite in Wales, along with further electron microprobe analyses, was presented by Bevins and Rowbotham (1983). Most of the analyses conform to Fe-pumpellyite compositions according to the classification of Passaglia and Gottardi (1973), although this classification scheme is difficult to apply rigorously in view of the lack of information concerning the oxidation state of iron from electron microprobe analyses.

Pyrargyrite   Trigonal
Ag_3SbS_3
A silver antimony sulphide which is dimorphous with pyrostilpnite, and which is found in low temperature mineral veins.

In Wales pyrargyrite is associated with freibergite and polybasite (into which it passes with increasing Cu content) in the Dolgellau Gold Belt, as for example at Tyddyn Gwladys Mine (Gilbey, 1968).

Pyrite   Cubic
FeS$_2$

Iron sulphide. Pyrite belongs to the pyrite group, is dimorphous with marcasite, and forms a series with cattierite. Pyrite forms in a wide variety of environments. It occurs as a low temperature diagenetic mineral in sedimentary rocks, as a common constituent in low grade and contact metamorphic rocks, as a minor constituent of igneous rocks, and in low temperature hydrothermal mineral veins.

Pyrite is a common mineral in Wales, occurring in a wide variety of settings, in igneous, sedimentary and metamorphic rocks. Only a few of the more notable occurrences are described.

On Anglesey, pyrite is the most common sulphide in the Parys Mountain ore deposit (Pointon and Ixer, 1980). At least four different types occur, reflecting different generations of pyrite growth.

In Snowdonia, pyrite occurs as cubes and modified cubes in slates of Cambrian and Ordovician age, for example at Penrhyn Quarry, Bethesda, and Oakley Quarry, Blaenau Ffestiniog. It is also a component of lead-zinc mineral veins cutting through the Lower Palaeozoic rocks. Notable specimens have been collected in particular from Parc Mine, where the pyrite occurs as fine coatings on either quartz or calcite. Other pyrite-bearing mineralized veins occur in the Snowdon area (see Howells *et al.,* 1991), and at the Tan-y-garth Mine, Bethesda (Dewey, 1920). The Cae Coch massive pyrite deposit, in north east Snowdonia, contrasts with the vein-type mineralization in that it largely comprises laminated pyrite-quartz ore, and has been likened to a Kuroko-type deposit (Ball and Bland, 1985). Of particular interest are tubes of pyrite, 5-10 mm in diameter, infilled with quartz. Such features are similar to tubes or pipes associated with 'black smokers'. More recently, however, Bottrell and Morton (1992) have argued that the Cae Coch pyrite deposit has a syn-diagenetic inhalative origin.

A pyrite specimen of particular note from Snowdonia is a single 5 cm cube from Llŷn Bochlwyd, Ogwen, now in the Mineral Collection of the National Museum of Wales.

In southern Snowdonia, pyrite occurs in gold-bearing veins across the Dolgellau Gold Belt. These veins show a regional variation from a pyrrhotite-chalcopyrite-pyrite-arsenopyrite/cobaltite-dominated assemblage in the southwest, passing northeastwards to one dominated by pyrite-sphalerite-galena (Gilbey, 1968).

To the west of the Gold Belt, pyrite is found in sedimentary rocks of Cambrian age, in particular in mudstones in association with bedded manganese ores (Woodland, 1938c; Bennett, 1987a). Pyrite is also a component of the Ordovician oolitic ironstones exposed across northern Wales, from Anglesey to Cadair Idris. Details of these pyrite occurrences are presented by Pulfrey (1933) and Trythall (1988).

Pyrite is widespread in the Central Wales Mining District, being recorded as abundant at the Penrhiw, Cwmystwyth, Brynyrafr and Ystumtuen mines, while good cubic crystals have been recorded from the Dylife and Plynlimon mines (Jones and Moreton, 1977).

Figure 98. Pyrite cube measuring 10 mm x 12 mm, embedded in Cambrian slate from Penrhyn Quarry, Bethesda, Gwynedd. I. Jones Collection, specimen 1376A.

Raybould (1973, 1976) noted that framboidal pyrite was the most common form present, occurring in wallrocks adjacent to veins and in rock fragments in hydraulic breccias. Cubes 2-3 cm across are found on the tips at Darren Mine, in mudstones of the Cwmsymlog Formation.

Further south, pyrite is abundant in auriferous pyritic shales at Dolaucothi, near Pumsaint. The pyrite shows a variety of forms, the most distinctive of which is as aggregates of euhedral crystals up to 10 mm across, exposed along bedding planes (see Annels and Roberts, 1989).

In South Wales, pyrite occurs in many coal seams. North (1916) recorded the presence of small octahedral crystals from Llanbradach. Lumps or nodules of pyrite are common in the Coal Measures and are known as 'coal brasses' (Adams, 1867). Excellent pyritohedra up to 25 mm across, from Cwmgwili Colliery, Llanelli, are now in the Mineral Collection of the National Museum of Wales. Pyrite was also a minor component in iron ores extracted at the Mwyndy and Llanharry Mines, near Llantrisant.

Finally, pyrite is a minor phase in many dolerites and gabbros in Wales. For example, Ixer (in Thorpe *et al.*, 1991) described pyrite aggregates up to 300 μm across in altered dolerite from Carn Menyn, in the Mynydd Preseli. On occasions the pyrite aggregates are larger, for example at Llechlwyd Quarry, Towyn, where pyrite aggregates are up to 20 mm across.

Pyrobelonite   Orthorhombic
PbMn(VO$_4$)(OH)
A lead manganese vanadate hydroxide belonging to the descloizite group. A rare mineral found in manganese ore deposits.

Only the second world-wide and the first British Isles occurrence of pyrobelonite was described from Tŷ Coch, Mid Glamorgan (Criddle and Symes, 1977), where it occurs as a minor constituent in manganese ore forming either discrete euhedral to anhedral grains or occurring in intergrowths with vanadinite. In addition it forms veinlets generally less than 0.5 mm thick, which can be traced for up to 3 cm. It has an adamantine to submetallic lustre, is black to deep red in colour and produces a bright orange powder. Associated minerals, in addition to vanadinite, include braunite, hausmannite, calcite, · manganocalcite, ferroan calcite, dolomite and barite.

Pyrochroite   Trigonal
Mn(OH)$_2$
A manganese hydroxide belonging to the brucite group which develops as a result of the oxidation of manganese ores.

In Wales pyrochroite is known only from the Benallt Mine, on Llŷn, with specimens preserved in the collections of the National Museum of Wales (specimen NMW 83.41G.M3750; *ex* King Collection specimen K5016), and the Natural History Museum, with hausmannite on specimen B.M. 1945, 133 (confirmed by X-ray diffraction no. x3404). These represent the first occurrences of pyrochroite in the British Isles.

Pyrolusite   Tetragonal
MnO$_2$
Manganese oxide belonging to the rutile group and trimorphous with akhtenskite and ramsdellite. A secondary mineral resulting from the alteration of other manganese minerals.

Pyrolusite is probably common in Wales, although specific records are few. It is known to occur at Benallt Mine, on Llŷn, and also at Tŷ Coch, Mid Glamorgan, both confirmed by X-ray diffraction at the Natural History Museum, X-ray nos. x4271 and x18701, respectively.

Pyromorphite   Hexagonal
Pb$_5$(PO$_4$)$_3$Cl
A lead phosphate chloride which develops as a secondary mineral after lead-bearing primary phases, particularly galena.

Pyromorphite is widely distributed in Wales, occurring as a secondary mineral in many of the lead mining districts. It is characteristically distinguished by its prismatic habit and a bright grass-green colour. However, varying shades through pale green to yellow are encountered, while at Frongoch Mine, Dyfed, brown to pale mauve pyromorphite is found. At certain mines in

Figure 99. Prismatic pyromorphite crystals on quartz from Bwlchglas Mine, near Talybont, in the Central Wales Mining District. The specimen measures 8 cm x 10 cm. Collected *c.* 1972. B.R. Moore Collection.

Figure 100. Prismatic pyromorphite crystals up to 2 mm in length from Bwlchglas Mine, near Talybont, in the Central Wales Mining District. Collected February 1983. NMW specimen 93.94G.M55, *ex* D. Lloyd Collection.

the Central Wales Mining District small yellow or orange wulfenite crystals are found associated with pyromorphite. A detailed account of one such occurrence, from Bwlchglas Mine near Talybont, was provided by Braithwaite (1982b). Here bright grass-green pyromorphite crystals up to 5-6 mm (average 1-2 mm) richly encrust quartz fragments in a breccia pipe, providing some of the best pyromorphites to be collected in the British Isles. It is specimens from this pipe which were readily available from mineral dealers in the early to mid 1970s, but which were only vaguely located as coming from 'near Plynlimon', or from 'Eisteddfa Gurig'. A few specimens from this locality have barrel-shaped crystal forms, similar to those of campylite. Further south pyromorphite associated with wulfenite has been described from dumps in the neighbourhood of Ysbyty Ystwyth (Ryback and Saville, 1967). Elsewhere in the Central Wales Mining District pyromorphite is known from numerous mines, including Aberdaunant, Alltycrib, Brynyrafr, Cwmdarren, Darren, East Glogfach, Esgairfraith, Nant-y-Cae, Pandy, Penybanc, South Nantycar, Ystrad Einion, Henfwlch, Mynyddgorddu, Dylife, Eaglebrook, Llanerch-yr-aur, Dyfngwm, Florida, Llechweddhelyg, and Esgair Hir (see for example Jones and Moreton, 1977, Mason, 1992, Clark and Rust, 1993). Hall (1868) recorded pyromorphite from Devil's Bridge.

At Llechweddhelyg, pyromorphite forms squat prisms on gossan matrix (J.S. Mason, *personal communication*).

Readwin (1888) listed pyromorphite among the many minerals he identified from the Dolgellau Gold Belt, in Gwynedd.

Further north pyromorphite is recorded from the Cwm Orog and Ochr Graig mines, at Llangynog, Powys and it is also known from a number of localities in the Halkyn district in Clwyd (Hall, 1868; G. Ryback, *personal communication*). It has, in fact, been known to occur in this latter region for a long time, record of its presence being provided by Pennant (1778), who reported a 'green lead ore' from Silver Rake, on Halkyn Mountain, and later by Traill (1821) who noted its presence in 'large quantity' at a mine called Gelly-Fowler Fields, also on Halkyn Mountain. Pyromorphite may also occur on Anglesey as a number of specimens in the National Museum of Wales are labelled as such, although no precise locality information is available.

Figure 101. Pale mauve to brown prismatic pyromorphite crystals up to 3 mm long from Frongoch Mine, in the Central Wales Mining District. J.S. Mason Collection, specimen JMFG505.

In South Wales pyromorphite is comparatively rare. It has been identified from the Vale of Towy or Nant Mine, to the east of Carmarthen, Dyfed, while arsenic-bearing pyromorphite is known from Nant-y-mwyn Mine, north of Llandovery, also in Dyfed (G. Ryback, *personal communication*). A specimen in the National Museum of Wales is labelled as from Rhiwsaeson, Llantrisant, Mid Glamorgan, although in fact no other specimens of pyromorphite are known from this area.

Pyrophanite   Trigonal
$MnTiO_3$
A manganese titanium oxide, belonging to the ilmenite group, and forming a series with ilmenite. A mineral found in manganese ore bodies.

Pyrophanite is found at Benallt Mine, near Rhiw, on Llŷn, forming small, tabular, orange-yellow crystals up to 0.25 mm in diameter and 0.15 mm in thickness. In thin section the crystals are characterized by very high birefringence and high refractive index ($n > 1.84$). Identification has been confirmed by X-ray diffraction powder photography (Natural History Museum X-ray no. x3576 on specimen B.M. 1944, 50) and positive chemical tests for manganese and titanium (see Campbell Smith *et al.*, 1946; Campbell Smith and Claringbull, 1947). This was the first reported occurrence in the British Isles.

Bennett (1987a and b) reported the presence of small, sparse, scattered opaque grains of Ti-Mn-Fe oxides ('ferropyrophanite') throughout the manganese ore and pyritic mudstones of the Hafotty Formation of Cambrian age, exposed in the Harlech Dome area of Gwynedd. Electron microprobe analyses presented in Bennett (1987a) indicate that the Harlech pyrophanites belong to the solid solution series between pyrophanite and ilmenite.

Pyrophyllite   Monoclinic and triclinic
$Al_2Si_4O_{10}(OH)_2$
A clay mineral, most abundantly developed in mudstones, although also found in some hydrothermal veins with quartz.

Gill *et al.* (1977) recorded pyrophyllite in small amounts in certain sandstones and shales of Coal Measures (Carboniferous) age from the anthracite zone (ie. the western area) of the South Wales Coalfield.

In Dyfed, pyrophyllite is present in sedimentary rocks of Silurian and Devonian age from the Marloes area (Nicholls, 1979; Robinson *et al.*, 1980). It has also been recorded from heavily altered rhyolites and rhyolitic tuffs in a borehole near Treffgarne (Brown and others, 1987).

In North Wales Merriman and Roberts (1985) reported pyrophyllite in Snowdonia and Llŷn, being developed in Ordovician pelitic rocks surrounding coeval igneous intrusions, such as the Penmaenmawr, Yr Eifl, Llanbedrog, and Bwlch Mawr Intrusions. Pyrophyllite also occurs in association with allanite, molybdenite and quartz in pod-like structures in the Ffestiniog Granite Quarry, Cefn Bychan, near Ffestiniog, Gwynedd (Roberts, 1979).

Pyrosmalite   Hexagonal
$(Fe^{+2},Mn)_8Si_6O_{15}(OH,Cl)_{10}$
An iron manganese silicate hydroxide chloride. A rare mineral.

The first occurrence of this rare mineral in the British Isles was reported by Brown (1959), from the Nant Ffrancon area in Gwynedd. It occurs in dark green Ordovician slates, affected by metamorphism as a result of the adjacent rhyolite intrusion, near the old Nant Ffrancon road, northwest of Blaen-y-nant, in association with an almandine-spessartine garnet, iron ore, apatite and an unidentified green micaceous mineral. The pyrosmalite, which forms only a very minor constituent of the rock, consists of clusters of radiating crystals up to 0.5 mm in length. Identification was on the basis of optical and X-ray powder diffraction photograph investigations, although it is not possible to determine whether ferropyrosmalite or manganopyrosmalite is present.

Pyrrhotite   Monoclinic and hexagonal
$Fe_{1-x}S$
An iron sulphide mineral which occurs as a minor phase in magmatic rocks, as well as in hydrothermal veins associated with other sulphides.

Pyrrhotite is relatively widespread in Wales, although specific descriptions in the literature are few.

Ixer (in Thorpe *et al.*, 1991) recorded the presence of discrete pyrrhotite masses up to 10 μm across, and 5-20 μm diameter chalcopyrite, pyrrhotite and pyrite aggregates in altered dolerite from Carn Menyn, in the Mynydd Preseli, Dyfed, and it is likely that many dolerites and gabbros in Wales contain this assemblage.

Pyrrhotite associated with other sulphides in ore bodies is more common in Wales. On Anglesey, pyrrhotite is present at Parys Mountain, where it occurs as 10-30 μm rounded inclusions associated with chalcopyrite in pyrite, and as aggregates up to 350 μm across replacing earlier pyrite (Pointon and Ixer, 1980). In northern Snowdonia, pyrrhotite is relatively rare, although it is a major component of mineral veins in the Nantlle Valley, such as at Drws-y-Coed (Braithwaite, 1982a) and Simmde Dylluan Mines (NMW collections), as well as occurring sparingly at Pant-y-Wrach Mine, near Penrhyndeudraeth, and Cwmdwyfor Mine, near Rhyd-ddu. Pyrrhotite also occurs associated with arsenopyrite at Tan-y-garth Mine near Bethesda (Dewey, 1920).

In southern Snowdonia, pyrrhotite is a common in gold-bearing veins in the Dolgellau Gold Belt. Gilbey (1968) noted the presence of pyrrhotite at numerous mines in the area, including Panorama, Foel Ispri, Clogau, Vigra, Caegwian, Prince Edward, and Wnion, while Naden (1988) reported two distinct pyrrhotite-bearing assemblages from Clogau Mine, namely a rutile-arsenopyrite-pyrite/pyrrhotite assemblage, and a chalcopyrite-pyrrhotite assemblage. Slightly further south, pyrrhotite was recorded as a constituent of a stilpnomelane-bearing mineral vein at Tyllau Mwn Mine, near Dolgellau (Matthews and Scoon, 1964).

In the Central Wales Mining District, pyrrhotite is relatively rare. Moreton (1982) noted the presence of hexagonal pyrrhotite crystals, up to 7 mm across, on mine dumps from the Dylife Mine, while pyrrhotite is also known from Erglodd Mine (J.S. Mason, *personal communication*).

In South Wales, pyrrhotite is found in clay ironstone nodules in the Coal Measures, forming hexagonal platy crystals at Parc Colliery, Cwm Parc, (Firth, 1971), Gelli Colliery, and on the Llanwynno Tips from the Ferndale Collieries (I. Jones, *personal communication*).

Quartz   Trigonal
SiO_2

Quartz is extremely widespread, occurring as gangue in mineral veins. It is also an important rock-forming mineral, occurring in many sedimentary, igneous and metamorphic rocks in varying amounts.

Probably the most spectacular quartz crystals in Wales come from the Snowdon area of North Wales. In particular, clear, faceted, prismatic crystals with pyramidal terminations occurring either as single crystals or in groups have been collected from Mynydd Drws-y-Coed, near Nantlle, with individual near perfect crystals reaching up to 7 cm in length (specimens in the Mineral Collection of the National Museum of Wales). In addition, however, excellent clear prismatic crystals occur in Alpine-type mineral veins at many localities in North Wales, such as Penrhyn, Gimlet, Minfordd, Votty

Figure 102. Colourless, terminated quartz crystal 6 cm long from Mynydd Drws-y-Coed, near Nantlle, in Snowdonia. NMW specimen 83.41G.M2043, *ex* R.J. King Collection specimen K3229-1970.

and Bowydd, and Manod Quarries. In some cases the quartz crystals are coloured in view of containing numerous small inclusions of other minerals, in particular chlorite or the TiO_2 polymorphs. Starkey and Robinson (1992) reported clear to milky, prismatic quartz crystals reaching up to 7-8 cm in Alpine-type veins at Fron Oleu, near Prenteg, while (Starkey *et al.*, 1991) also noted fine colourless euhedral crystals up to 20 mm in length in fractures at Hendre Quarry, near Glyn Ceiriog, Clwyd.

Elsewhere in North Wales excellent quartz specimens have been collected from mines in the Llanrwst district, in particular from Trecastell and Parc Mines, where the quartz, sometimes coated with marcasite and pyrite, occurs as aggregates of terminated crystals on sphalerite and galena.

In Central Wales, quartz is widespread, although spectacular crystal specimens are few. Jones and Moreton (1977) reported good crystals from Snowbrook, Blaenceulan, Grogwynion and Copa Hill, although some of the most attractive specimens have been collected from Brynyrafr and from Cefngwyn (J.S. Mason, *personal communication*). Further south, attractive specimens are known from mines at Rhandirmwyn, where crystals up to 15 cm in height have been collected from the Upper Boat Level tip.

Figure 103. Doubly-termintaed quartz crystal 2 cm long in a cavity in a clay ironstone nodule from the International Colliery, Blaengarw, Mid Glamorgan. Collected 1990. I. Jones Collection.

Excellent quartz specimens have previously been collected from old iron mines to the northwest of Cardiff, in particular the Llanharry and Mwyndy Mines. The quartz is associated with hematite and goethite, and commonly contains inclusions of iron minerals, colouring the quartz pink, buff or black. In some cases the quartz has an amethystine colour. At the nearby 'Steetley' Quarry, at Taff's Well, well formed quartz crystals coat pink, bladed barite. Of particular interest in South Wales, however, are prismatic, clear quartz crystals, up to 3-4 cm in length, sometimes showing double terminations, known as 'Merthyr Diamonds', identical in nature to so-called 'Herkimer Diamonds', from Herkimer County, New York State, USA. Firth (1971) described and illustrated some of the forms seen in the South Wales examples. The crystals occur in cavities associated with millerite in ironstone nodules across much of the South Wales Coalfield region, and have been collected from waste tips from numerous collieries. On occasions the crystals show visible fluid inclusions and trapped vapour bubbles.

Other varieties of quartz occur locally in Wales. The Precambrian sequences of North Wales locally contain jasper, as at Aberdaron, on Llŷn (Matley, 1928), and Newborough, on Anglesey (Greenly, 1902). Jasper is also found associated with doleritic rocks in the Strumble Head region, near Fishguard, in Dyfed (Bevins, 1979), while prase has been found in this region occurring between pillows in the lava sequence. Agate is only rarely found in Wales. Poorly formed agate occurs in so-called 'Potato Stones' in the Triassic rocks of South Wales, and the stones can be collected from beaches in the Porthcawl area. Elsewhere, small agate nodules occur in lavas at Llanelwedd Quarry, Builth Wells, as well as in rhyolitic rocks at Pen-ychain, on Llŷn.

Ramsbeckite Monoclinic
$(Cu,Zn)_{15}(SO_4)_4(OH)_{22}.6H_2O$
A rare copper zinc sulphate hydroxide hydrate which occurs in the secondary oxidation zone of copper- and zinc-bearing ore bodies.

Ramsbeckite was reported from two localities in Wales by Rust (1992), being two of the three first known occurrences in the British Isles. At Dylife Mine, Powys, it forms bright green, pseudo-orthorhombic crystals, as well as elongate, rod-like prisms. At Brynarian Mine, near Talybont, Dyfed, it occurs in association with schulenbergite, linarite, anglesite, cerussite and brochantite as rare, poorly-crystallized masses and also as scattered single crystals. More recently, ramsbeckite has been confirmed from the Penrhiw Mine, near Ystumtuen, Dyfed, forming dark green, lustrous, diamond-shaped crystals up to 2 mm (NMW X-ray no.793), associated with linarite and schulenbergite. It has also been identified visually at Nantycagl (Eaglebrook), Ystrad Einion, and Frongoch (J.S. Mason, *personal communication*). At all of these localities ramsbeckite is most likely of post-mining origin.

Rectorite Monoclinic
A clay mineral, being a 1:1 regular interstratification of dioctahedral mica and dioctahedral smectite. Rectorite forms a component of the clay mineral fraction in certain mudstones.

Gill *et al.* (1977) noted the presence of allevardite associated with pyrophyllite in anchizone pelites from the anthracite area of the South Wales Coalfield; allevardite is now called rectorite. This represented the first occurrence of rectorite in the British Isles. Elsewhere in Wales, Merriman and Roberts (1985) recorded the presence of rectorite in a number of Arenig and Llanvirn (Ordovician) age pelites from Snowdonia and Llŷn, on the basis of X-ray diffraction analysis. It is restricted, however, to pelites which were affected by contact metamorphism by intrusions prior to regional metamorphism. Microprobe analyses presented by Merriman and Roberts (1985) show that in the Arenig

samples the expansible component is a Ca-smectite, while in the Llanvirn samples it is a Na-smectite. A more recent investigation has recorded rectorite in a pelite sample from the valley of the Afon Seiont, 2 km southeast of Caernarfon Castle, again on the basis of X-ray diffraction studies (Jiang *et al.*, 1990).

Rhodochrosite Trigonal
$MnCO_3$
Manganese carbonate belonging to the calcite group, which forms two series, one with calcite, the other with siderite. Rhodochrosite develops in a variety of environments, but chiefly in manganese-bearing mineral veins.

The principal occurrences of rhodochrosite in Wales are in manganese ore bodies of the Harlech Dome region. In the Harlech ores rhodochrosite is the principal constituent, along with spessartine. Dewey and Bromehead (1915) had originally considered these ores to be composed principally of 'mixed carbonate (dialogite) and silicate (rhodonite)', although Woodland (1935) subsequently identified the silicate phase as being spessartine garnet. Further details of these rhodochrosite-bearing ores are provided by Woodland (1939b, 1956), Allen and Jackson (1985), and Bennett (1987a and b). Bennett (1987b) remarked that the stratiform manganese ores of the Harlech district consist of alternating red laminated bands and creamy-yellow concretions. In the red layers kutnohorite is the principal carbonate mineral, while in the creamy-yellow concretions it is calcian rhodochrosite (with <20 mol% Ca). In addition, Bennett (1987b) recorded rhodochrosite in late veins and joints cutting the manganese ores.

Manganiferous sediments of Cambrian age are also found on the St. Tudwal's Peninsula, Llŷn. Bennett (1987b) has shown that carbonates in the manganiferous shales of the Mulfran Formation are manganoan calcites and calcian rhodochrosites. Elsewhere on Llŷn, rhodochrosite is a component of the manganese ore at the Benallt and Nant Mines (Woodland, 1939a, 1956).

An interesting account of rhodochrosite 'from a mine on Llanymynech Hill' is provided by Campbell Smith (1913), in his description of 'Dark greyish copper ore, mixed with a pale red....' on a specimen in the mineral collection of Thomas Pennant. Arthur Russell identified the specimen as containing rhodochrosite.

Elsewhere in Wales, Readwin (1888) reported rhodochrosite from the Dolgellau Gold Belt, while a single specimen in the Mineral Collection of the National Museum of Wales is rhodochrosite from the Cambrian Slate Quarry, Glyn Ceiriog, Clwyd. Hall (1971) reported the presence of rhodochrosite at Talachddu, near Brecon, in South Wales. X-ray diffraction at the National Museum of Wales, however, has recorded only the presence of pink dolomite (see also Hall, 1993).

Rhodonite Triclinic
$(Mn^{+2},Fe^{+2},Mg,Ca)SiO_3$
A manganese iron magnesium calcium silicate, which is a component of manganese-bearing ore bodies.

It was long thought that rhodonite was a major

component of the manganese ores of the Harlech Dome region, occurring in association with rhodochrosite. Halse (1887) noted that manganese ore exposed near Barmouth contains 4% silicate of manganese, although the first mention of rhodonite appears to have been by Dewey and Bromehead (1915), who remarked that the ore consisted of 'mixed carbonate (dialogite) and silicate (rhodonite)'. This interpretation was later re-iterated by Dewey and Dines (1923) and Cox and Wells (1927). However, Woodland (1935) reported that the major silicate phase in the ore beds is, in fact, the manganese garnet spessartine. Although rhodonite is present in the manganese ore beds of the Harlech Dome, it is now recognised as being only a minor phase (Woodland, 1939a; Woodland, 1956; Allen and Jackson, 1985; Bennett, 1987b). To the east, rhodonite is a minor component of the Vigra gold-bearing lode at Vigra Mine, in the Dolgellau Gold Belt (Andrew, 1910).

Further north, rhodonite is also present in the manganese ores at the Benallt and Nant Mines, on Llŷn (Russell, 1946). Rhodonite was first recorded from Nant Mine by the late Sir Arthur Russell in 1911.

Riebeckite   Monoclinic
$Na_2(Fe^{+2},Mg)_3Fe_2^{+3}Si_8O_{22}(OH)_2$

A sodium iron magnesium silicate hydroxide of the amphibole group which forms a series with magnesioriebeckite. Riebeckite is a rock-forming mineral which occurs in acidic igneous rocks, such as granite or rhyolite.

In a description of the Mynydd Mawr microgranite, Gwynedd, Harker (1888a) referred to the presence of both hornblende and tourmaline, although Bonney (1888) considered both minerals in fact to be varieties of hornblende, possibly arfvedsonite. Harker (1888b) subsequently identified that the true identity of the black and blue crystals which he had observed in the Mynydd Mawr microgranite was riebeckite. This represented the first description of riebeckite in the British Isles. More recently identification has been confirmed by electron microprobe analysis (R.S. Thorpe, *personal communication*).

Robinsonite   Monoclinic
$Pb_4Sb_6S_{13}$

Robinsonite is a rare lead antimony sulphide mineral which occurs in association with other antimony-bearing sulphides.

Robinsonite has been identified from Bwlch Mine, near Deganwy, Gwynedd, where it occurs with stibnite and other sulphosalt minerals including semseyite, plagionite and zinkenite. All of these sulphosalt minerals have similar physical and optical properties and consequently identification is difficult and relies on determinative analyses. To date, electron microprobe analyses of a phase which recalculate as robinsonite have been determined but the occurrence has yet to be verified by X-ray diffraction investigations (Bevins *et al.*, 1988). If confirmed, this represents the first occurrence of robinsonite in the British Isles.

Romanèchite   Monoclinic
$(Ba,H_2O)(Mn^{+4},Mn^{+3})_5O_{10}$

A barium hydrate manganese oxide which develops as an alteration product after carbonates and silicates in manganese ore bodies.

Criddle and Symes (1977) described romanèchite from the disused manganese mine at Tŷ Coch near South Cornelly, Mid Glamorgan, where it occurs as cavity fillings interlayered with goethite, associated with white fibrous calcite lining cavities, and as botryoidal and compound crystallites. This represented the first published record of romanèchite in the British Isles. Romanèchite also occurs on Natural History Museum specimen B.M. 1944, 28 (X-ray no. x13062), from Benallt Mine, near Rhiw, Llŷn.

Römerite   Triclinic
$Fe^{+2}Fe_2^{+3}(SO_4)_4.14H_2O$

An iron sulphate hydrate, developed as an oxidation product of pyritic ore.

Bor (1950) reported a chestnut-brown alteration mineral from Parys Mountain, Anglesey, which he considered to be römerite. However, this record requires confirmation in the absence of appropriate analytical data.

Rosasite   Monoclinic
$(Cu,Zn)_2(CO_3)(OH)_2$

A copper zinc carbonate hydroxide belonging to the rosasite group which forms as a result of oxidation of primary copper- and zinc-bearing minerals.

Rosasite has been reported from Bute Quarry, Llantrisant, Mid Glamorgan, and from a borehole at Locks Common, Porthcawl, Mid Glamorgan (Fletcher and Young, 1988). In both examples the rosasite occurs as a secondary alteration product after primary chalcopyrite and sphalerite and is associated with aurichalcite and zincian malachite, in cavities in Carboniferous Limestone. In the same area, bluish-green spherules from Hendy Quarry, near Miskin, give infrared patterns which are different to either malachite or aurichalcite, and may indicate the presence of rosasite (*British Micromount Society Newsletter*, No. 35). In the Central Wales Mining District, rosasite has been identified from Gwaithyrafon Mine (S.A. Rust, *personal communication*), confirmed by X-ray diffraction at the Natural History Museum.

Rutile   Tetragonal
TiO_2

Titanium dioxide, a member of the rutile group, and trimorphous with anatase and brookite. Rutile is a common accessory mineral in many igneous rocks, and is a minor constituent in certain metamorphic rocks. Rutile is also found in heavy mineral concentrates, and forms a minor component in mineral deposits.

Rutile is a common mineral in Wales, although records are relatively few. Many of the basic igneous rocks in Wales probably carry minor amounts of rutile, most probably related to the breakdown of primary iron-titanium oxide minerals such as ilmenite, as described by

Ixer (in Thorpe *et al.*, 1991) from Carn Menyn, in the Mynydd Preseli district of north Pembrokeshire, and by Pointon and Ixer (1980) from the Parys Mountain district of Anglesey. Pointon and Ixer (1980) also recorded rutile at Parys Mountain occurring in association with pyrite and chalcopyrite. Elsewhere in North Wales, rutile has been described as an important component in altered basaltic tuffs of the Bedded Pyroclastic Formation exposed at the base of the sequence northeast of Lliwedd (Williams, 1927), while Starkey and Robinson (1992) recorded minor acicular, silvery-yellow crystals of rutile in the brookite-bearing veins at Fron Oleu, near Prenteg, in Gwynedd. Further east, Starkey *et al.* (1991) described the presence of minor acicular, silvery-metallic crystals of rutile from Hendre Quarry, near Glyn Ceiriog, in Clwyd.

Naden (1988) described the presence of individual needles of 'rutile' up to 10 μm long and aggregates of needles up to 100 μm across in vein assemblages also carrying arsenopyrite, pyrite/pyrrhotite and cobaltite at the Clogau Mine, in the Dolgellau Gold Belt. However, Naden (1988) noted that he referred generally to the TiO_2 polymorphs and had not determined the particular species present.

Rutile is rare in the Central Wales Mining District, although it has been recorded from Brynyrafr Mine, near Ponterwyd, Dyfed (*British Micromount Society Newsletter*, No. 35) and Darren Mine (J.S. Mason, *personal communication*).

Sanidine Monoclinic
$KAlSi_3O_8$
A potassium aluminium silicate belonging to the feldspar group of minerals. Sanidine is a common component of rhyolites and trachytes, being a high temperature feldspar; however sanidine usually inverts to a low temperature polymorph. Sanidine also occurs in high temperature metamorphic rocks belonging to the sanidinite facies.

In Wales, sanidine is very rarely preserved, although Davies and Bloxam (1990) reported that Precambrian rhyolitic lavas exposed in the St. David's area, Dyfed, contain sanidine and albite phenocrysts.

Saponite Monoclinic
$(Ca/2,Na)_{0.3}(Mg,Fe^{+2})_3(Si,Al)_4O_{10}(OH)_2.4H_2O$
A calcium sodium magnesium iron silicate hydroxide hydrate belonging to the smectite group. Saponite occurs chiefly in altered basic igneous rocks as a result of low temperature alteration.

Roberts (1981) reported saponite-bearing metadolerite sills from near Pwllheli and Dinas, on Llŷn, Gwynedd, in assemblages also containing actinolite ± albite ± ankerite ± calcite ± chlorite ± prehnite ± quartz ± titanite. In these rocks saponite occurs either in intergranular patches or pseudomorphing olivine. A specimen of saponite from Gimlet Quarry, Llŷn is in the Mineral Collection of the Natural History Museum, registration number B.M. 1909, 462.

Saponite has also been identified associated with talc

in quartz-calcite veins cutting altered basic lavas at Llanelwedd Quarry, Builth Wells (Metcalfe, 1990).

Scapolite (group name) Tetragonal
General formula $(Na,Ca)_4Al_3(Al,Si)_3Si_6O_{24}(Cl,SO_4,CO_3)$
A group of complex feldspathoid minerals, typically found in calcium-rich metamorphic rocks.

Stamp and Wooldridge (1923) reported the presence of scapolite 'in fair quantity' in a dolerite intrusion at Pen-y-banc Farm near Llanwrtyd Wells, Powys. However, detailed examination of samples from this intrusion has so far failed to prove its presence; only prehnite has been located and this might possibly have been incorrectly identified for scapolite.

Scheelite Tetragonal
$CaWO_4$
A calcium tungstate mineral, which forms a series with powellite. Scheelite occurs in tungsten-bearing mineral veins, and also in contact metamorphic mineral deposits.

Bennett (1987a) recorded the presence of rare scheelite in pyritic mudstones of the Haffoty Formation of Cambrian age, exposed in the Harlech Dome area, Gwynedd. The dominant mineralogy of the pyritic mudstone is pyrite, chlorite and quartz, associated with rare chalcopyrite, 'ferroan pyrophanite', scheelite and an yttrium-rich phosphate.

Schmiederite Monoclinic
$Pb_2Cu_2(Se^{+3}O_3)(Se^{+6}O_4)(OH)_4$
A rare lead copper selenide selenate hydrate, found in the oxidized zone of copper and lead bearing ore bodies.

Deep blue spheres from Llechweddhelyg Mine in the Central Wales Mining District have been shown by X-ray analysis to fall between schmiederite and linarite, with analysis by the Natural History Museum X-ray no. 7530F (see *British Micromount Society Newsletter*, No. 25). Analysis of this material suggests in fact it is sulphatian schmiederite (Rust, 1990b). A similar X-ray pattern was also obtained from material from Esgair Hir Mine, with X-ray analysis again by the Natural History Museum, X-ray no. 7157F. Confirmation of schmiederite from Eaglebrook and Dyfngwm, in the Central Wales Mining District, and from Machen, in South Wales, has been provided by X-ray diffraction analyses at the National Museum of Wales.

Schulenbergite Trigonal
$(Cu,Zn)_7(SO_4,CO_3)_2(OH)_{10}.3H_2O$
A rare copper zinc sulphate carbonate hydroxide hydrate, developed in the oxidized zone of copper- and zinc-bearing ore bodies.

Schulenbergite has recently been reported from Nantycagl (Eaglebrook) Mine, Dyfed, as 'bright blue-green, slightly twisted hexagonal crystals in rosettes covering areas to 4 mm' (*British Micromount Society Newsletter*, No. 22), from Dylife Mine, Powys (S.A. Rust, *personal communication*), and also from Brynarian Mine, Talybont (Rust, 1992). It is also known from Copa Hill, Cwmystwyth, Dyfed. All of these occurrences have been confirmed by X-ray diffraction at the Natural

Figure 104. Schulenbergite (turquoise) aggregates up to 0.5 mm across, associated with linarite (dark blue) and ramsbeckite (green) from Penrhiw Mine, near Ystumtuen, in the Central Wales Mining District. J.S. Mason Collection, specimen JMPR515.

History Museum. In addition, schulenbergite has been identified at Penrhiw Mine, with identification confirmed by X-ray diffraction at the National Museum of Wales. There is no formal record of the first occurrence of schulenbergite in the British Isles; specimens identified by the Natural History Museum from Dylife Mine and from Ecton Mine, in Staffordshire, appear to have been about the same time, in 1987.

Scorodite   Orthorhombic
$FeAsO_4.2H_2O$
An iron arsenate hydrate, which belongs to the variscite group, and forms a series with mansfieldite. It generally develops in the oxidized zone of arsenic-bearing sulphide ore bodies.

Gilbey (1968) reported scarce scorodite, along with quartz, calcite, chlorite and lepidocrocite-goethite, replacing cracked and veined arsenopyrite from the Dolgellau Gold Belt, Gwynedd (eg. from Clogau Mine). National Museum of Wales specimen NMW 78.85G.M20 is scorodite from Gerlan, Bethesda, Gwynedd, with identification confirmed by X-ray diffraction (NMW X-103), an occurrence noted as an alteration product of arsenopyrite (R.S.W. Braithwaite, *personal communication*).

Semseyite   Monoclinic
$Pb_9Sb_8S_{21}$
A lead antimony sulphide which occurs in association with other lead antimony sulphosalts in low temperature ore veins.

Semseyite occurs associated with stibnite and other lead antimony sulphosalts at Bwlch Mine, Deganwy, Gwynedd where it forms either massive patches up to 3 cm in diameter showing well-defined cleavages, or flat, prismatic crystals up to 2 mm in length. Originally described by Russell (1944), recent investigations of material from Bwlch Mine (Bevins *et al.*, 1988) have confirmed the original description by X-ray diffraction and electron microprobe techniques.

Senarmontite   Cubic
Sb_2O_3
An antimony oxide, dimorphous with valentinite. A secondary mineral resulting from the oxidation of antimony sulphide or antimony-bearing sulphosalts.

Senarmontite has been recorded from the Dolgellau Gold Belt, Gwynedd (Readwin, 1888).

Serpierite   Monoclinic
$Ca(Cu,Zn)_4(SO_4)_2(OH)_6.3H_2O$
A calcium copper zinc sulphate hydroxide hydrate, dimorphous with orthoserpierite. Serpierite forms in the oxidized zones of ore bodies containing copper and zinc.

Jones and Moreton (1977) described the presence of serpierite at Dylife Mine, Powys, forming tufted aggregates of sky-blue, lath-like crystals, and botryoidal, silky crusts associated with calcite. Braithwaite (1982a) found serpierite at Eaglebrook Mine, Dyfed, as pale blue, microscopic, radiating blade-like crystals. More recently it has been reported from Esgair Hir Mine, Dyfed as masses of light blue, intergrown, lath-like crystals in cavities (Rust and Mason, 1988), and also from Ystrad Einion Mine (*British Micromount Society Newsletter*, No. 35) and Frongoch (J.S. Mason, *personal communication*).

Siderite   Trigonal
$FeCO_3$
An iron carbonate belonging to the calcite group and forming two series, one with magnesite and one with rhodochrosite. Siderite is of widespread occurrence, in particular in sedimentary rocks.

Siderite is the principal carbonate component in the clay ironstone nodules of the South Wales Coalfield (North, 1916; Firth, 1971); consequently, it is widely developed over much of South Wales. Siderite is also an important component of Ordovician ironstones exposed in Gwynedd, from Anglesey in the north to Cadair Idris in the south (Pulfrey, 1933). Along this outcrop siderite has been recorded from many localities, including Tremadog, Maes y Gaer (near Aber), Llandegai (Anglesey), Bryn Poeth (Anglesey), Pen y Gaer (Llangian) and the Garreg Fawr and Ystrad mines near Betws Garmon. Jones and Moreton (1977) noted that siderite forms a gangue mineral in certain veins in the Central Wales Mining District, such as Ystrad Einion,

Figure 105. Six-rayed siderite crystal 1.5 mm across from International Colliery, Blaengarw, Mid Glamorgan. Collected July 1990. I. Jones Collection.

Geufron and Siglenlas, although this may well have been ferroan dolomite (J.S. Mason, *personal communication*).

Figure 106. Rhombs of siderite up to 5 mm on edge from Llantrisant, Mid Glamorgan. NMW specimen 48.264.GR141, *ex* Cymmer Welfare Library and Institute.

Siegenite   Cubic
$(Ni,Co)_3S_4$
Nickel cobalt sulphide, belonging to the linnaeite group of minerals. Siegenite occurs in low temperature mineral veins in association with other nickel- and cobalt-bearing sulphides.

Siegenite has been identified in clay-ironstone nodules from Wyndham Colliery, Mid Glamorgan (Bevins and Horák, 1985), forming small (up to 0.5 mm diameter),

silvery-white octahedral crystals in association with siderite, millerite and chalcopyrite. In addition, analysis by Bevins and Horák (1985) of so-called linnaeite described by Des Cloizeaux (1880) from the 'Rhonda Valley, Glamorganshire' shows that this too is in fact siegenite. Consequently siegenite may be widely distributed in the central and eastern parts of the South Wales Coalfield, considering the distribution of 'linnaeite' listed by Howarth (1928), North and Howarth (1928) and Firth (1971).

Cobalt-bearing sulphide minerals from the Central Wales Mining District, previously described as linnaeite, are in fact siegenite (J.S. Mason, *personal communi-*

Figure 107. A cubo-octahedral siegenite crystal 1.5 mm across in a cavity in a clay ironstone nodule from Gelli Colliery, Mid Glamorgan. Collected June 1988. I. Jones Collection.

cation). It is known to occur at a number of mines, including Erglodd, Esgair Hir, Esgairfraith, Eaglebrook, Brynarian and Loveden. At Erglodd Mine, siegenite occurs as scattered crystals up to 1.5 mm across, associated with chalcopyrite in quartz (J.S. Mason, *personal communication*); this occurrence was reported by Rust (1991).

Sillimanite   Orthorhombic
Al_2SiO_5

An aluminium silicate, trimorphous with andalusite and kyanite. Sillimanite is a high grade metamorphic mineral which develops in pelitic rocks.

Sillimanite is developed in biotite-garnet gneisses of the Coedana Complex, Anglesey which represent some of the highest grade metamorphic rocks in Wales (Greenly, 1896, 1919). The 'richest' localities, according to Greenly (1919), occur in coastal regions of the Nebo Inlier, and in the area south-east of Llechcynfarwydd *(sic.)* Church. It forms slender, needle-like crystals associated with quartz, biotite, garnet, oligoclase and ilmenite at Porth Helgyn and Llechcynfarwy (Horák, 1993).

Silver   Cubic
Ag

Native silver, which forms a series with gold. Silver occurs in the oxidized zone of mineral deposits, as well as being a primary constituent of some hydrothermal veins.

The only record of native silver in Wales is from Frongoch Mine, in the Central Wales Mining District (see *British Micromount Society Newsletter*, No. 36).

Smithsonite   Trigonal
$ZnCO_3$

A zinc carbonate belonging to the calcite group of minerals. Smithsonite is found in the oxidized zone of zinc-bearing mineral veins.

Smithsonite is found at a number of localities in North and Central Wales, although to date there are very few records of the mineral from South Wales.

In North Wales smithsonite is found in the mineral veins of the Halkyn district. Campbell Smith (1913), in describing the mineral collection of Thomas Pennant, noted smithsonite from numerous localities in 'Flintshire', namely Talargoch, near Dyserth; Moel-y-crio, on Halkyn Mountain; Talacre Mine, near Gronant; Trelogan; Pen-y-bryn, Holywell; Coetia-mawr, Holywell; Coetia Butler, Holywell; Clawdd-ffordd, near Holywell; and from near Cilcain. The specimens from Talargoch are canary-yellow and botryoidal, while most from Moel-y-crio are pseudomorphous after calcite, although one is an 'epimorph of green calamine on cubes of purple fluor' (Campbell Smith, 1913, p.339). Specimens in the National Museum of Wales from this district are from West Halkyn Mine, Rhosesmor Mine and Halkyn United Mine. Mountain (1924) described the presence of botryoidal and pseudomorphous smithsonite from Milwr Mine in the Holywell district, Clwyd. Further to the southeast smithsonite is known from

Minera Mine, near Wrexham, while Greg and Lettsom (1858) described smithsonite from Llanymynech Hill near Oswestry.

Smithsonite occurs in the mineral veins of the Llangynog district (Williams, 1985); a specimen from Craig Rhiwarth is in the British Micromount Society reference collection (see *British Micromount Society Newsletter*, No. 22).

Figure 108. Botryoidal smithsonite from Halkyn Mountain, Clwyd. The specimen measures 8.5 cm x 4.5 cm. NMW specimen 85.70G.M35, *ex* R.W. Barstow Collection.

In the Central Wales Mining District smithsonite has been reported from a number of sites including Esgairfraith, Copa Hill, Brynyrafr, and Eaglebrook (Jones and Moreton, 1977), Dylife (Rust and Rust, 1987), and Esgair Hir (Rust and Mason, 1988).

Smithsonite is recorded from South Wales on a specimen in the Mineral Collection of the National Museum of Wales, labelled as coming from 'Llantrisant' and confirmed by X-ray diffraction, as well as being identified by Natural History Museum X-ray diffraction analyses of specimens from Rhyd-y-Gwern Mine, near Machen, Mid Glamorgan, and from 'Ochr-Chwith, Glamorgan' (? = Ochrwyth, near Risca, Gwent), X-ray nos x15836 and x14629, respectively. It has also been recorded from Machen Quarry, at Machen (*British Micromount Society Newsletter*, No. 36).

Sonolite   Monoclinic
$Mn_9(SiO_4)_4(OH,F)_2$
A manganese silicate fluoride hydroxide belonging to the humite group, dimorphous with jerrygibbsite.

Bennett (1987a) reported the presence of rare orange-yellow Mn-humite associated with barite in a microconcretion and in adjacent carbonate-rich red laminated ore in the manganese ore bed of the Hafotty Formation of Cambrian age, Llŷn Dywarchen near Moel Ysgyfarnogod, Gwynedd (on National Museum of Wales specimen NMW 24.479.GR32; Bennett analysis 12459). This represents the first occurrence of sonolite in the British Isles.

Spessartine   Cubic
$Mn_3Al_2(SiO_4)_3$
A manganese aluminium silicate which is a member of the garnet group, and forms a series with almandine. Spessartine results from metamorphism of manganiferous pelitic rocks.

Spessartine is widely developed in Wales. In Snowdonia, spessartine occurs along with magnetite in a thick grit band in the lowermost (Talgau) lavas exposed behind the cottage of Tan-yr-allt, near Nant Peris (Williams, 1927; Williams, 1930).

Spessartine is widely developed in the Harlech Dome region of Gwynedd, forming a major component of the bedded manganese ores of Cambrian age. Originally, the silicate component of these ores was considered to be rhodonite (see Dewey and Bromehead, 1915; Cox and Wells, 1927); subsequently, however, it was shown to be spessartine (Woodland, 1935; Matley and Wilson, 1946). More recently, electron microprobe analyses have been presented by de Béthune (1972) and Bennett (1987a), while Bennett (1987b) provided further account of these spessartine-bearing Harlech Dome manganese ores.

Elsewhere in Wales, spessartine has been identified as a component of metamorphosed pelitic rocks associated with blueschists exposed in a temporary road cutting near Llanfairpwllgwyngyll, in southeast Anglesey (Gibbons and Horák, unpublished field guide), while Roach (1969) described the presence of spessartine in pelitic rocks affected by contact metamorphism adjacent to the St. David's Head Intrusion in Dyfed.

Sphalerite   Cubic
(Zn,Fe)S
Zinc iron sulphide, belonging to the sphalerite group and trimorphous with matraite and wurtzite. Sphalerite occurs in low-temperature sulphide-bearing veins.

Sphalerite is widely developed in Wales, chiefly associated with galena or chalcopyrite in mineral veins.

In Clwyd, sphalerite is an important component of the mineral veins which cut the Carboniferous Limestone. At Minera, near Wrexham, for example, excellent resinous red-brown sphalerite is abundantly developed, while in the Halkyn area small, 2-3 mm sized, red ruby-blende crystals were once in abundance, although they are now difficult to collect. In Gwynedd, sphalerite is a component of the massive "bluestone" ore of Parys

Figure 109. Small sphalerite crystals, up to 0.2 mm, on millerite from Coed Ely Colliery, Llantrisant, Mid Glamorgan. Collected 1982. I. Jones Collection, specimen 994.

Mountain (Greenly, 1919), while it occurs also in mineral veins of Llanrwst district, associated with galena. Further south, in the Dolgellau Gold Belt, sphalerite is present in abundance in veins commonly associated with gold, as for example at Gwynfynydd Mine (Readwin, 1888).

Figure 110. A large mass of sphalerite measuring 80 mm x 45 mm, with a single colourless fluorite crystal from Trelogan Mine, at Trelogan, Clwyd. NMW specimen 27.111.GR164, *ex* G.J. Williams Collection.

Sphalerite is a major component of the mineral veins of the Central Wales Mining District (Jones and Moreton, 1977), being present at most mine sites. It appears, however, that the veins are richer in zinc towards the east, and richer in lead towards the west. Typically it is dark brown and massive, although occasionally it is shows crystal form when present in cavities. At some mines, for example Dylife, Frongoch and Bwchrhennaid, sphalerite is found as radiating aggregates of crystals, forming spherules up to several centimetres across. Small, red sphalerite crystals are known, however, from Van Mine, while black sphalerite crystals occur at Dolwen Mine, near Devil's Bridge (J.S. Mason, *personal communication*).

In South Wales, sphalerite is found as small, dark brown well-formed crystals in cavities in ironstone nodules of the coalfield district (North, 1916).

Spinel   Cubic
$MgAl_2O_4$
A magnesium aluminium oxide, belonging to the spinel group, forming three series, with magnesiochromite, gahnite, and with hercynite. Spinel is a minor component of mafic igneous rocks.

Spinel is probably present in most ultramafic and mafic igneous rocks in Wales, although records are few. Hawkins (1970) noted the presence of small, euhedral to subhedral spinels in the hornblende-picrite unit of the Rhiw Intrusion, on Llŷn, Gwynedd. They form small (0.05-0.20 mm) octahedra or cubes, typically enclosed by larger olivine crystals. Semi-quantitative analysis indicates the presence also of iron and titanium, suggesting a possible intergrowth with ilmenite. More recently, Ixer (in Thorpe *et al.*, 1991) noted the presence of spinel in altered dolerite from the Carn Menyn, in the Mynydd Preseli area of Dyfed. Elsewhere in South Wales chrome spinels are recorded as a minor component in magnesian peridotites in the diatreme exposed at Great House and Glen Court, near Usk (D.T. Moffat, *personal communication*).

Spionkopite   Hexagonal
$Cu_{39}S_{28}$
A copper sulphide mineral which occurs as an alteration mineral associated with chalcopyrite in copper deposits.

Blaubleibender covelline (= spionkopite) has been identified associated with other copper-bearing minerals at Great Ormes Head, Llandudno, Gwynedd (R.A. Ixer, *personal communication*).

Staurolite   Monoclinic
$(Fe^{+2},Mg,Zn)_2Al_9(Si,Al)_4O_{22}(OH)_2$
An iron magnesium zinc aluminium silicate hydroxide which typically develops in medium to high grade metamorphic rocks.

No *in situ* occurrence of staurolite is known in Wales. However, Greenly (1919) reported the presence of staurolite in the heavy residue from glacial sands exposed around Ty'n-y-caeau, near Menai, on Anglesey. In South Wales Griffiths (1939) identified staurolite as a major component of Irish Sea Drift in the region between the Afon Neath and the Afon Tywi, while Griffiths and Stuart (1940) reported detrital staurolite from glacial deposits at Ludchurch, Dyfed.

Stibiconite   Cubic
$Sb^{+3}Sb_2^{+5}O_6(OH)$
Antimony hydroxide, belonging to the stibiconite group which occurs as an alteration product of stibnite.

Russell (1944) described the presence of thin yellow resinous crusts of stibiconite coating stibnite obtained from the old dump at Bwlch Mine, near Deganwy, Gwynedd; this report requires verification.

Stibnite   Orthorhombic
Sb_2S_3
An antimony sulphide, dimorphous with metastibnite. Stibnite is generally found in low temperature hydrothermal veins.

Stibnite occurs in coarsely bladed masses, up to 4 mm in width and 30 mm in length, in association with various lead-antimony sulphosalts at Bwlch Mine, near Deganwy, Gwynedd (Russell, 1944; Bevins *et al.*, 1988). A fine specimen of stibnite (with bladed crystals up to 6 cm in length) in the G.J. Williams Collection in the

Figure 111. Steel-grey stibnite, partially altered to kermesite (cherry-red), in Ordovician rhyolitic ignimbrite from Bwlch Mine, near Deganwy, Gwynedd. Collected 1980. The specimen measures 11 cm x 6 cm. NMW specimen 85.70G.M34, *ex* R.W. Barstow Collection.

National Museum of Wales is labelled as 'picked up from the shore between Rhôs-mynach Mine and Dulas, Anglesey'. However, no trace of other such specimens from this locality has been detected and this occurrence remains to be verified. Stibnite is also reported from the Dolgellau Gold Belt, Gwynedd (Readwin, 1888).

Stilpnomelane Monoclinic and triclinic
$K(Fe^{+2},Mg,Fe^{+3})_8(Si,Al)_{12}(O,OH)_{27}$
A potassium iron magnesium aluminium silicate hydroxide. It is typically developed in iron-rich igneous rocks which have suffered metamorphic alteration.

Hallimond (1924) identified the presence of a brittle dark-brown mineral in Ordovician pisolitic ironstones exposed at Pen-yr-allt iron mine, Llanfrothen near Penrhyndeudraeth, Gwynedd which strongly resembled biotite but which he identified as being stilpnomelane. This represented the first published account of the

mineral in the British Isles, although Hallimond remarked that the presence of this mineral had already been observed by Mr G.J. Williams (former Inspector of Mines for Wales) and by Sir Arthur Russell. Russell also passed on to Hallimond a stilpnomelane specimen from the oolitic ironstones exposed at Cross Foxes, Dolgellau, Gwynedd. Stilpnomelane specimens from the G.J. Williams Collection, currently housed in the National Museum of Wales, are labelled as being from Bryn Castell Mine, Cross Foxes (near Dolgellau, Gwynedd) and Cwm Mawr Mine, Llanbedr (also in Gwynedd). In oolitic iron ores of the same age, Pulfrey (1933) reported blades and veins of stilpnomelane in ore from mines at Pen-yr-allt and Betws Garmon (both in Gwynedd).

Natural History Museum X-ray no. x19863 is stilpnomelane from 'Moelfre', which is presumably from Moelfre Mine in the Harlech Dome region of Gwynedd. Bloxam and Price (1961) described stilpnomelane from the Cregenen granophyre, exposed near Arthog, Gwynedd, as well as in certain Ordovician acidic ash flow tuffs in the same region, remarking that the so-called biotite in the Cregenen granophyre and other minor intrusions (see Cox and Wells, 1920) is almost certainly stilpnomelane. Similarly the description of biotite in many of the intrusions of the Snowdon district (eg. Williams, 1930) is probably an erroneous identification of stilpnomelane. Bloxam and Price (1961) described the Cregenen stilpnomelane as forming sharply terminated laths, arranged either in radiating sheafs or as 'bow-tie' aggregates, and as being strongly pleochroic from pale yellow to deep golden brown or even black when observed under the polarizing microscope.

Subsequently, Matthews and Scoon (1964) reported a further locality for stilpnomelane in the Dolgellau area, in a lenticular mass of Ordovician sedimentary ironstone from approximately 3.2 km south-west of the former station at Drws-y-nant, at an old mine by the name of Tyllau Mwn. It occurs associated with magnetite, chamosite, pyrrhotite, ilmenite and fluorapatite. Both ferro- and ferristilpnomelane were identified.

More recently Roach (1969) and Bevins and Roach (1982) identified abundant stilpnomelane in the more fractionated parts of the St. David's Head Intrusion (Dyfed); in the granophyric gabbros it forms up to 13% of the mode. Bevins and Rowbotham (1983) emphasised the sporadic occurrence of stilpnomelane across the whole of Wales, in relatively fractionated igneous rocks, principally of Ordovician age, which have been affected by low-grade Caledonian metamorphism. They presented representative analyses of stilpnomelane from the St. David's Head Intrusion and from the Treseissyllt Intrusion, both in Dyfed, and from the summit of Cadair Idris, Gwynedd. Further demonstration of the restriction of stilpnomelane to the relatively more fractionated igneous rocks is provided by its occurrence only in the ferrodolerite horizon of the Tal y Fan Intrusion, Gwynedd, reported by Merriman *et al.* (1986) and Bevins and Merriman (1988).

Strontianite   Orthorhombic
$SrCO_3$

A strontium carbonate mineral belonging to the aragonite group. Strontianite is usually found in veins associated with barite, calcite and celestine cutting limestone.

In Wales strontianite is rare. Strontianite specimens in museum collections are Natural History Museum specimen B.M. 1985, M1 11289, from Pennant Mine, near St. Asaph, Clwyd, and National Museum of Wales specimen NMW 85.41G.M1, which is strontianite from Penarth Head, South Glamorgan (collected and donated by A. Dean). The latter comprises a radiating mass 1 mm across of white, acicular crystals, detached from matrix. Natural History Museum X-ray no. x2980 confirms the presence of strontianite at Benallt Mine, Llŷn, while X-ray no. x7903 is strontianite from Nant Mine, 'Llanfairly, Carnarvonshire', which is presumably Nant Mine at Llanfaelrhys, on Llŷn.

Strüverite   Tetragonal
$(Ti,Ta,Fe^{+3})_3O_6$

A titanium tantalum iron oxide which forms a series with ilmenorutile. A rare mineral, typically found in granitic pegmatites.

Small prisms in altered microgranite, associated with brookite and gibbsite from Y Llymllwyd, Nant Ffrancon, Gwynedd have been identified as strüverite on the basis of X-ray diffraction analysis (D.A. Jenkins, *personal communication*). This represents the first occurrence of the mineral in the British Isles.

Sulfur   Orthorhombic
S

Native sulphur. Sulfur is most commonly found in active volcanic regions, associated with fumaroles and hot springs. It is also found associated with salt domes and more rarely with hydrothermal mineral deposits.

Records of sulfur in Wales are few. Greenly (1919) reported that sulfur was a component in the gossan capping to the Parys Mountain ore body, although all of the gossan has long since been removed. Wedd *et al.* (1929) described the presence of sulfur in a galena-bearing vein at Nant-y-blaidd Mine, near Llanrhaeadr-ym-Mochnant, Clwyd. In South Wales, sulfur has been identified from galena-bearing veins at the Dan-y-graig and Ochrwyth quarries, near Risca, in Gwent (Alabaster, 1983).

Sulfur is probably quite widespread in the oxidized zone of lead-bearing veins in the Central Wales Mining District, although no written records are known. It has been visually identified from Frongoch Mine (J.S. Mason, *personal communication*), although this requires confirmation.

Susannite   Trigonal
$Pb_4(SO_4)(CO_3)_2(OH)_2$

A secondary lead sulphate carbonate hydroxide typically found in the oxidized zone of lead-bearing ore deposits.

Susannite has been reported from Esgair Hir Mine, Dyfed, by Rust and Mason (1988). It forms groups of

Figure 112. Pale yellow hexagonal susannite crystal 0.5 mm across from Frongoch Mine, in the Central Wales Mining District. J.S. Mason Collection, specimen JMFG136.

rod-like to prismatic crystals, associated with caledonite and leadhillite. This represented the first reported occurrence of susannite in Wales. However, susannite is now known from other localities in the Central Wales Mining District, being confirmed also from Llechweddhelyg, Hendrefelen and Frongoch Mines by X-ray diffraction at the Natural History Museum. At Frongoch Mine white, pale blue or pale yellow hexagonal plates and prisms up to 1 mm coat altered galena (J.S. Mason, *personal communication*). A brief account of the Llechweddhelyg occurrence is provided by Rust (1990b), while reference to the Hendrefelen occurrence is reported by Clark and Rust (1993).

Sylvanite   Monoclinic
$(Au,Ag)_2Te_4$

A silver gold telluride occurring in hydrothermal veins, commonly associated with native gold.

Pryor (1988) has provided the only reported occurrence of sylvanite in Wales, occurring in association with gold, acanthite and various other telluride minerals including hessite, at Gwynfynydd Mine near Dolgellau, Gwynedd. This represents the first occurrence of sylvanite in the British Isles.

Figure 113. Tapering, prismatic susannite crystals up to 0.75 mm long from Frongoch Mine, in the Central Wales Mining District. J.S. Mason Collection, specimen JMFG010.

Synchysite   Orthorhombic
Ca(La,Ce,Nd,Y)(CO$_3$)$_2$ F
A calcium rare earth carbonate fluoride. Synchysite occurs in pegmatites, carbonatites, and low-temperature alpine-type mineral veins.

Synchysite occurs intergrown with quartz and K-feldspar forming radiating sheaves in an altered rhyolite of Ordovician age from Beddgelert Forest, Gwynedd (A.T. Kearsley, *personal communication*). Energy dispersive analysis shows it to have high yttrium contents and so it is likely to be the species synchysite-(Y). This represents the first occurrence of the synchysite in the British Isles. Synchysite in rhyolite from Snowdonia, occurring in radiating sheaves and along cracks, is illustrated by Howells *et al.* (1991). Synchysite-(Ce) has been recorded from Manod Quarry, at Blaenau Ffestiniog, Gwynedd (N. Hubbard, *personal communication*), which if verified would represent the first occurrence of synchysite-(Ce) in the British Isles.

Szomolnokite   Monoclinic
Fe^{2+}SO$_4$.H$_2$O
A hydrous iron sulphate typically associated with pyrite and other secondary sulphates. Szomolnokite is usually precipitated from highly acidic solutions, such as mine waters.

Szomolnokite is found as white, powdery efflorescences on Natural History Museum specimens B.M. 1985,MI 33592 and B.M. 1985,MI 33593 from Seam 'x', Ebbw Vale Main, and '40 yd outbye 1st crosscut on Ebbw Vale Return' at Crumlin Colliery, Ebbw Vale, Gwent. The latter was identified by X-ray diffraction investigation and constitutes the first verified occurrence of the mineral in the British Isles.

Talc   Monoclinic and triclinic
Mg$_3$Si$_4$O$_{10}$(OH)$_2$
A magnesium silicate hydroxide typically developed in ultrabasic rocks as a result of hydrothermal alteration.

Talc was described by Readwin (1888) as occurring in the Dolgellau Gold Belt, in Gwynedd. Later, Greenly (1919) reported the presence of talc-marbles at Llanfwrog, talc in altered gabbros at Porth-delisc and at Cliperau, and talc-bearing schists north of Bronddel, all on Anglesey. Maltman (1977) also identified talc in various altered basic and ultrabasic rocks of the Mona Complex on Anglesey, associated with tremolite, chlorite, epidote, carbonate and other secondary minerals. Elsewhere in Gwynedd talc has been described in association with calcite and quartz occurring in thin veins (>1.5 cm thick) cutting the Penmaenmawr Intrusion (Sargent, 1925).

Talc occurs as a replacement of olivine in xenolithic gabbros in the St. David's Head Intrusion, Dyfed (Roach, 1969) with confirmation by electron microprobe analysis (author's unpublished data).

In Powys talc has been identified associated with saponite in quartz-calcite veins cutting altered basaltic lavas at Llanelwedd Quarry, Builth Wells (Metcalfe, 1990).

Tapiolite   Tetragonal
(Fe,Mn)(Ta,Nb)$_2$O$_6$
An iron manganese tantalum niobium oxide which forms the series ferrotapiolite-mangantapiolite. It occurs typically in quartz-albite mineral veins and pegmatites.

Natural History Museum X-ray no. 3244F is tapiolite from 'near Tremadoc', Wales. No further details are known, although this represents the first account of tapiolite from the British Isles. However, whether it is ferrotapiolite or mangantapiolite which is present has not been determined.

Tellurobismuthite   Trigonal
Bi$_2$Te$_3$
A bismuth telluride mineral belonging to the tetradymite group, which forms a series with tellurantimony.

Kingsbury (1965) first reported tellurobismuthite from the Clogau and Vigra Mines, near Dolgellau, Gwynedd, occurring in association with gold, and considered previous descriptions of tetradymite from these mines (eg. Readwin, 1860; Forbes, 1867) to have been misidentifications of tellurobismuthite. Readwin (1860) had previously referred to the presence of 'telluric-bismuth'. Gilbey (1968), however, demonstrated the presence of both minerals, recording tellurobismuthite and tetradymite from the Clogau, Caegwian, Vigra, Cefn Coch and Fridd-goch mines, the former as brilliant, metallic silver flakes (up to 1.5 mm), peppered in quartz and calcite and associated with galena, other telluride minerals, and occasionally gold. Kingsbury (1965) and Embrey (1978) recorded this as the first description of tellurobismuthite in Britain; however, Siddiqui (1964) had previously reported the mineral from Gwavas Quarry, Cornwall.

Tennantite   Cubic
$(Cu,Ag,Fe,Zn)_{12}As_4S_{13}$
A copper silver iron zinc arsenic sulphide which belongs to the tetrahedrite group, and which forms a series with tetrahedrite. Tennantite occurs in hydrothermal mineral veins, associated with other sulphide minerals.

Carruthers *et al.* (1915) described the presence of 'fahl-ore' associated with argentiferous galena, chalcopyrite and sphalerite at Cystanog Mine, near Carmarthen, Dyfed, although whether this was tennantite or tetrahedrite is not known. Tennantite has been reported from the Parys Mountain copper deposit on Anglesey, by Wheatley (1971), Sivaprakash (1977) and Pointon and Ixer (1980). It is present in the chalcopyrite-rich and more rarely in the sphalerite- and galena-rich portions of the ore body, forming thin (up to 20 μm) rims between chalcopyrite and galena or sphalerite, small inclusions or veinlets in sphalerite, and isolated anhedral grains up to 400 μm (see Pointon and Ixer, 1980). Electron microprobe analyses are presented by Wheatley (1971) and Sivaprakash (1977). Tennantite and tetrahedrite are both present at Parys Mountain, although the former is more common. Lately, tennantite has been identified from the Great Ormes Head copper mine, Llandudno, Gwynedd (R.A. Ixer, *personal communication*).

Minor tennantite-barite-chalcopyrite mineralization has been reported from Old Radnor, Powys (Parnell and Eakin, 1989).

Tenorite   Monoclinic
CuO
A copper oxide mineral which commonly develops in the oxidized zone of copper deposits.

One of the earliest descriptions of tenorite in Wales is the record of 'melaconite' (a synonym of tenorite) from the Great Ormes Head, at Llandudno (Greg and Lettsom, 1858).

Greenly (1919) mentioned the former presence of 'melaconite' in gossan associated with the Great Lode from the Parys Mountain copper deposit, on Anglesey, Gwynedd, although Greenly's comments were based on an earlier account of the deposit by Lentin (1800), as at the time he wrote the Anglesey Memoir no gossan was present at Parys Mountain.

In the Central Wales Mining District melaconite has been reported from the Darren, Esgairfraith, and Snowbrook Mines, all in Dyfed (Jones and Moreton, 1977). At Esgairfraith, it occurs as masses up to 10 cm

associated with chrysocolla (J.S. Mason, *personal communication*). More recently, black bituminous masses up to 5 mm coating chalcopyrite and chalcocite at Esgair Hir Mine, Dyfed, have been interpreted as being tenorite (Rust and Mason, 1988).

Tephroite   Orthorhombic
Mn_2SiO_4
A manganese silicate belonging to the olivine group, and forming a series with fayalite. Typically tephroite is of contact metamorphic origin, occurring in iron-manganese skarns.

Tephroite is recorded from the Benallt Mine, Llŷn, where it occurs 'on the foot-wall side of no. 1 ore-body by no. 1 Chute, 50-60 feet west of the main shaft, and some 10-20 feet above the 130-foot level' (Campbell Smith *et al.*, 1944b). It occurs intimately associated with alleghanyite, and forms composite, dark, narrow, blade-like crystals up to 2 cm in length and varying in thickness from 2 mm down to microscopic sizes. The tephroite is olive-green, and weakly pleochroic about pale olive-green in thin section. Crystals are elongated parallel to the c-axis. This represented the first recorded occurrence of tephroite in the British Isles. Campbell Smith *et al.* (1944) also recorded tephroite associated with alleghanyite from 'near the foot-wall of no. 2 ore-body, located 40 to 80 feet west of the Court Shaft'.

Tetradymite   Trigonal
Bi_2Te_2S
A bismuth tellurium sulphide belonging to the tetradymite group of minerals. Tetradymite commonly occurs in mineral veins, in association with gold, sulphides, and various telluride minerals.

Smyth (1862) first described the occurrence of tetradymite associated with gold at Clogau Mine, near Dolgellau, Gwynedd, an occurrence which was reported in numerous later publications (eg. Forbes, 1867; Readwin, 1888; Andrew, 1910) and represented the first occurrence of the mineral in the British Isles. Its presence was subsequently questioned by Kingsbury (1965), who examined a number of specimens in his possession from both the Clogau and Vigra Mines, in which he only identified tellurobismuthite. However Gilbey (1968) reported tetradymite associated with tellurobismuthite from numerous gold-bearing lodes in the Dolgellau area, typically occurring with galena as a complex, exsolved intergrowth in tellurobismuthite. At Clogau Mine, Gilbey (1968) identified an assemblage of tetradymite-tellurobismuthite-galena-altaite-hessite-gold-nagyagite. Recent detailed mineralogical studies of an ore shoot from the 4th mine level at Clogau Mine have revealed an assemblage of major tellurobismuthite-tetradymite-galena-chalcopyrite-pyrrhotite and minor hessite-altaite-gold-cobaltite-native bismuth-matildite (Naden, 1988) with the tetradymite containing up to *c*.11 wt% lead.

Tetrahedrite   Cubic
$(Cu,Fe,Ag,Zn)_{12}Sb_4S_{13}$
Copper iron silver zinc antimony sulphide, belonging to the tetrahedrite group and forming two series, one with freibergite, and one with tennantite. Typically tetra-

hedrite occurs in low temperature hydrothermal veins in association with various sulphide minerals.

The earliest report of tetrahedrite in Wales appears to be that by Lentin (1800), from the Parys Mountain copper deposit on Anglesey. Subsequently, this was confirmed by Greenly (1919), Wheatley (1971), Sivaprakash (1977) and Pointon and Ixer (1980). It occurs in chalcopyrite and, more rarely, in the sphalerite- and galena-rich portions of the ore body, forming thin ($c.20$ μm) rims between chalcopyrite and galena or sphalerite, small inclusions or veinlets in sphalerite, and isolated anhedral grains, up to 400 μm (see Pointon and Ixer, 1980). Electron microprobe analyses are presented by Wheatley (1971) and Sivaprakash (1977). Tetrahedrite forms a solid solution series with tennantite, and both end members are present at Parys Mountain; tennantite, however, is more common than tetrahedrite.

Figure 114. Tetrahedrite (steel-grey, bottom right) associated with galena (steel-grey, top left), from Darren Mine, in the Central Wales Mining District. NMW specimen 86.100G.M8, *ex* J.S. Mason.

Tetrahedrite has also been identified as occurring in the Dolgellau region, first by Readwin (1888) and later by Andrews (1910) and Gilbey (1968). The latter reported the presence of tetrahedrite as inclusions in galena at Foel Ispri Mine, and as inclusions in sphalerite at Gwynfynydd Mine. Rice and Sharp (1976) also made reference to the presence of tetrahedrite in the Coed-y-Brenin area. Commonly the mineral has a high silver content and is more correctly termed argentian tetrahedrite. When the silver content is sufficient, argentian tetrahedrite passes into freibergite. In view of the fact that an analysis of 'polytelite' from Tyddyn Gwladys Mine near Dolgellau by Forbes (1868) contained 11.25% Ag it is most likely that this was in fact argentian tetrahedrite. More recently tetrahedrite has been reported from the Clogau Mine, near Dolgellau, on the basis of electron microprobe analysis (Naden, 1988), on a specimen (K2) in the Kingsbury Collection, in the Natural History Museum.

So-called argentiferous galena from Darren, South Darren, Cwmerfin, Goginan, Cwmsymlog and other mines in the Central Wales Mining District has been shown to contain abundant tetrahedrite inclusions (Mason and Hughes, 1990; J.S. Mason, *personal communication*). The presence of tetrahedrite at the Bwlchrhennaid Mine, near Goginan, has been confirmed by X-ray diffraction at the Natural History Museum, X-ray no. 6338F.

Carruthers *et al.* (1915) recorded the presence of 'fahlore' at the Cystanog Mine, near Carmarthen, Dyfed, although it is not certain whether this represents tetrahedrite or tennantite.

Thaumasite   Hexagonal
$Ca_6Si_2(CO_3)_2(SO_4)_2(OH)_{12}.24H_2O$
A calcium silicate carbonate sulphate hydroxide hydrate.

Thaumasite has been identified in weathered furnace slag from the 'White Tip' from the Dowlais and Cyfarthfa Iron Works at Merthyr Tydfil, Mid Glamorgan (Wilson, 1978). It is present as white fluffy or felty, fibrous, vesicle infillings. Individual acicular fibres range in width from 5-10 μm and up to 500 μm in length, and occur associated with calcite. It also occurs as white, powdery, acicular crystals in a mineralized breccia, or possibly a post-mining cemented aggregate, at Glasdir mine dumps, near Dolgellau, Gwynedd (G. Ryback, *personal communication*).

Thomsonite   Orthorhombic
$NaCa_2Al_5Si_5O_{20}.6H_2O$
A sodium calcium aluminium silicate hydrate, belonging to the zeolite group. Typically thomsonite occurs in vesicles or veins in basic igneous rocks affected by low temperature alteration.

Thomsonite forms radiating, fibrous aggregates infilling vesicles (up to 2 cm in diameter) in the Marchlyn Dyke, an olivine dolerite dyke of Tertiary age, exposed in Central Snowdonia, Gwynedd (Williams, 1924, 1930). A chemical analysis of the mineral is presented by Williams (1924). More recently thomsonite has been reported from amygdales in monchiquitic basanite from dyke rocks at Great House and Glen Court near Usk, Gwent (D.T. Moffat, *personal communication*).

Thorianite   Cubic
ThO_2
A thorium oxide mineral, forming a series with uraninite.

Thorianite is commonly found in pegmatites.

Thorianite has been identified associated with thorite occurring as inclusions (between 2-5 μm across) within spherical bitumen nodules in the Folly Sandstone of Llandovery age, exposed in the Presteigne area, Powys (Parnell and Eakin, 1989).

Thorite   Tetragonal
(Th,U)SiO$_4$
A thorium uranium silicate, dimorphous with huttonite. Generally thorite is found as a primary accessory mineral in acidic igneous rocks, in particular in pegmatites.

Thorite has been identified by back-scatter electron microscopy combined with energy-dispersive analysis as small overgrowths on primary zircon in a rhyolitic ash-flow tuff of Ordovician age from Ramsey Island, Dyfed (author's unpublished data). Thorite is also found as inclusions less than 2 μm across associated with thorianite within spherical bitumen nodules in the Folly Sandstone of Llandovery age, exposed in the Presteigne area of Powys (Parnell and Eakin, 1989). Howells *et al.* (1991) reported the presence of thorite as an alteration mineral in rhyolitic rocks from Snowdonia, on the basis of energy-dispersive analysis. Finally, thorite has been recognised as overgrowths on xenotime crystals in Ordovician mudstones from the Aberangell district, Gwynedd (A.T. Kearsley, *personal communication*).

Titanite (syn. sphene)   Monoclinic
CaTiSiO$_5$
A calcium titanium silicate which is found as an accessory mineral in acidic igneous rocks. In addition, titanite develops in rocks as a result of contact metamorphism, and also of regional low-grade metamorphism.

Titanite is present as an accessory phase in various rhyolitic rocks in Snowdonia, Gwynedd (Campbell *et al.*, 1987; Howells *et al.*, 1991), where it forms euhedra up to 200 μm across, with some crystals showing well-

Figure 115. Scanning electron micrograph of sector-zoned titanite from altered rhyolite from Beddgelert Forest, central Snowdonia, Gwynedd. British Geological Survey specimen KB454. Field of view is 350 μm across.

developed sector zoning, having tin-rich cores, with up to 3.5% SnO$_2$ (A.T. Kearsley, *personal communication*). In addition it is widely developed as a low-grade metamorphic mineral in rocks of basaltic composition. In such occurrences it typically forms anhedral dusty granules up to 0.1 mm across associated with chlorite in the groundmass of the rock, or pseudomorphing primary iron-titanium oxides. Electron microprobe analyses of titanites in altered basaltic rocks are presented by Bevins and Rowbotham (1983) and Bevins and Merriman (1988). These data show that there is considerable substitution of Al and Fe for Ti, which has been reported elsewhere in titanites developed in low-grade metamorphic rocks.

Starkey and Robinson (1992) recorded titanite in Alpine-type veins at Fron Oleu, near Prenteg, Gwynedd.

Todorokite   Monoclinic
(Mn^{+2},Ca,Mg)Mn$_3$$^{+4}O_7$.H$_2$O
A manganese calcium magnesium oxide hydrate, which occurs as a secondary mineral resulting from alteration of other manganese minerals.

Glasby (1974) reported that the chief alteration product of bedded manganese ore (chiefly rhodochrosite, spessartine and rare rhodonite) of Cambrian age in the Harlech Dome region of Gwynedd is todorokite, and not pyrolusite, as had been previously suggested by Woodland (1938c). The presence of todorokite in this area has also been reported by Allen and Jackson (1985) and Bennett (1987a).

Topaz   Orthorhombic
Al$_2$SiO$_4$(F,OH)$_2$

An aluminium silicate fluoride hydroxide, most commonly occurring as an accessory phase in granites, granitic pegmatites, and rhyolites.

Williams (1930) described the presence of topaz in the Bwlch y Cywion Intrusion, Snowdonia, Gwynedd which he identified in heavy mineral residue following separation from the crushed rock. Williams (1930) also reported topaz from a garnet-biotite rock developed in the contact aureole of the Bwlch y Cywion Intrusion, forming irregular, colourless grains up to 3 mm across commonly hosting smaller almandine garnet crystals.

Topaz was also reported by Griffiths and Stuart (1940) along with diaspore and other detrital minerals in sandy boulder clay from Ludchurch, Dyfed.

Tourmaline   Trigonal
A group name for borosilicates with the general formula (Ca,Na,K)(Al,Fe^{+2},Fe^{+3},Li,Mg,Mn^{+2})$_3$(Al,Cr^{+3},Fe^{+3},V^{+3})$_6$ (BO$_3$)$_3$Si$_6$O$_{18}$(O,OH,F)$_4$.
Tourmaline commonly develops in pegmatites and pneumatolytic veins associated with granites. It can also result from boron metasomatism. In addition, it is an important detrital component in sedimentary rocks.

One of the earliest records of tourmaline in Wales was by Fearnsides (1908), who, by examining detrital minerals in river gravels in Snowdonia, determined the presence of tourmalinized-grits at Cwm Dwythwc. A more detailed description was subsequently provided by Williams (1927), who reported the presence of well-formed, zoned blue to brown tourmaline in grits of Arenig age, tracing them from Bwlch Gwyn to Brithdir. Further tourmalinized grits in the same region were identified by Beavon (1963) in the vicinity of Aberglaslyn, as well as in blocks in the slightly younger Llŷn Dinas Breccias exposed to the east of Beddgelert. Subsequently Bromley (1969) located similar brecciated and tourmalinized rocks in the contact aureole of the Tan-y-Grisiau microgranite. In all these cases the tourmaline is zoned from blue-green to brown. Bromley (1969) considered that tourmalinization was related to pneumatolytic activity associated with contemporary acidic magmatism.

On Anglesey, tourmaline has been identified as a minor component in various rock units of the Mona Complex, such as the Holyhead Quartzite, the South Stack Series, the Tyfry Beds, the Gwna Grits and Quartzites, and the Mona gneisses, as well as in hornfelses surrounding the Coedana Granite (Greenly, 1919).

Woodland (1938a) reported minute euhedral pleochroic pale yellowish-green to greenish-brown tourmaline prismatic crystals (0.020-0.035 mm in length, and 0.005-0.015 mm in width) in mudstones of the Harlech Grits Group, of Cambrian age, exposed in the Harlech Dome region, as for example on the east side of Diphwys. Its presence in the Harlech region was subse-quently confirmed by de Béthune (1972).

In Powys, tourmaline-bearing altered gabbros have been described from Hanter Hill (Holgate and Hallowes, 1941; Holgate, 1977). In these rocks, blue-black tourmaline forms clots up to 15 mm across which consist either of a single crystal or groups of crystals in near parallel orientation. The crystals are pleochroic from slate blue-grey to olive-grey to deep slate-green. Chemical analysis and X-ray diffraction studies indicate that this tourmaline is close to dravite in the schorlite-dravite series.

Tremolite   Monoclinic
$Ca_2(Mg,Fe^{+2})_5Si_8O_{22}(OH)_2$

A calcium magnesium iron silicate hydroxide belonging to the amphibole group. Tremolite develops in contact and regionally metamorphosed carbonate-bearing rocks, in particular metamorphosed limestones and dolomites.

On Anglesey, tremolite occurs in various carbonate-rich rocks formed as a result of serpentinization and carbonatization of a suite of ultramafic (peridotitic) and mafic (gabbroic) intrusions on Holy Island. Greenly (1919) recorded tremolite-schists and tremolitic marbles from numerous localities, including: the vicinity of Rhyd-y-Bont; near Fadog; near Pwllpillo; a few metres southeast of Gareg-lwyd House; and in a small quarry c. 250 metres north of Bronddel. Maltman (1977) gave further account of tremolite in this suite of intrusions, although he considered it to be more extensively developed within and at the margins of altered gabbroic

Figure 116. Radiating sprays of tyrolite crystals up to 2 mm in diameter on quartz, from Gwaithyrafon Mine, at Cwmsymlog, in the Central Wales Mining District. J.S. Mason Collection, specimen JMGA520.

bodies, particularly in fault zones. Greenly (1919) also reported the presence of tremolite from a small number of localities associated with a belt of basic intrusions in the northern part of Anglesey, including a green serpentinite at Mynachdy; a tremolite-schist at Cefn-coch mill; and forming a tremolitic serpentine in massive ophicalcite at Tyddyn-dai. Finally, Greenly (1919) provided further occurrences of tremolite in Anglesey in a serpentine intrusion at Bodrwyn, near Cerrigceinwen, and in another serpentine intrusion exposed to the west-southwest of Tyfry, near Pentraeth.

Tschermakite   Monoclinic
$Ca_2(Mg,Fe)_3Al_2(Si_6,Al_2)O_{22}(OH)_2$
A calcium iron aluminium silicate hydroxide belonging to the amphibole group and forming a series with ferrotschermakite. Tschermakite is a rock-forming mineral, found typically in basic igneous rocks.

Tschermakite has been determined by electron microprobe analysis as being a component in the Rhiw Intrusion, Llŷn, where it occurs as a late stage magmatic mineral in the gabbros (author's unpublished data). In addition, Horák (1993) recorded the presence of tschermakite in ultrabasic gneisses exposed at Parwyd, on Llŷn.

Tucekite   Tetragonal
$Ni_9Sb_2S_8$
An iron antimony sulphide belonging to the hauchecornite group.

Tucekite has been identified as a component of complex sulphide assemblages in the Central Wales Mining District, in particular from the Nantycagl (Eaglebrook), Henfwlch, Esgair Hir, Esgairfraith and Hyddgen mines with X-ray diffraction and electron microprobe confirmation on specimens from Nantycagl. Optical identifications from the other localities are based on the distinctive anisotropy of tucekite (J. S. Mason, *personal communication*). This represents the first occurrence of the mineral in the British Isles and only the third occurrence world-wide.

Tyrolite   Orthorhombic
$CaCu_5(AsO_4)_2(CO_3)(OH)_4.6H_2O$
A calcium copper arsenate carbonate hydroxide hydrate. A rare secondary mineral which develops in the oxidized zone of copper-bearing ore bodies.

Tyrolite has been reported from Gwaithyrafon Mine, at Cwmsymlog, in the Central Wales Mining District, as radiating, lath-like blue crystals up to 2 mm in length, on joints associated with chrysocolla and iron oxides, confirmed by X-ray diffraction at the Natural History Museum X-ray no. 6878F. A tyrolite-like mineral has also been reported from a trial level near Bontddu, Gwynedd (Saich and Rust, 1987), forming bright blue spherules up to 0.3 mm, and botryoidal masses up to 2 mm.

Ullmannite   Cubic
NiSbS
A nickel antimony sulphide, which forms a series with

willyamite. Ullmannite is found in mineral veins along with other nickel-bearing sulphide minerals.

Ashton (1981) first reported the occurrence of ullmannite from the Central Wales Mining District, describing it as being present at Goginan Mine, Dyfed. Subsequently it has been confirmed from numerous other mines, including the Dolclettwr, Ynystudur and Pandy Mines at Tre'r-ddol, Mynyddgorddu Mine at Bontgoch, Grogwynion Mine at Pontrhydygroes, and at Glogfawr Mine, Devil's Bridge. It forms either discrete cubic

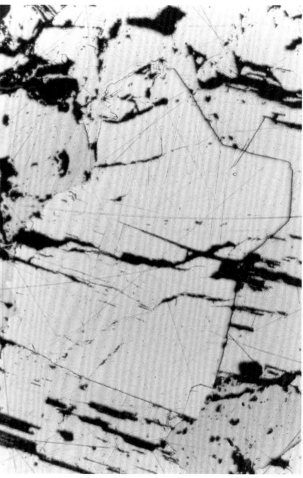

Figure 117. Ullmannite (centre) overgrown by galena (grey, surrounding) and chalcopyrite (yellow), from Ynystudur Mine, in the Central Wales Mining District. Reflected light photomicrograph. Field of view 2.5 mm across. *Ex* J.S. Mason Collection, now National Museum of Wales specimen 93.90G.M71.

crystals up to 1 cm across, or cubic inclusions or cores up to 0.7 mm across in galena. It is usually part of an assemblage including tetrahedrite, bournonite, boulangerite, galena, chalcopyrite and linnaeite group minerals (J.S. Mason, *personal communication*).

Rust and Mason (1988) have described the presence of ullmannite at Esgair Hir Mine, Talybont, also in the Central Wales Mining District. Here, it forms idiomorphic inclusions within galena or larger grains along boundaries with chalcopyrite; the larger grains contain inclusions of chalcopyrite or siegenite. A note in the *British Micromount Society Newsletter*, No. 25, for 1989 records ullmannite as grey metallic masses up to 5 mm and rare cubes up to 1 mm from an un-named trial at [SN 720 693] near Ysbyty Ystwyth. Clark and Rust (1993) described the presence of bottinoite as an alteration product on ullmannite at the Mynyddgorddu and Hendrefelen Mines.

Uraninite   Cubic
UO_2

An oxide of uranium which forms a series with thorianite. Uraninite occurs in hydrothermal veins, as well as in association with other secondary uranium minerals in sandstones.

Uranium enrichment of hydrocarbons at Great Ormes Head, Llandudno has been known for some time (Sylvester-Bradley and King, 1963; Parnell, 1983). This has subsequently been identified as being due to uraninite, occurring as regular arrays of inclusions (1-10 μm in diameter) in hydrocarbons in the Ty Gwyn Mine. These hydrocarbons contain up to 1.37 wt% uranium, and associated minerals include annabergite and gersdorffite, which are found as coatings and fractures in the hydrocarbon (P. Eakin, *personal communication*), and in cobaltian niccolite (Parnell, 1988). Parnell (1988) has also reported uraninite in hydrocarbons in the Carboniferous Limestone elsewhere in North Wales, including Minera and Halkyn, both in Clwyd. Eakin (1989) listed a total of 9 localities where uraniferous hydrocarbons are found in North Wales. Uraniferous bitumen, containing probable uraninite, has more recently been described by Eakin and Gize (1992) from Llandulas, Clwyd, with an alteration rim of probable brannerite.

Vanadinite   Hexagonal
$Pb_5(VO_4)_3Cl$

A lead vanadate chloride belonging to the vanadinite group. Vanadinite occurs in the oxidized zone of lead-bearing mineral deposits.

Criddle and Symes (1977) described the presence of vanadinite at a disused manganese mine at Tŷ Coch, Mid Glamorgan, occurring as: pale yellow euhedral to anhedral crystals intimately associated with pyrobelonite, braunite, hausmannite, calcite, manganocalcite, ferroan calcite, dolomite and barite; grey crystals, with a greasy lustre occupying cavities in psilomelane; and in brecciated manganese ore as bright yellow encrustations.

Vanadinite forms small brown hexagonal prisms associated with gold from 'mines near Dolgelly' on Natural History Museum specimen B.M. 67960.

Vesuvianite (syn. idocrase)   Tetragonal
$Ca_{10}Mg_2Al_4(SiO_4)_5(Si_2O_7)_2(OH)_4$

A calcium magnesium aluminium silicate hydroxide. Typically vesuvianite is found in contact metamorphosed limestones.

Clear, glassy, grass-green porphyroblasts (up to 4 mm in diameter) in gneisses of the Mona Complex at Porth Helygyn, on Anglesey, were identified by Greenly (1919) as vesuvianite. It occurs associated with sillimanite, biotite, and a rose-coloured garnet. Recent detailed studies of these gneisses, however, have failed to identify vesuvianite in any of the gneisses of the Nebo Inlier (J.M. Horák, *personal communication*).

Vivianite   Monoclinic
$Fe_3(PO_4)_2.8H_2O$

An iron phosphate hydrate, belonging to the vivianite group of minerals.

Vivianite occurring on an iron fragment found in a peat bog at Valley, on Anglesey, is preserved in the Mineral Collection of the National Museum of Wales as specimen NMW 43.282.GR1 (confirmation by X-ray diffraction analysis number NMW X-283). A more recent identification, again confirmed by X-ray diffraction in the National Museum of Wales, is in boulder clay during excavation of a culvert at Threapwood, in Clwyd (S. Conway, *personal communication*).

Wavellite   Orthorhombic
$Al_3(PO_4)_2(OH,F)_3.5H_2O$

An aluminium phosphate hydroxide fluoride hydrate, typically found as globular thin radiating aggregates on fractures or joints in aluminium-rich sedimentary or metamorphic rocks.

The first written record of wavellite in Wales was by W.E. Logan in 1837, in a report in the Swansea

Figure 118. Radiating aggregates of wavellite, up to 8 mm in diameter, from Cil Ifor Hill, Llanrhidian, West Glamorgan. Collected July 1987. I. Jones Collection.

Philosophical and Literary Institution Proceedings of the Second Annual Meeting, describing (p. 23) the presence of the mineral at Cil Ifor Hill, near Llanridian, on the Gower Peninsula, in West Glamorgan, occurring in fractures in a whitish yellow sandstone. Logan stated that the mineral 'has been observed to abound in all the quarries in which the rock is exposed, to the distance of two miles east of Cil Ifor'. He stated also that the identification is of interest because 'they confirm Mr Conybeare's discovery of this mineral in the South Wales coal basin'. This is almost certainly a reference to W.D. Conybeare, although no published account of his discovery is known, neither are any more specific details of Conybeare's discovery.

De La Beche (1846) made a passing reference to Logan's report of wavellite from the Gower, while Strahan (1907) described wavellite from roadside sections between Clyne Common and Bishopston, also on Gower, occurring as 'discs of radiating crystals' in joints of the harder bands of a sequence of bedded clays with thin seams of limestone and chert. During subsequent road widening, Trueman (1930) noted that the wavellite was most abundant at this locality along faults, where the cherts are brecciated, and that it forms botryoidal masses filling the spaces between the chert clasts. Strahan (1907) also reported wavellite from the cliff top at Pwll-du Head, Gower, present in cracks in the clayey matrix of light-coloured clays and sandstones, forming sea-green acicular, radiating crystals.

Further west, wavellite was recorded by Dixon (1921) from three localities in Dyfed; firstly, in a lane west of Gumfreston in striped cherts of Carboniferous age; secondly in chert-debris at Lydstep Lodge; and thirdly in shales exposed in the valley-bottom a short distance to the north-west.

Winchite   Monoclinic
$NaCa(Mg,Fe^{+2})_4AlSi_8O_{22}(OH)_2$
A sodium calcium iron magnesium aluminium silicate hydroxide of the amphibole group, forming a series with ferrowinchite. Winchite is a rock-forming mineral, found in certain igneous and metamorphic rocks.

Greenly (1919) reported that blue amphiboles in mica schists of the Mona Complex exposed beneath the Marquis of Anglesey's Monument near Llanfairpwllgwyngyll on Anglesey possess green hornblende cores. Electron microprobe analyses by Gibbons and Gyopari (1986) demonstrated, however, that these green amphiboles fall in the range barroisite-ferrobarroisite-winchite. Further occurrences of such amphiboles were reported by Gibbons and Gyopari (1986) from temporary roadcuttings related to construction of the Llanfairpwllgwyngyll bypass. These occurrences represented the first verified description of winchite in the British Isles.

Witherite   Orthorhombic
$BaCO_3$
A barium carbonate belonging to the aragonite group of minerals, found in low temperature mineral veins associated with barite and calcite.

One of the earliest records of witherite in Wales is by Greg and Lettsom (1858), from 'Flintshire, near St. Asaph', which almost certainly was referring to Pennant Mine, located some 5 km east of St. Asaph, Clwyd. Carruthers *et al.* (1915) confirmed the presence of witherite at Pennant Mine, where it occurs in pockets in association with barite in lead- and zinc-bearing veins. Carruthers *et al.* (1915) also reported witherite from various mines in the Llangynog district, namely the Cwm Orog, Craig Rhiwarth, Craig-y-Mwyn and Llangynog Mines. Fine specimens of witherite from Cwm Orog are preserved in the Mineral Collection of the National Museum of Wales as specimens NMW 87.21G.M24 and M29. In addition, a specimen in the National Museum of Wales, registration number NMW 83.41G.M5435 (formerly in the R.J. King Collection, number K1093) is labelled 'witherite with calcite, Halkyn Mines, Flintshire'.

In Mid Wales, witherite is recorded from the eastern part of the Central Wales Mining District (Carruthers *et al.,* 1915), in particular abundance at the Pen-y-clun and Gorn Mines, and in lesser amounts at the Aberdaunant and Bryntail Mines. At these localities it is again associated with barite in lead- and zinc-bearing veins. Morgan and Starkey (1991) recorded colourless to white, translucent to transparent witherite crystals up to 20 mm across from Pen-y-clun Mine.

In South Wales, the only known occurrence of witherite is from the Llantrisant area of Mid Glamorgan (Bowler and Kingston, 1971; Alabaster, 1990), where it occurs in cavities in Triassic Dolomite Conglomerate, associated with alstonite, calcite, barite, galena, pyrite, and sphalerite at various mine sites (eg. Cefn Parc Mine, and from an old mine dump in the vicinity of Rhiwsaeson).

Woodwardite   ?
$Cu_4Al_2(SO_4)(OH)_{12}.2\text{-}4H_2O(?)$
An inadequately described copper aluminium sulphate hydroxide hydrate.

Braithwaite (1982a) described the occurrence of pale blue botryoidal coatings at Nantycagl (Eaglebrook) Mine, Dyfed, which give an infra-red spectrum and X-ray diffraction pattern similar to that of woodwardite. The 'woodwardite' X-ray diffraction powder pattern in the JCPDS file, from Simmde Dylluan, Drws-y-Coed, near Nantlle, Gwynedd (from National Museum of Wales specimen NMW 27.111.GR464) is almost certainly not woodwardite (Nickel, 1976), and has been identified as the copper analogue of glaucocerinite (Raade *et al.,* 1985). Similar material was also collected from Drws-y-Coed Mine in 1969 (G. Ryback, *personal communication*), on a specimen now in the Mineral Collection of the National Museum of Wales as NMW 86.58G.M1.

Wroewolfeite   Monoclinic
$Cu_4(SO_4)(OH)_6.2H_2O$
A copper sulphate hydroxide hydrate, dimorphous with langite and found in the oxidized zone of copper-bearing ore deposits.

Figure 119. Wroewolfeite crystals up to 1 mm long, collected in 1970 from Nantycagl Mine, near Ponterwyd, in the Central Wales Mining District. NMW specimen 87.43G.M36, *ex* A. Dean Collection.

The first description of the mineral wroewolfeite was by Dunn and Rouse (1975), on material from Loudville lead mine, Loudville, Massachusetts, U.S.A. In their account, however, Dunn and Rouse made reference to 'a recent communication' from the late Dr M.H. Hey, of the Natural History Museum, stating the existence of samples of wroewolfeite from Ladywell Mine, Shelve, Shropshire and from Nantycagal (Eaglebrook) Mine, Ceulanymaesmawr, Dyfed in the collections of the Natural History Museum. These specimens were collected by Dr R.S.W. Braithwaite and colleagues during the early to mid 1960s, and were sent to the Natural History Museum for identification. It was not until the work of Dunn and Rouse (1975), however, that their true identity was established. A more complete description of these and other occurrences of wroewolfeite in Britain is provided by Braithwaite (1982a). At Nantycagl (Eaglebrook) Mine, Dyfed, wroewolfeite forms clear, sharp, greenish-blue blades with rectangular, chisel-shaped terminations, associated with linarite and brochantite. Elsewhere in the Central Wales Mining District wroewolfeite has been found at Esgair Hir (see Rust and Mason, 1988), Dylife (Rust and Rust, 1987), Frongoch and Darren Mines, all confirmed by X-ray diffraction at the Natural History Museum, and also Llechweddhelyg Mine (J.S. Mason, *personal*

communication). At Drws-y-Coed Mine in Gwynedd, Braithwaite (1982) described wroewolfeite forming greenish-blue blades between 0.1 and 1 mm in length on calcite.

Wroewolfeite has also been identified at Glasdir Mine, Gwynedd as aggregates of blue microcrystals with malachite on shale, with identification confirmed by infrared spectra analysis (G. Ryback, *personal communication*).

Wulfenite   Tetragonal
$PbMoO_4$
A lead molybdate, typically found in the oxidized zone of lead-bearing ore deposits.

The first mention of supposed wulfenite in Wales was by Perceval (1866a), who identified small, well-formed, tabular, brown to honey-yellow bevelled crystals in rhyolite from Treffgarne Rocks, Dyfed, as being wulfenite. In the same year, however, he corrected his original identification, stating that the crystals were in fact brookite (Perceval, 1886b).

The first confirmed report of wulfenite from Wales was much later, by Ryback and Saville (1967), who identified the mineral from workings and dumps in the

Figure 120. Bipyramidal wulfenite crystals on pyromorphite from Bwlchglas Mine, near Talybont, in the Central Wales Mining District. Field of view 0.3 mm across. NMW specimen 83.24G.M1, *ex* R.E. Starkey.

Figure 121. Tabular wulfenite crystal from Llechweddhelyg Mine, in the Central Wales Mining District. The crystal measures 5 mm along the edge. J.S. Mason Collection.

colour and are characterised by an acute bipyramidal habit. Further reports of wulfenite in the Central Wales Mining District include those from Bwlchrhennaid Mine (*British Micromount Society Newsletter*, No. 20), Llechweddhelyg Mine (Jones, 1987), Mynyddgorddu Mine (Clark and Rust, 1993), and Esgair Hir Mine (Rust and Mason, 1988). Recently, Mason (1992) has provided an extensive review of the distribution of wulfenite in the Central Wales Mining District, reporting additional occurrences, invariably in association with pyromorphite, at the following mines in Dyfed: Alltycrib (Talybont), Cwmdarren (Trefeirig), Darren (Pen-Bont Rhydy-beddau), Esgairfraith (Talybont), Henfwlch (Talybont), Nantycagl (Eaglebrook, Talybont), Pandy Mine (Tre'r-ddol), and Penybanc Mine (Talybont), and in Powys: Aberdaunant (Llanidloes), Geufron (Llanidloes), South Nantycar (Rhayader), and Ystrad Einion (Eglwysfach).

Wulfenite has also been recorded from the Llangynog district, Powys, at Cwm Orog Mine (*British Micromount Society Newsletter*, No. 20).

Figure 122. Tabular wulfenite crystals up to 1 mm across from the Bwlchglas Mine, near Talybont, in the Central Wales Mining District. J.S. Mason Collection.

vicinity of Ysbyty Ystwyth, Dyfed. They described three occurrences: on the dumps of the Eastern or Pen-y-bwlch shaft on the Glogfawr lode, as very thin, clear rectangular plates and orange-brown translucent elongated bipyramids with convex curved edges, associated with pyromorphite on shale or gossan; from a small dump along the lode towards Pen-y-bwlch shaft, as groups of clear, honey-brown, thick, bevelled plates or orange-brown translucent bipyramids, on shales and cavernous mudstones with pyromorphite and drusy quartz; and on a dump from an adit driven 100 yards ENE of Taylor's or East Glog-Fach shaft, as orange-brown translucent bipyramids with pyromorphite. Jones and Moreton (1977) also record the mineral as yellow microcrystals from Dyfngwm Mine, Powys, and as microcrystals from Dylife, Powys.

A later description of wulfenite from the Central Wales Mining District was provided by Braithwaite (1982), on the basis of identification of the mineral at Bwlchglas Mine, Dyfed, in 1968. As elsewhere in the district, it is typically closely associated with pyromorphite and cerussite. Braithwaite (1982b) identified two generations of crystals, the earlier ones being yellowish-orange and of bipyramidal habit, although a few of short prismatic form terminated with basal planes were also encountered, while the later ones are reddish-orange in

The first occurrence of wulfenite in Mid Glamorgan was reported by Braithwaite and Lamb (1986) from Tŷ Coch Mine, where it occurs associated with calcite, forming orange to yellow to greyish-white, bevelled, rectangular, platy crystals up to 3 x 3 x 0.5 mm (although most typically 1-2 mm across) in size.

Xenotime-(Y)   Tetragonal
YPO_4
An yttrium phosphate which forms a series with chernovite-(Y). Xenotime-(Y) is found typically as an accessory phase in acidic igneous rocks, such as granites, pegmatites and rhyolites.

Xenotime has been identified by back-scatter electron microscopy combined with energy dispersive analysis in rhyolitic tuffs of Ordovician age exposed on Ramsey Island, Dyfed (author's unpublished data). In Snowdonia xenotime occurs overgrowing rounded zircons in altered

Figure 123. Pale brown, prismatic xenotime crystal (left of centre) associated with red-brown anatase crystal (1.5 mm in size) and colourless prismatic quartz crystal from Hendre Quarry, near Glyn Ceiriog, Clwyd. Collected January 1988. N. Hubbard Collection.

rhyolites from Cerrig Cochion, and as small dispersed grains in altered rhyolites from Castell Yr Arddu (A.T. Kearsley, *personal communication*; Howells *et al.*, 1991), as well as forming small detrital and diagenetic grains in Ordovician mudstones from the Aberangell area (National Museum of Wales specimens NMW 85.13G.M1-M3). Bennett (1987a) recorded an yttrium-rich phosphate mineral (presumably xenotime) in pyritic mudstones of the Haffoty Formation of Cambrian age exposed in the Harlech Dome area of Gwynedd.

Recently sharp, golden, tetragonal, prismatic xenotime crystals up to 0.5 mm in length on albite associated with anatase have been reported from low temperature alter-

ation veins cutting dolerite at Hendre Quarry near Glyn Ceiriog, Clwyd (Starkey *et al.*, 1991). A specimen of xenotime from this locality is preserved in the Mineral Collection of the National Museum of Wales, registration number NMW 87.36G.M1 (donated by N. Hubbard).

Zinkenite   Hexagonal
$Pb_9Sb_{22}S_{42}$
A lead antimony sulphosalt, typically found in association with stibnite and other sulphosalt minerals in low temperature mineral veins.

Zinkenite occurs at Bwlch Mine, near Deganwy, Gwynedd, where it is present in association with stibnite, semseyite, plagionite, jamesonite and possible robinsonite (Bevins *et al.*, 1988).

Zircon   Tetragonal
$ZrSiO_4$
A zirconium silicate which is a common accessory mineral in igneous rocks such as granite and granodiorite, and also in pegmatites. Zircon is also found as a detrital mineral in sedimentary rocks.

Zircon is probably widespread in Wales, although specific references are few. It occurs widely as an accessory mineral in volcanic rocks, such as rhyolite and rhyolitic tuffs, and also in intrusive rocks such as microgranite and granite.

In North Pembrokeshire, zircon is a minor component of many of the more silicic igneous rocks, such as rhyolites of the Fishguard area (Bevins, 1982), intrusive porphyritic rhyolites on Ramsey Island (Kokelaar *et al.*, 1985), and more silicic compositions in the St. David's Head Intrusion (Bevins *et al.*, 1991).

In Snowdonia zircon is again a minor component in many silicic igneous rocks. Bromley (1969) recorded zircon as a common accessory mineral in various microgranites and granophyres, as well as in certain extrusive rhyolitic rocks in the area. This was supported by the more recent work of Howells *et al.* (1991). In southern Snowdonia, zircon, overgrown by xenotime and thorite, is found in Ordovician mudstones in the Aberangell district (A.T. Kearsley, *personal communication*). Elsewhere in North Wales, Croudace (1982) noted zircon to be an accessory mineral in many of the microtonalitic and granitoid rocks of Lower Palaeozoic age exposed across the Llŷn Peninsula.

Zircon is also found as a detrital phase in certain sandstones. Boswell (1927) recorded detrital purple zircon in sandstones of Silurian, Devonian, Carboniferous and Triassic age in different parts of Wales. More specifically, Heard (1922) reported the presence of abundant detrital zircon in sandstones of Carboniferous ('Pennant') age, east of the River Taff, in South Wales. Griffiths and Stuart (1940) also found zircon to be a component of sandy boulder clay exposed at Ludchurch, in Dyfed. Finally, zircon is probably abundant in many soils across Wales, in particular those in areas where volcanic rocks are present, for example in Snowdonia (see Jenkins, 1964).

Zoisite   Orthorhombic
Ca$_2$Al$_3$(SiO$_4$)$_3$OH
Zoisite is a calcium aluminium silicate hydroxide, typically a product of low to medium grade metamorphism.

Greenly (1919) reported the presence of zoisite in various units on Anglesey, as for example in mica schists of the New Harbour Group, in diorites, mica-schists and hornblende schists in the Penmynydd Zone, and in hornblende gneisses of the Mona Complex. However, Greenly stated that in the hornblende schists it is 'always a clino-zoisite', and thus is not specifically referring to the presence of true zoisite.

Sargent (1925) described the presence of zoisite forming thin tabular imbricated crystals in association with axinite and quartz in veins cutting the Penmaenmawr Intrusion, Gwynedd.

REFERENCES

ADAMS, W. 1867. On the "Coal Brasses" of the South Wales coal fields. *Transactions of the South Wales Institute of Engineers,* **5**, 190-196.

ADAMS, W.A., AND KASSIM, J.K. 1984. Iron oxyhydroxides in soils developed from Lower Palaeozoic sedimentary rocks in mid-Wales and implications for some pedogenetic processes. *Journal of Soil Science,* **35**, 117-126.

AIKIN, A. 1797. *Journal of a tour through North Wales and part of Shropshire, with observations in mineralogy and other branches of natural history.* London, 231pp.

ALABASTER, C. 1983. Native sulphur from Stancombe Quarry, Flax Bourton and Dan-y-graig Quarry, Risca (South Wales). *Proceedings of the Bristol Naturalists' Society,* **43**, 13-27.

ALABASTER, C. 1990. Alstonite and barytocalcite from Llantrisant, South Wales and barytocalcite from Holwell, Mendip Hills, England. *Journal of the Russell Society,* **3**, 1-6.

ALKATTAN, M.M. 1976. *The geochemistry of lower Keuper Marl at Lavernock Point, Glamorgan, South Wales.* Unpublished M.Sc. thesis, University of Wales.

ALLEN, P.M., and EASTERBROOK, G.D. 1978. Mineralised breccia pipe and other intrusion breccias in the Harlech Dome, N. Wales. *Transactions of the Institution of Mining and Metallurgy (Section B; Applied earth science),* **87**, B157-B161.

ALLEN, P.M., and JACKSON, A.A. 1985. Geology of the country around Harlech. *Memoirs of the British Geological Survey.* Explanation of Sheet 135, with part of 149, 112pp.

ALWAN, A.K., and WILLIAMS, P.A. 1979. Nickeloan hydrozincite: a new variety. *Mineralogical Magazine,* **43**, 397-398.

ANDREW, A.R. 1910. The geology of the Dolgelley gold-belt, North Wales. *Geological Magazine,* **47**, 159-171, 201-221, 261-271.

ANNELS, A.E., and ROBERTS, D.E. 1989. Turbidite-hosted gold mineralization at the Dolaucothi Gold Mines, Dyfed, Wales, United Kingdom. *Economic Geology,* **84**, 1293-1314.

ARCHER, A.A., and ELLIOT, R.W. 1965. The occurrence of olivine-dolerite dykes near Llanrwst, North Wales. *Bulletin of the Geological Survey of Great Britain,* **23**, 145-152.

ASHTON, J.H. 1981. *Wallrock geochemistry and ore geology of certain mineralized veins in Wales.* Unpublished Ph.D. thesis, University of Wales, Aberystwyth.

BALL, D.F. 1964. Gibbsite in altered granitic rock in North Wales. *Nature,* **204**, 673-674.

BALL, D.F. 1969. Basaluminite from Cambrian rocks near Harlech. *Mineralogical Magazine,* **37**, 291-293.

BALL, T.K., and BLAND, D.J. 1985. The Cae Coch volcanogenic massive sulphide deposit, Trefriw, North Wales. *Journal of the Geological Society, London,* **142**, 889-898.

BALL, T.K., and NUTT, M.J.C. 1976. Preliminary mineral reconnaisance of Central Wales. *Report of the Institute of Geological Sciences,* No. 75/14, 12pp.

BANNISTER, F.A. 1943. Brammallite (sodium-illite), a new mineral from Llandebie, South Wales. *Mineralogical Magazine,* **26**, 304-307.

BANNISTER, F.A., HEY, M.H., and CAMPBELL SMITH, W. 1955. Grovesite, the manganese-rich analogue of berthierine. *Mineralogical Magazine,* **30**, 645-647.

BAQRI, R., and HODSON, F. 1979. Apatite in South Wales anthracite. *Geological Magazine,* **116**, 483-486.

BAYLISS, P. 1975. Nomenclature of the trioctahedral chlorites. *Canadian Mineralogist,* **13**, 178-180.

BEAVON, R.V. 1963. The succession and structure east of the Glaslyn River, North Wales. *Quarterly Journal of the Geological Society of London,* **119**, 479-512.

BENNETT, M.A. 1987a. *The Cambrian manganese deposits of North Wales.* Unpublished Ph.D. thesis, University of Leeds.

BENNETT, M.A. 1987b. Genesis and diagenesis of the Cambrian manganese deposits, Harlech, North Wales. *Geological Journal,* **22**, 7-18.

BÉTHUNE, S. de. 1972. Etude a la microsonde électronique des minéraux métamorphiques du Cambrien de Harlech (Pays de Galles). *Bulletin de la Société Belge de Géologie de Paléontologie et d'Hydrologie,* **81**, 255-265.

BEVINS, R.E. 1978. Pumpellyite-bearing basic igneous rocks from the Lower Ordovician of North Pembrokeshire. *Mineralogical Magazine,* **42**, 81-83.

BEVINS, R.E. 1979. *The geology of the Strumble Head-Fishguard region, Dyfed, Wales.* Unpublished Ph.D. thesis, University of Keele, 256pp.

BEVINS, R.E. 1982. Petrology and geochemistry of the Fishguard Volcanic Complex, Wales. *Geological Journal,* **17**, 1-21.

BEVINS, R.E. 1985. Pumpellyite-dominated metadomain alteration at Builth Wells, Wales - evidence for a fossil submarine hydrothermal system? *Mineralogical Magazine,* **49**, 451-456.

BEVINS, R.E., and HORÁK, J.M. 1985. Siegenite in clay-ironstone nodules from the South Wales Coalfield. *Journal of the Russell Society,* **1**, 83-85.

BEVINS, R.E., and MERRIMAN, R.J. 1988. Compositional controls on coexisting prehnite-actinolite and prehnite-pumpellyite facies assemblages in the Tal y Fan metabasite intrusion, North Wales: implications for Caledonian metamorphic field gradients. *Journal of Metamorphic Geology,* **6**, 17-39.

BEVINS, R.E., and ROACH, R.A. 1982. Ordovician igneous

activity in south-west Dyfed. *In:* Bassett, M.G. (ed.) *Geological excursions in Dyfed, south-west Wales.* National Museum of Wales, Cardiff, 65-80.

BEVINS, R.E., and ROBINSON, D. 1993. Parageneses of Ordovician sub-greenschist to greenschist facies metabasites from Wales, U.K. *European Journal of Mineralogy,* **5,** 925-935.

BEVINS, R.E., and ROWBOTHAM, G. 1983. Low-grade metamorphism within the Welsh sector of the paratectonic Caledonides. *Geological Journal,* **18,** 141-167.

BEVINS, R.E., and STANLEY, C.J. 1990. Aleksite, a lead bismuth sulfotelluride: a second world occurrence from the Dolgellau Gold Belt, Gwynedd, Wales. *Journal of the Russell Society,* **3,** 67-69.

BEVINS, R.E., ALDERTON, D.H.M., and HORÁK, J.M. 1988. Lead-antimony mineralization at Bwlch Mine, Deganwy, Wales. *Mineralogical Magazine,* **52,** 391-394.

BEVINS, R.E., LEES, G.J., and ROACH, R.A. 1991. Ordovician bimodal volcanism in SW Wales: geochemical evidence for petrogenesis of the silicic rocks. *Journal of the Geological Society, London,* **148,** 719-729.

BEVINS, R.E., LEES, G.J., ROACH, R.A., ROWBOTHAM, G., and FLOYD, P.A. *In press.* Petrogenesis of the St. David's Head Layered Intrusion, Wales: a complex history of multiple magma injection and *in situ* crystallization. *Transactions of the Royal Society of Edinburgh.*

BEVINS, R.E., METCALFE, R., and ROBINSON, D. 1993. Temporal variations in water-rock interaction as a control on pumpellyite formation. *Terra Abstracts,* **5,** 413.

BEVINS, R.E., O'BRIEN, P., TURGOOSE, S., and WILLIAMS, P.A. 1982. A new find of nickeloan hydrozincite in the Parc Mine, North Wales. *Journal of the Russell Society,* **1,** 19-21.

BEVINS, R.E., ROWBOTHAM, G., STEPHENS, F.S., TURGOOSE, S., AND WILLIAMS, P.A. 1985. Lanthanite-(Ce), $(Ce,La,Nd)_2(CO_3)_3.8H_2O$, a new mineral from Wales, U.K. *American Mineralogist,* **70,** 411-413.

BEVINS, R.E., TURGOOSE, S., and WILLIAMS, P.A. 1982a. Namuwite, $(Zn,Cu)_4SO_4(OH)_6.4H_2O$, a new mineral from Wales. *Mineralogical Magazine,* **46,** 51-54.

BEVINS, R.E., TURGOOSE, S., and WILLIAMS, P.A. 1982b. Some new minerals from Wales. *Nature in Wales (new series),* **1** (2), 66-68.

BICK, D.E. 1974. *The Old Metal Mines Of Wales. Part 1, Cardiganshire - South of Devil's Bridge.* Pound House, Newent.

BICK, D.E. 1975. *The Old Metal Mines Of Wales. Part 2, The Rheidol to Goginan.* Pound House, Newent.

BICK, D.E. 1976. *The Old Metal Mines Of Wales. Part 3, Cardiganshire - North of Goginan.* Pound House, Newent.

BICK, D.E. 1977. *The Old Metal Mines Of Wales. Part 4, West Montgomeryshire.* Pound House, Newent.

BICK, D.E. 1978. *The Old Metal Mines Of Wales. Part 5, Aberdovey, Dinas Mawddwy and Llangynog.* Pound House, Newent.

BICK, D.E. 1982. *The Old Copper Mines of Snowdonia.* Pound House, Newent.

BICK, D.E. 1991. *The Old Metal Mines Of Wales. Part 6, A Miscellany.* Pound House, Newent.

BINSTOCK, J.L.H. 1977. *Petrology and sedimentation of the Cambrian manganese-rich sediments of the Harlech Dome, North Wales.* Unpublished Ph.D. thesis, Harvard University.

BLAKE, J.F. 1888. The occurrence of a glaucophane-bearing rock in Anglesey. *Geological Magazine,* **5,** 125-127.

BLOXAM, T.W., AND DIRK, M.H.J. 1988. The petrology and geochemistry of the St. David's granophyre and the Cwm Bach rhyolite, Pembrokeshire, Dyfed. *Mineralogical Magazine,* **52,** 563-575.

BLOXAM, T.W., and PRICE, N.B. 1961. Stilpnomelane in North Wales. *Nature,* **190,** 525-526.

BONNEY, T.G. 1888. On a peculiar variety of hornblende from Mynydd Mawr, Carnarvonshire. *Mineralogical Magazine,* **8,** 103-107.

BOR, L. 1950. Pisanite from Parys Mountain, Anglesey. *Mineralogical Magazine,* **29,** 63-67.

BOSWELL, P.G.H. 1927. On the distribution of purple zircon in British sedimentary rocks. *Mineralogical Magazine,* **21,** 310-317.

BOTTRELL, S.H. 1986. *The origin of the gold mineralization of the Dolgellau district, North Wales: the chemistry and role of the fluids.* Unpublished Ph. D. thesis, University of East Anglia.

BOTTRELL, S.H., and MILLER, M.F. 1990. The geochemical behaviour of nitrogen compounds during the formation of black shale-hosted quartz vein deposits in North Wales. *Applied Geochemistry,* **5,** 289-296.

BOTTRELL, S.H., AND MORTON, M.D.B. 1992. A reinterpretation of the genesis of the Cae Coch pyrite deposit, North Wales. *Journal of the Geological Society, London,* **149,** 581-584.

BOTTRELL, S.H., and SPIRO, B. 1988. A stable isotope study of black shale-hosted gold mineralization in the Dolgellau Gold Belt, North Wales. *Journal of the Geological Society, London,* **145,** 941-949.

BOTTRELL, S.H., GREENWOOD, P.B., YARDLEY, B.W.D., SHEPHERD, T.J., and SPIRO, B. 1990. Metamorphic and post-metamorphic fluid flow in low grade rocks of the Harlech Dome, N. Wales. *Journal of Metamorphic Geology,* **8,** 131-143.

BOTTRELL, S.H., SHEPHERD, T.J., YARDLEY, B.W.D., and DUBESSY, J. 1988. A fluid inclusion model for the genesis of the ores of the Dolgellau Gold Belt, North Wales. *Journal of the Geological Society, London,* **145,** 139-145.

BOULTON, W.S. 1911. On a monchiquite intrusion in the Old Red Sandstone of Monmouthshire. *Quarterly Journal of the Geological Society of London,* **67,** 460-476.

BOWLER, C.M.L., and KINGSTON, G.A. 1971. Mineralisation in the Triassic rocks of the Llantrisant area, Glamorgan. *1970 Gregynog Mineral Exploitation Colloquium Report.* University College Cardiff, 30-34.

BRAITHWAITE, R.S.W. 1982a. Wroewolfeite in Britain. *Mineralogical Record,* **13,** 167-174.

BRAITHWAITE, R.S.W. 1982b. Pyromorphite, wulfenite and other minerals from the Bwlch-Glas Mine, Central Wales. *Mineralogical Record,* **13,** 151-153.

BRAITHWAITE, R.S.W., and LAMB, R.P.H. 1986. Wulfenite from Tŷ Coch, Glamorgan (Powys), South Wales.

Mineralogical Magazine, **50,** 180-181.

BRAMMALL, A., LEECH, J.G.C., and BANNISTER, F.A. 1937. The paragenesis of cookeite and hydromuscovite associated with gold at Ogofau, Carmarthenshire. *Mineralogical Magazine,* **24,** 507-521.

BREARLEY, A.J. 1988. Chloritoid from low-grade pelitic rocks in North Wales. *Mineralogical Magazine,* **52,** 394-396.

BROMLEY, A.V. 1964. Allanite in the Tan-y-Grisiau Microgranite, Merionethshire, North Wales. *American Mineralogist,* **49,** 1747-1752.

BROMLEY, A.V. 1969. Acid plutonic igneous activity in the Ordovician of North Wales. *In:* Wood, A. (ed.) *The Pre-Cambrian and Lower Palaeozoic rocks of Wales.* University of Wales Press, 387-408.

BROWN, G. 1953. The occurrence of lepidocrocite in some British soils. *Journal of Soil Science,* **4,** 220-228.

BROWN, G., and SMITHSON, F. 1953. Distribution of dickite in some British sandstones. *Nature,* **172,** 317.

BROWN M.J., and EVANS, A.D. 1989. Geophysical and geochemical investigations of the manganese deposits of Rhiw, western Llŷn, North Wales. *British Geological Survey Technical Report WF/89/14 (BGS Mineral Reconnaissance Programme Report,* No. 102).

BROWN, M.J., and OTHERS. 1987. Volcanogenic mineralisation in the Treffgarne area, south-west Dyfed, Wales. *Mineral Reconnaissance Programme Report, British Geological Survey,* No. 86.

BROWN, P.E. 1959. A note on pyrosmalite from Nant Francon, North Wales. *Mineralogical Magazine,* **32,** 242-244.

CALVERT, J. 1853. *Gold rocks in Great Britain and Ireland.* London, 324pp.

CAMPBELL, S.D.G., REEDMAN, A.J., HOWELLS, M.F., and MANN, A.C. 1987. The emplacement of geochemically distinct groups of rhyolites during the evolution of the Lower Rhyolitic Tuff Formation caldera (Ordovician), North Wales, U.K. *Geological Magazine,* **124,** 501-511.

CAMPBELL SMITH, W. 1913. The mineral collection of Thomas Pennant (1726-1798). *Mineralogical Magazine,* **16,** 331-342.

CAMPBELL SMITH, W. 1945. Banalsite crystals from Wales. *Mineralogical Magazine,* **27,** 63-64.

CAMPBELL SMITH, W. 1948. Ganophyllite from the Benallt Mine, Rhiw, Caernarvonshire. *Mineralogical Magazine,* **28,** 343-352.

CAMPBELL SMITH, W., and CLARINGBULL, G.F. 1947. Pyrophanite from the Benallt mine, Rhiw, Carnarvonshire. *Mineralogical Magazine,* **28,** 108-110.

CAMPBELL SMITH, W., BANNISTER, F.A., and HEY, M.H. 1944a. A new barium-feldspar from Wales. *Nature,* **154,** 336-337.

CAMPBELL SMITH, W., BANNISTER, F.A., and HEY, M.H. 1944b. Banalsite, a new barium-felspar from Wales. *Mineralogical Magazine,* **27,** 33-46.

CAMPBELL SMITH, W., BANNISTER, F.A., and HEY, M.H. 1946. Pennantite, a new manganese-rich chlorite from Benallt mine, Rhiw, Carnarvonshire. *Mineralogical Magazine,* **27,** 217-220.

CAMPBELL SMITH, W., BANNISTER, F.A., and HEY, M.H. 1949. Cymrite, a new barium mineral from the Benallt manganese mine, Rhiw, Carnarvonshire. *Mineralogical Magazine,* **28,** 676-681.

CARRUTHERS, R.G., EASTWOOD, T., WILSON, G.V., POCOCK, R.W., and WRAY, D.A. 1915. Barytes and witherite. *Memoirs of the Geological Survey. Special Reports on the Mineral Resources of Great Britain,* **2.**

CARRUTHERS, R.G., POCOCK, R.W., and WRAY, D.A. 1916. Fluorspar. *Memoirs of the Geological Survey. Special Reports on the Mineral Resources of Great Britain,* **4.**

CATTERMOLE, P.J. 1976. The crystallization and differentiation of a layered intrusion of hydrated alkali olivine-basalt parentage at Rhiw, North Wales. *Geological Journal,* **11,** 45-70.

CLARK, A.M., and RUST, S.A. 1993. Bottinoite, a new mineral to Britain. *Mineralogical Magazine,* **57,** 543-544.

CLARK, A.M., EASTON, A.J., JONES, G.C., and MOUNT, M. 1978. A study of the neotocite group. *Mineralogical Magazine,* **42,** M26-M30.

CLAXTON, C.W. 1963. An occurrence of regionally metamorphosed Pre-Cambrian schists in South-West Pembrokeshire. *Geological Magazine,* **100,** 219-223.

CLOIZEAUX, A.L. DES. 1880. *Bulletin de la Société Française de Minéralogie,* **3,** 170-171.

CLOIZEAUX, A.L. DES. 1893. *Manuel de Minéralogie,* **II.** Paris, 305-306.

CONYBEARE, J.J. 1821. Description of a new substance found in ironstone. *Annals of Philosophy,* **1,** 136-137.

CONYBEARE, J.J. 1823. On hatchettine. *Annals of Philosophy,* **5,** 190.

CONYBEARE, W.D., and PHILLIPS, W. 1822. *Outlines of the geology of England and Wales.* W. Phillips, London, 471pp.

COOPER, D.C., BASHAM, I.R., and SMITH, T.K. 1983. On the occurrence of an unusual form of monazite in panned stream sediments in Wales. *Geological Journal,* **18,** 121-127.

COPE, J.C.W. 1982. The geology of the Llanstephan Peninsula. *In:* Bassett, M. G. (ed.) *Geological Excursions in Dyfed, South-West Wales, National Museum of Wales,* 259-269.

COPE, J.C.W., and BEVINS, R.E. 1993. The stratigraphy and setting of the Precambrian rocks of the Llangynog Inlier, Dyfed, South Wales. *Geological Magazine,* **130,** 101-111.

COX, A.H. 1954. The Usk monchiquite, a 'pipe intrusion'. *Geological Magazine,* **91,** 519.

COX, A.H., and TRUEMAN, A.E. 1936. The Mesozoic Rocks. *In:* Tattersall, W.M. (ed.) *Glamorgan County History, No. 1, Natural History.* William Lewis, Cardiff, 19-59.

COX, A.H., and WELLS, A.K. 1920. The Lower Palaeozoic rocks of the Arthog-Dolgelley district. *Quarterly Journal of the Geological Society of London,* **76,** 254-324.

COX, A.H., and WELLS, A.K. 1927. The geology of the Dolgelley district, Merionethshire. *Proceedings of the Geologists' Association,* **38,** 265-318.

CRIDDLE, A.J., and SYMES, R.F. 1977. Mineralization at Tŷ Coch, Glamorgan (Mid Glamorgan), Wales: the second occurrence of pyrobelonite. *Mineralogical Magazine*, **41**, 85-90.

CROUDACE, I.W. 1982. The geochemistry and petrogenesis of the Lower Palaeozoic granitoids of the Lleyn Peninsula, North Wales. *Geochimica et Cosmochimica Acta*, **46**, 609-622.

DANA, J.D. 1868. *A System of Mineralogy*. 5th Edition. John Wiley, New York.

DAVIES, E.C., and BLOXAM, T.W. 1990. Petrology and geochemistry of late Precambrian volcanic rocks of the St. David's area, Pembrokeshire, South Wales (U.K.). *Geologie en Mijnbouw*, **69**, 407-416.

DAVIES, H. 1948. A gold mining legend of Pembrokeshire. *Quarry Manager's Journal*, **December**, 328-331.

DEAN, A. 1845. Notice on the discovery of gold ores in Merionethshire, North Wales. *Report of the British Association for the Advancement of Science* (for 1844), 56.

DE LA BECHE, H.T. 1846. On the formation of the Rocks of South Wales and South Western England. *Memoirs of the Geological Survey*, **1**, 296pp.

DEWEY, H. 1920. Arsenic and antimony ores. *Memoirs of the Geological Survey. Special Reports on the Mineral Resources of Great Britain*, **15**.

DEWEY, H., and BROMEHEAD, C.E.N. 1915. Tungsten and manganese ores. *Memoirs of the Geological Survey. Special Reports on the Mineral Resources of Great Britain*, **1**.

DEWEY, H., and DINES, H.G. 1923. Tungsten and manganese ores. Third Edition. *Memoirs of the Geological Survey. Special Reports on the Mineral Resources of Great Britain*, **1**.

DEWEY, H., and EASTWOOD, T. 1925. Copper ores of the Midlands, Wales, the Lake District and the Isle of Man. *Memoirs of the Geological Survey. Special Report on the Mineral Resources of Great Britain*, **30**.

DEWEY, H., and SMITH, B. 1922. Lead and zinc ores in the pre-Carboniferous rocks of West Shropshire and North Wales. Part II, North Wales. *Memoirs of the Geological Survey. Special Report of the Mineral Resources of Great Britain*, **23**.

DICK, A. 1888. On kaolinite. *Mineralogical Magazine*, **8**, 15-27.

DICK, A. 1908. Supplementary note on the mineral kaolinite. *Mineralogical Magazine*, **15**, 124-127.

DIXON, E.E.L. 1921. The Geology of the South Wales Coalfield. Part XIII. The Country around Pembroke and Tenby. *Memoirs of the Geological Survey of England and Wales*. Explanation of Sheets 244 and 245.

DOWN, C.G. 1980. *The Manganese Mines of North Wales*. British Mining Monograph No.14, Northern Mine Research Society.

DUNN, P.J., and ROUSE, R.C. 1975. Wroewolfeite, a new copper sulphate hydroxide hydrate. *Mineralogical Magazine*, **40**, 1-5.

DUNN, P.J., PEACOR, D.R., NELEN, J.E., and RAMIK, R.A. 1983. Ganophyllite from Franklin, New Jersey; Pajsberg, Sweden; and Wales: new chemical data. *Mineralogical Magazine*, **47**, 563-566.

EAKIN, P.A. 1989. Isotopic and petrographic studies of uraniferous hydrocarbons from around the Irish Sea Basin. *Journal of the Geological Society, London*, **146**, 663-673.

EAKIN, P.A., and GIZE, A.P. 1992. Reflected-light microscopy of uraniferous bitumens. *Mineralogical Magazine*, **56**, 85-99.

ELSDEN, J.V. 1904. On the age of the Llyn-Padarn dykes. *Quarterly Journal of the Geological Society of London*, **60**, 372-388.

EMBREY, P.G. 1978. Fourth supplementary list of British minerals. *Mineralogical Magazine*, **42**, 169-177.

EVANS, C.D.R. 1968. *Geological succession and structure of the area east of Bethesda*. Unpublished Ph.D. thesis, University of Wales, Aberystwyth.

EVANS, R.B., and CHACKSFIELD, B.C. 1987. Magnetic anomalies in Snowdonia, North Wales, and their relationship to magnetite-rich sediments. *Report of the Regional Geophysics Research Group, British Geological Survey*, No.87/20.

EYLES, V.A., and BLUNDELL, C.R.K. 1957. On a volcanic vent and associated monchiquite intrusions in Monmouthshire. *Geological Magazine*, **94**, 54-57.

FEARNSIDES, W.G. 1908. The tourmaline rocks of Cwm Dwythwc, near Llanberis (North Wales). *Geological Magazine*, New Series, Decade 5, **5**, 465-466.

FEARNSIDES, W.G. 1910. Excursion to North Wales. *Proceedings of the Geologists' Association*, **21**, 368-390.

FEARNSIDES, W.G. 1912. Report on an excursion to the Portmadoc and Criccieth district of south-east Carnarvonshire. *Proceedings of the Geologists' Association*, **23**, 199-217.

FIRTH, J. N. M. 1971. *The Mineralogy of the South Wales Coalfield*. Unpublished Ph.D. thesis, University of Bristol.

FIRTH, J.N.M., AND EGLINTON, G. 1971. Hatchettite from the South Wales Coalfield. *Advances in Organic Geochemistry*, 613-628.

FLEISCHER, M., AND MANDARINO, J.A. 1991. *Glossary of mineral species, 1991*. Mineralogical Record Inc.

FLETCHER, C.J.N. 1988. Tidal erosion, solution cavities and exhalative mineralization associated with the Jurassic unconformity at Ogmore, South Glamorgan. *Proceedings of the Geologists' Association*, **99**, 1-14.

FLETCHER, C.J.N., and YOUNG, B.R. 1988. Rosasite from Bute Quarry, Mid Glamorgan. The first reported occurrence in Wales. *Journal of the Russell Society*, **2**(1), 19-23.

FLETCHER, C. J. N., SWAINBANK, I. G., and COLMAN, T. B. 1993. Metallogenic evolution in Wales: constraints from lead isotope modelling. *Journal of the Geological Society, London*, **150**, 77-82.

FORBES, D. 1867. Researches on British Mineralogy. *The London, Edinburgh and Dublin Philosophical Magazine and Journal of Science*, **34**, 329-354.

FORBES, D. 1868. Researches in British Mineralogy. *The London, Edinburgh and Dublin Philosophical Magazine and Journal of Science*, **35**, 171-184.

FOSTER, C. LE NEVE. 1882. On the occurrence of cobalt ores in Flintshire. *Transactions of the Royal Geological Society of Cornwall*, **10**, 107-112.

FREY, M. 1969. A mixed-layer paragonite/phengite of low-grade metamorphic origin. *Contributions to Mineralogy and Petrology*, **24**, 63-65.

GAYER, R.A., and CRIDDLE, A.J. 1970. Mineralogy and genesis of the Llanharry iron ore deposits, Glamorgan. *Proceedings of the Ninth Commonwealth Mining and Metallurgy Congress, London, 1969,* **2,** 605-626.

GAYER, R.A., and RICKARD, D. 1993. Gold in South Wales coal. *Nature,* **364,** 395.

GIBBONS, W. 1983. Stratigraphy, subduction and strike-slip faulting in the Mona Complex of North Wales - a review. *Proceedings of the Geologists' Association,* **94,** 147-163.

GIBBONS, W. 1987. Menai Strait fault system: an early Caledonian terrane boundary in North Wales. *Geology,* **15,** 744-747.

GIBBONS, W., AND GYOPARI, M. 1986. A greenschist protolith for blueschist on Anglesey, U.K. *In:* Evans, B.W. and Brown, E.H. (eds), Blueschists and Eclogites. *Geological Society of America Memoir,* **164,** 217-228.

GIBBONS, W., and MANN, A. 1983. Pre-Mesozoic lawsonite in Anglesey, northern Wales: Preservation of ancient blueschists. *Geology,* **11,** 3-6.

GILBEY, J.W.G. 1968. *The mineralogy, paragenesis and structure of the ores of the Dolgellau Gold Belt, Merionethshire, and associated wall rock alteration.* Unpublished Ph.D. thesis, University of London.

GILL, W.D., KHALAF, F.I., AND MASSOUD, M.S. 1977. Clay minerals as an index of the degree of metamorphism of the carbonate and terrigenous rocks in the South Wales coalfield. *Sedimentology,* **24,** 675-691.

GLASBY, G.P. 1974. A geochemical study of the manganese ore deposits of the Harlech Dome, North Wales. *Journal of Earth Science,* **8,** 445-450.

GREENLY, E. 1896. On the occurrence of sillimanite gneisses in central Anglesey. *Geological Magazine,* Decade 4, **3,** 494-496.

GREENLY, E. 1902. The origin and associations of the jaspers of south-eastern Anglesey. *Quarterly Journal of the Geological Society of London,* **58,** 425-440.

GREENLY, E. 1919. The Geology of Anglesey. *Memoirs of the Geological Survey of Great Britain,* 980pp (2 volumes).

GREG, R.P., AND LETTSOM, W.G. 1858. *Manual of the Mineralogy of Great Britain and Ireland.* John van Voorst, London, 483pp.

GRIFFITHS, J.C. 1939. The mineralogy of the glacial deposits of the region between the Rivers Neath and Towy, South Wales. *Proceedings of the Geologists' Association,* **50,** 433-462.

GRIFFITHS, J.C., and STUART, A. 1940. An occurrence of detrital diaspore in South Wales. *Geological Magazine,* **77,** 74-76.

GROVES, A.W. 1947. Results of magnetometric survey at Benallt manganese mine, Rhiw, Caernarvonshire. *Bulletin of the Institution of Mining and Metallurgy,* No.484, 1-24, No.486, 37-47, No.490, 29-32.

GROVES, A.W. 1952. Wartime investigations into the hematite and maganese ore resources of Great Britain and Northern Ireland. *Ministry of Supply, Permanent Records of Research and Development,* Monograph No. 20-703.

HAIDINGER, W. 1845. *Handbuch der bestimmenden Mineralogie.* Vienna.

HALL, G.W. 1971. *Metal Mines of Southern Wales.* Privately Published.

HALL, G.W. 1975. *The Gold Mines of Merioneth.* Griffin, Gloucester.

HALL, G.W. 1993. *Metal Mines of Southern Wales.* Griffin Publications.

HALL, T.M. 1868. *The Mineralogists' Directory.* London, 168pp.

HALLIMOND, A.F. 1924. On stilpnomelane from North Wales. *Mineralogical Magazine,* **20,** 193-197.

HALLIMOND, A.F. 1925. Iron ores: Bedded Ores of England and Wales: Petrography and Chemistry. *Memoirs of the Geological Survey. Special Reports on the Mineral Resources of Great Britain,* **29.**

HALSE, E. 1887. On the occurrence of manganese ore in the Cambrian rocks of Merionethshire. *Transactions of the North of England Institute of Mining and Mechanical Engineering,* **36,** 103-107.

HARKER, A. 1887. On some Anglesey dykes. *Geological Magazine,* New Series, Decade 3, **4,** 409-416.

HARKER, A. 1888a. Notes on the geology of Mynydd Mawr and the Nantlle Valley. *Geological Magazine,* New Series, Decade 3, **5,** 221-226.

HARKER, A. 1888b. Additional note on the blue hornblende of Mynydd Mawr. *Geological Magazine,* New Series, Decade 3, **5,** 455-456.

HARKER, A. 1889. *The Bala Volcanic Series of Caernarvonshire.* Cambridge University Press, 130pp.

HARRISON, W.J. 1894. New localities for the minerals brookite, natrolite and barytes. *Geological Magazine,* New Series, Decade 4, **1,** 567.

HARRISON, W.J. 1897. An occurrence of prehnite in Wales. *Mineralogical Magazine,* **11,** 198.

HASLETT, S.K. 1992. Petrology of a monchiquite from the Welsh Borderlands. *Mercian Geologist,* **13,** 43-46.

HAWKINS, T.R.W. 1970. Hornblende gabbros and picrites at Rhiw, Caernarvonshire. *Geological Journal,* **7,** 1-24.

HEARD, A. 1922. The petrology of the Pennant Series, east of the River Taff. *Geological Magazine,* **59,** 83-94.

HENRY, W. 1830. On the magnesite discovered in Anglesey. *Edinburgh Journal of Science,* new series, **2,** 155-156.

HENSLOW, J.S. 1822. Geological description of Anglesea. *Transactions of the Cambridge Philosophical Society,* **1,** 359-452.

HEY, M.H. 1932. Studies on the zeolites. Part III. Natrolite and metanatrolite. *Mineralogical Magazine,* **23,** 243-289.

HEY, M.H. 1954. A new review of the chlorites. *Mineralogical Magazine,* **30,** 277-292.

HOLGATE, N. 1951. On crossite from Anglesey. *Mineralogical Magazine,* **29,** 792-798.

HOLGATE, N. 1977. Tourmaline from amphibolized gabbro at Hanter Hill, Radnorshire. *Mineralogical Magazine,* **41,** 124-127.

HOLGATE, N., and HALLOWES, K.A.K. 1941. The igneous rocks of the Stanner-Hanter District, Radnorshire. *Geological Magazine,* **78,** 241-267.

HORÁK, J.M. 1993. *The Late Precambrian Coedana and Sarn Complexes, Northwest Wales - a geochemical and petrological study.* Unpublished Ph. D. thesis, University of Wales, 415pp.

HORÁK, J.M., and GIBBONS, W. 1986. Reclassification of blueschist amphiboles from Anglesey, North Wales. *Mineralogical Magazine,* **50,** 532-535.

HOWARD, F.T. 1895. The geology of Barry Island. *Transactions of the Cardiff Naturalists' Society,* **27,** 42-55.

HOWARD, F.T. 1899. Note on the lead deposits of the eastern fringe of the South Wales Coalfield. *Transactions of the Cardiff Naturalists' Society,* **30,** 46-47.

HOWARTH, W.E. 1928. On the occurrence of linnaeite in the Coal-measures of South Wales. *Geological Magazine,* **65,** 517-518.

HOWARTH, W.E. 1954. On the occurrence of linnaeite in the Coal Measures of South Wales. *Geological Magazine,* **91,** 407.

HOWELLS, M.F., REEDMAN, A.J., and CAMPBELL, S.D.G. 1991. *Ordovician (Caradoc) marginal basin volcanism in Snowdonia (north-west Wales).* HMSO for the British Geological Survey, 191pp.

HUBBARD, N. 1991. Phosgenite, the first Welsh occurrence. *Journal of the Russell Society,* **4,** 35.

HUGHES, W.J. 1959. The non-ferrous mining possibilities of Central Wales. *In: The Future of Non-ferrous Mining in Great Britain and Ireland.* Institution of Mining and Metallurgy, London, 227-294.

IXER, R.A., and VAUGHAN, D.J. 1993. Lead-zinc-fluorite-baryte deposits of the Pennines, North Wales and the Mendips. *In:* Pattrick, R.A.D., and Polya, D.A. (eds) *Mineralization in the British Isles,* Chapman and Hall, 355-418.

JENKINS, D.A. 1964. *Trace element studies on some Snowdonian rocks, their minerals, and related soils.* Unpublished Ph.D. thesis, University of Wales.

JENKINS, D.A., and BALL, D.F. 1964. Pumpellyite in Snowdonian soils and rocks. *Mineralogical Magazine,* **33,** 1093-1096.

JENKINS, D.A., and JOHNSON, D.B. 1993. Abandoned metal mines: a unique mineralogical and microbiological resource. *Journal of the Russell Society,* **5,** 40-44.

JIANG, W.-T., and PEACOR, D.R. 1993. Formation and modification of metastable intermediate sodium potassium mica, paragonite, and muscovite in hydrothermally altered metabasites from northern Wales. *American Mineralogist,* **78,** 782-793.

JIANG, W-T., PEACOR, D.R., MERRIMAN, R.J., and ROBERTS, B. 1990. Transmission and analytical electron microscopic study of mixed-layer illite/smectite formed as an apparent replacement product of diagenetic illite. *Clays and Clay Minerals,* **38,** 449-468.

JOHNSON, D.B., KELSO, W.I., and JENKINS, D.A. 1979. Bacterial streamer growth in a disused pyrite mine. *Environmental Pollution,* **18,** 107-118.

JOHNSTON, J.F.W. 1838. On the composition of certain mineral substances of organic origin. II. Hatchettine. *Philosophical Magazine,* **12,** 338-339.

JONES, A.D. 1987. The minerals of Llechweddhelyg. *U.K. Journal of Mines and Minerals,* **No. 3,** 25-27.

JONES, G., and LEWIS, P. 1971. Roman gold mines at Dolaucothi. *Publication of Carmarthen County Museum,* **1,** 23pp.

JONES, J.A., AND MORETON, N.J.M. 1977. *The Mines and Minerals of Mid-Wales,* 40pp.

JONES, O.T. 1922. Lead and zinc. The mining district of North Cardiganshire and West Montgomeryshire. *Memoirs of the Geological Survey. Special Report of the Mineral Resources of Great Britain,* **20.**

JORDAN, H.K. 1876. Pencoed, Mynydd-y-Gaer and Gilfach-Goch mineral districts. *Proceedings of the South Wales Institute of Engineers,* **9,** 250-270.

KENDALL, A. 1988. Aragonite in Ogof Daren Cilau. *Cave Science,* **15,** 83-84.

KINGSBURY, A.W.G. 1965. Tellurbismuth and meneghinite, two minerals new to Britain. *Mineralogical Magazine,* **35,** 424-426.

KIRTON, S.R., and DONATO, J.A. 1985. Some buried Tertiary dykes of Britain and surrounding waters deduced by magnetic modelling and seismic reflection methods. *Journal of the Geological Society, London,* **142,** 1047-1057.

KOKELAAR, B.P. 1977. *The igneous history of the Rhobell Fawr area, Merioneth, North Wales.* Unpublished Ph.D. thesis, University of Wales.

KOKELAAR, B.P. 1986. Petrology and geochemistry of the Rhobell Volcanic Complex: Amphibole-dominated fractionation at an early Ordovician arc volcano in North Wales. *Journal of Petrology,* **27,** 887-914.

KOKELAAR, B.P., BEVINS, R.E., and ROACH, R.A. 1985. Submarine silicic volcanism and associated sedimentary and tectonic processes, Ramsey Island, SW Wales. *Journal of the Geological Society, London,* **142,** 591-613.

LANGFORD, J.I. 1973. The accuracy of cell dimensions determined by Cohen's method of least squares and the systematic indexing of powder data. *Journal of Applied Crystallography,* **6,** 190-196.

LEAKE, B.E. 1978. Nomenclature of amphiboles. *Mineralogical Magazine,* **42,** 533-563.

LEE, M.K., PHARAOH, T.C., and SOPER, N.J. 1990. Structural trends in central Britain from images of gravity and aeromagnetic fields. *Journal of the Geological Society, London,* **147,** 241-258.

LENTIN, A.G.L. 1800. *Briefe über die Insel Anglesea, vorzuglich über die dasigen Kupferbergwerke und die dazu gehorigen Schmelzwerke und Fabriken.* Leipzig.

LÉVY, M. 1825. An account of a new mineral. *Annals of Philosophy,* **9,** 140-142.

LEWIS, A. 1990. Underground exploration of the Great Orme Copper Mines. *In:* Crew, P and Crew, S. (eds), *Early Mining in the British Isles.* Plas Tan y Bwlch Occasional Paper No. 1, 5-10.

LEWIS, W.J. 1967. *Lead mining in Wales.* University of Wales Press, 415pp.

LYNAS, B.D.T. 1973. The Cambrian and Ordovician rocks of the Migneint area, North Wales. *Journal of the Geological Society, London,* **129,** 481-503.

MACPHERSON, H.G. 1983. References for, and updating of, L.J. Spencer's 1st and 2nd supplementary list of British Minerals. *Mineralogical Magazine,* **47,** 243-257.

MALTMAN, A.J. 1977. Serpentinites and related rocks of Anglesey. *Geological Journal,* **12,** 113-128.

MASON, J.S. 1992. Wulfenite in the British Isles. Part Two: Wales. *U.K. Journal of Mines and Minerals,*

No. 11, 38-41.

MASON, J.S. and HUGHES, S.J.S. 1990. Geology of the Darren District. *In:* Hughes, S.J.S. *The Darren Mines.* British Mining No. 40. Northern Mine Research Society, 131-141.

MATLEY, C.A. 1928. The Pre-Cambrian complex and associated rocks of south-western Lleyn (Carnarvonshire). *Quarterly Journal of the Geological Society of London,* **84,** 440-504.

MATLEY, C.A., and WILSON, T.S. 1946. The Harlech Dome, north of the Barmouth Estuary. *Quarterly Journal of the Geological Society of London,* **102,** 1-40.

MATTHEWS, D.W., and SCOON, J.H. 1964. Notes on a new occurrence of stilpnomelane from North Wales. *Mineralogical Magazine,* **33,** 1032-1037.

MEDENBACH, O., and GEBBERT, W. 1993. Lautenthalite, $PbCu_4[(OH)_6/(SO_4)_2].3H_2O$, the Pb analogue of devellite - A new mineral from the Harz mountains, Germany. *Neues Jahrbuch für Mineralogie Monatshefte,* **9,** 401-407.

MERRIMAN, R.J., and ROBERTS, B. 1985. A survey of white mica crystallinity and polytypes in pelitic rocks of Snowdonia and Llŷn, North Wales. *Mineralogical Magazine,* **49,** 305-319.

MERRIMAN, R.J., BEVINS, R.E., and BALL, T.K. 1986. Petrological and geochemical variations within the Tal y Fan Intrusion: a study of element mobility during low-grade metamorphism with implications for petro-tectonic modelling. *Journal of Petrology,* **27,** 1409-1436.

METCALFE, R. 1990. *Fluid/rock interaction and metadomain formation during low-grade metamorphism in the Welsh marginal basin.* Unpublished Ph.D. thesis, University of Bristol.

MILLER, W.H. 1842. On the specific gravity of sulphuret of nickel. *The London, Edinburgh and Dublin Philosophical Magazine and Journal of Science,* **20,** 378-379.

MOHR, P.A. 1964. Genesis of the Cambrian manganese carbonate rocks of North Wales. *Journal of Sedimentary Petrology,* **34,** 819-829.

MONNET, M. 1779. *Nouveau Systême de Minéralogie.* Paris.

MORETON, N.J.M. 1982. Metal mines of the British Isles. No. 1, Dylife (Powys). *Journal of the Russell Society,* **1,** 8.

MORGAN, D., and STARKEY, R. 1991. Harmotome from Pen-y-Clun Mine, Llanidloes, Dyfed, Wales. *U.K. Journal of Mines and Minerals,* **No. 10,** 4-6.

MORIMOTO, N. 1988. Nomenclature of pyroxenes. *American Mineralogist,* **73,** 1123-1133.

MORRISON, T.A. 1975. *Goldmining in West Merioneth.* Privately Published, Llandyssul, 98pp.

MOTTANA, A. 1986. Blueschist facies metamorphism of manganiferous cherts: a review of the alpine occurrences. *In:* Evans, B.W. & Brown, E.H. (eds). Blueschists and Eclogites. *Memoirs of the Geological Society of America,* **164,** 267-299.

MOUNTAIN, E.D. 1924. Calcite crystals from Holywell, North Wales. *Mineralogical Magazine,* **20,** 212-216.

NADEN, J. 1988. *Gold mineralisation in the Caledonides of the British Isles with reference to the Dolgellau Gold Belt and the Southern Uplands of Scotland.* Unpublished Ph.D. thesis, University of Aston.

NATARAJ, T.S. 1967. *Glaucophanic metamorphism in Anglesey.* Unpublished Ph.D. thesis, University of Leeds, 103pp.

NICHOLLS, G.D. 1957. Autometasomatism in the Lower Spilites of the Builth Volcanic Series. *Proceedings of the Geological Society of London,* **1543,** 8-10.

NICHOLLS, G.D. 1958. Autometasomatism in the Lower Spilites of the Builth Volcanic Series. *Quarterly Journal of the Geological Society of London,* **114,** 137-162.

NICHOLLS, R.A. 1979. *Geochemistry and clay mineralogy of some Silurian sedimentary rocks, Dyfed, S.W. Wales.* Unpublished Ph.D. thesis, University of Bristol.

NICKEL, E. 1976. New data on woodwardite. *Mineralogical Magazine,* **43,** 644-647.

NIEDERMAYER, R.-O., and LANGBEIN, R. 1989. Probable microbial origin of Ordovician (Arenig) phosphatic pebble coats ('Bolopora') from North Wales, U.K. *Geological Magazine,* **126,** 691-698.

NOCKOLDS, S.R. 1938. On the occurrence of acmite in the riebeckite-microgranite of Mynydd Mawr, Caernarvonshire. *Mineralogical Magazine,* **25,** 35-37.

NORTH, F.J. 1916. The minerals of Glamorgan. *Transactions of the Cardiff Naturalists' Society,* **49,** 16-51.

NORTH, F.J., and HOWARTH, W.E. 1928. On the occurrence of millerite and associated minerals in the Coal Measures of South Wales. *Proceedings of the South Wales Institute of Engineers,* **44,** 325-348.

NUTT, M.J.C., INESON, P.R., and MITCHELL, J.G. 1979. The age of mineralization at Parys Mountain, Anglesey. *In:* Harris, A.L., Holland, C.H., and Leake, B.E. (eds) *The Caledonides of the British Isles - reviewed.* Geological Society of London Special Paper, **8,** 619-627.

OAKLEY, K.P. 1934. Phosphatic calculi in Silurian Polyzoa. *Proceedings of the Royal Society of London,* Series B, **116,** 296-314.

PALACHE, C., and VASSAR, H.E. 1925. Some minerals of the Keweenawan copper deposits: pumpellyite, a new mineral; sericite; saponite. *American Mineralogist,* **10,** 412.

PARNELL, J. 1983. The distribution of hydrocarbon minerals in the Welsh Borderlands and adjacent areas. *Geological Journal,* **18,** 129-139.

PARNELL, J. 1988. Mineralogy of uraniferous hydrocarbons in Carboniferous-hosted mineral deposits, Great Britain. *Uranium,* **4,** 197-218.

PARNELL, J., and EAKIN, P. 1989. Thorium-bitumen mineralization in Silurian sandstones, Welsh Borderland. *Mineralogical Magazine,* **53,** 111-116.

PASSAGLIA, E., and GOTTARDI, G. 1973. Crystal chemistry and nomenclature of pumpellyites and julgoldites. *Canadian Mineralogist,* **12,** 219-223.

PEACOR, D.R., ESSENE, E.J., SIMMONS, W.B., and BIGELOW, W.C. 1974. Kellyite, a new Mn-Al member of the serpentine group from Bald Knob, North Carolina, and new data on grovesite. *American Mineralogist,* **59,** 1153-1156.

PENNANT, T. 1778. *A Tour in Wales.* London.

PERCEVAL, S.G. 1866a. Discovery of wulfenite, etc., in Pembrokeshire. *Geological Magazine*, **3,** 377-378.

PERCEVAL, S.G. 1866b. Correspondence in *Geological Magazine*, **3,** 518.

POINTON, C.R., and IXER, R.A. 1980. Parys Mountain mineral deposit, Anglesey, Wales: geology and ore mineralogy. *Transactions of the Institution of Mining and Metallurgy (Section B: Applied earth science)*, **89,** B143-B155.

POLLARD, A.M., THOMAS, R.G., WILLIAMS, P.A., BEVINS, R.E., and TURGOOSE, S. 1989. Carbonatian connellite, a new variety, from the Britannia Mine, North Wales, and from the Botallack Mine, Cornwall. *Journal of the Russell Society,* **2**(2), 23-27.

PRIOR, G.T. 1906. Dundasite from North Wales. *Mineralogical Magazine,* **14,** 167-169.

PRYOR, M.J. 1988. Geological and fluid inclusion studies at Ogofau and Gwynfynydd gold mines, Wales. *South African Journal of Geology,* **91,** 450-464.

PULFREY, W. 1933. The iron-ore oolites and pisolites of North Wales. *Quarterly Journal of the Geological Society of London,* **89,** 401-430.

RAADE, G., ELLIOTT, C.J., and DIN, V.K. 1985. New data on glaucocerinite. *Mineralogical Magazine,* **49,** 583-590.

RAMSAY, A.C. 1854. On the geology of the gold-bearing district of Merionethshire, North Wales. *Quarterly Journal of the Geological Society of London,* **10,** 242-247.

RANKIN, A.H., and CRIDDLE, A.J. 1985. Mineralizing fluids and metastable low-temperature inclusion brines at Llanharry iron deposit, South Wales. *Transactions of the Institution of Mining and Metallurgy (Section B: Applied earth science),* **94,** B126-B132.

RAYBOULD, J.G. 1973. Framboidal pyrite associated with lead-zinc mineralisation in mid-Wales. *Lithos,* **6,** 175-181.

RAYBOULD, J.G. 1976. Ore textures, paragenesis and zoning in the lead-zinc veins of mid-Wales. *Transactions of the Institution of Mining and Metallurgy (Section B: Applied earth science),* **85,** B112-B119.

READ, D., COOPER, D.C., and McARTHUR, J.M. 1987. The composition and distribution of nodular monazite in the Lower Palaeozoic rocks of Great Britain. *Mineralogical Magazine,* **51,** 271-280.

READWIN, T.A. 1860. The gold discoveries in Merionethshire. *Transactions of the Manchester Geological and Mining Society,* **2,** 97-101.

READWIN, T.A. 1862. *The Gold-Bearing Strata of Merionethshire.*

READWIN, T.A. 1864. On the recent discovery of gold near Bala Lake, Merionethshire. *Report of the British Association for the Advancement of Science* (for 1862), 86-87.

READWIN, T.A. 1888. *Gold in Wales.* London, 12pp.

REED, F.R.C. 1895. The geology of the country around Fishguard, Pembrokeshire. *Quarterly Journal of the Geological Society of London,* **51,** 149-195.

REEDMAN, A.J., COLMAN, T.B., CAMPBELL, S.D.G., and HOWELLS, M.F. 1985. Volcanogenic mineralization related to the Snowdon Volcanic Group (Ordovician), Gwynedd, North Wales. *Journal of the Geological Society, London,* **142,** 875-888.

RICE, R., and SHARP, G.J. 1976. Copper mineralization in the forest of Coed-y-Brenin, North Wales. *Transactions of the Institution of Mining and Metallurgy, (Section B: Applied earth science),* **85,** B1-B13.

ROACH, R.A. 1969. The composite nature of the St. David's Head and Carn Llidi intrusions of North Pembrokeshire. *In:* Wood, A. (ed.) *The Pre-Cambrian and Lower Palaeozoic rocks of Wales,* University of Wales Press, Cardiff, 409-433.

ROBERTS, B. 1979. *The geology of Snowdonia and Llŷn: an outline and field guide.* Adam Hilger, Bristol.

ROBERTS, B. 1981. Low grade and very low grade regional metabasic Ordovician rocks of Llŷn and Snowdonia, Gwynedd, North Wales. *Geological Magazine,* **118,** 189-200.

ROBERTS, B., and MERRIMAN, R.J. 1990. Cambrian and Ordovician metabentonites and their relevance to the origins of associated mudrocks in the northern sector of the Lower Palaeozoic Welsh marginal basin. *Geological Magazine,* **127,** 31-43.

ROBERTS, B., EVANS, J.A., MERRIMAN, R.J., and SMITH, M. 1989. Discussion of 'Low grade metamorphism of the Welsh Basin Lower Palaeozoic succession: an example of diastathermal metamorphism'. *Journal of the Geological Society, London,* **146,** 885-890.

ROBERTS, D. 1986. *Geochemistry of recent freshwater manganese tunnel deposits.* Unpublished Ph.D. thesis, University of Wales.

ROBINSON, D., AND BEVINS, R.E. 1986. Incipient metamorphism in the Lower Palaeozoic marginal basin of Wales. *Journal of Metamorphic Geology,* **4,** 101-113.

ROBINSON, D., NICHOLLS, R.A., and THOMAS, L.J. 1980. Clay mineral evidence for low-grade Caledonian and Variscan metamorphism in south-western Dyfed, South Wales. *Mineralogical Magazine,* **43,** 857-863.

ROGERS, E., SALTER, J.W., and others. 1861. The Iron Ores of Great Britain. Part 3, Iron Ores of South Wales. *Memoirs of the Geological Survey.*

ROSS, C.S., and KERR, P.F. 1930. Dickite, a kaolin mineral. *American Mineralogist,* **15,** 34-39.

RUSSELL, A. 1911. An occurrence of the barium-felspar celsian in North Wales. *Nature,* **86,** 180.

RUSSELL, A. 1944. Notes on some minerals either new or rare to Britain. *Mineralogical Magazine,* **27,** 1-10.

RUSSELL, A. 1946. On rhodonite and tephroite from Treburland manganese mine, Altarnun, Cornwall; and on rhodonite from other localities in Cornwall and Devonshire. *Mineralogical Magazine,* **27,** 221-235.

RUST, S.A. 1990a. Mattheddleite from the Darren Mine, Dyfed, Wales. *U.K. Journal of Mines and Minerals,* **No. 8,** 47-48.

RUST, S.A. 1990b. Susannite and sulphatian schmeiderite from Llechwedd Helyg Mine, Tir-y-Mynach, Dyfed, Wales. *U.K. Journal of Mines and Minerals,* **No. 8,** 48.

RUST, S.A. 1991. Siegenite from Erglodd Mine, Talybont, Dyfed, Wales. *U.K. Journal of Mines and Minerals,* **No. 9,** 4.

RUST, S.A. 1992. Ramsbeckite, the first three British

occurrences. *U.K. Journal of Mines and Minerals,* **No. 11,** 24-25.

RUST, S., and MASON, J.S. 1988. The Minerals of Esgair Hir Mine, Bwlch-y-Esgair Hir, Ceulanymaesmawr, Dyfed, Wales. *U.K. Journal of Mines and Minerals,* **No. 5,** 35-43.

RUST, S., and RUST, D. 1987. Micro-minerals from Dyfngwm Mine. *U.K. Journal of Mines and Minerals,* **No. 2,** 28-32.

RYBACK, G., and SAVILLE, G. 1967. Wulfenite from Ysbyty Ystwyth, Cardiganshire. *Mineralogical Magazine,* **36,** 458-459.

SAICH, D.A., and RUST, S.A. 1987. Micro-minerals from a trial level in Wales. *U.K. Journal of Mines and Minerals,* **No. 3,** 3-4.

SARGENT, H.C. 1915. The Penmaenmawr Intrusion. *Geological Magazine,* New Series, Decade 6, **2,** 15-27.

SARGENT, H.C. 1916. Axinite veins in the Penmaenmawr Porphyrite. *Geological Magazine,* New Series, Decade 6, **3,** 5-7.

SARGENT, H.C. 1924. Notes on the petrology of Penmaenmawr Mountain (Part 1). *Proceedings of the Liverpool Geological Society,* **14,** 82-89.

SARGENT, H.C. 1925. Notes on the petrology of Penmaenmawr Mountain (Part II). *Proceedings of the Liverpool Geological Society,* **14,** 123-142.

SCHAUB, L. 1905. Ueber den Quartznorit von Penmaenmawr in Wales und seine Schlierenbildungen. *Neues Jahrbuch für Mineralogie,* **1,** 93-121.

SHEPHERD, T.J., and BOTTRELL, S.H. 1993. Dolgellau Gold-belt, Harlech district, North Wales. *In:* Pattrick, R.A.D., and Polya, D.A. (eds) *Mineralization in the British Isles.* Chapman and Hall, 187-207.

SIBLY, T.F. 1919. Iron ores - the haematites of the Forest of Dean and South Wales. *Memoirs of the Geological Survey. Special Reports on the Mineral Resources of Great Britain,* **10.**

SIBLY, T.F. AND LLOYD, W. 1927. Iron ores - the haematites of the Forest of Dean and South Wales. *Memoirs of the Geological Survey. Special Reports on the Mineral Resources of Great Britain,* **10,** 2nd edit.

SIDDIQUI, S.F.A. 1964. *The geology and mineralisation of the area between Newlyn and Mousehole, Cornwall.* Unpublished Ph.D. thesis, University of London.

SIVAPRAKASH, C. 1977. *Geochemistry of some sulphides and sulphosalts from Parys Mountain, Anglesey.* Unpublished M.Phil. thesis, University of Aston in Birmingham.

SMITH, B. 1921. Lead and zinc ores in the Carboniferous rocks of North Wales. *Memoirs of the Geological Survey. Special Report of the Mineral Resources of Great Britain,* **19.**

SMITH, B., and CARRUTHERS, R.G. 1925. Copper ores of the Midlands, Wales, The Lake District and the Isle of Man. *Memoirs of the Geological Survey. Special Report on the Mineral Resources of Great Britain,* **30.**

SMITH, F.W. 1973. Fluid inclusion studies on fluorite from the North Wales ore field. *Transactions of the Institution of Mining and Metallurgy (Section B: Applied earth sciences),* **82,** B174-B176.

SMITH, M. 1988. *The tectonic evolution of the Cambrian and Ordovician rocks in Southern Central Snowdonia.* Unpublished Ph.D. thesis, University of Wales, Aberystwyth.

SMITHSON, F. 1954. The petrography of dickitic sandstones in North Wales and Northern England. *Geological Magazine,* **91,** 177-188.

SMITHSON, F., and BROWN, G. 1957. Dickite from sandstones in Northern England and North Wales. *Mineralogical Magazine,* **31,** 381-391.

SMYTH, W.W. 1862. Gold mining at Clogau, North Wales. *Mining and Smelting Magazine,* **1,** 359-366.

SOUTHWOOD, M.J. 1982. *The geological setting of the sulphide deposits at Morfa Du, Parys Mountain, Anglesey.* Unpublished Ph.D. thesis, University of Wales.

SOUTHWOOD, M.J. 1984. Basaltic lavas at Parys Mountain, Anglesey: trace-element geochemistry, tectonic setting and exploration implications. *Transactions of the Institution of Mining and Metallurgy, (Section B: Applied earth sciences),* **93,** B51-B54.

SOWERBY, G.B. 1838. Locality for brookite. *Annals and Magazine of Natural History,* series 2, **2,** 293.

SOWERBY, J. 1809. *British Mineralogy.* Volume III. Richard Taylor, London.

SOWERBY, J. 1811. *British Mineralogy.* Volume IV. Richard Taylor, London.

SOWERBY, J. 1817. *British Mineralogy.* Volume V. Richard Taylor, London.

SPENCER, L.J. 1942. Barium-felspars (celsian and paracelsian) from Wales. *Mineralogical Magazine,* **26,** 231-245.

STAMP, L.D., and WOOLDRIDGE, S.W. 1923. The igneous and associated rocks of Llanwrtyd, Brecon. *Quarterly Journal of the Geological Society of London,* **79,** 16-46.

STARKEY, R.E., AND ROBINSON, G.W. 1992. Famous mineral localities, Prenteg, Tremadog, Gwynedd, Wales. *Mineralogical Record,* **23,** 391-399.

STARKEY, R.E., HUBBARD, N., AND BAYLEY, M.P. 1991. Mineralization at Hendre Quarry, Glyn Ceiriog, Clwyd, Wales. *U.K. Journal of Mines and Minerals,* **No. 10,** 48-51.

STEED, G.M., ANNELS, A.E., SHRESTHA, P.L., and TATER, P.S. 1976. Geochemical and biochemical prospecting in the area of the Ogofau gold mines, Dyfed, Wales. *Transactions of the Institution of Mining and Metallurgy (Section B: Applied earth science),* **85,** B109-B117.

STORRIE, J. 1895. Notes on the occurrence of grains of native gold in the New Red Marl strata during the boring of an artesian well at the Phoenix Brewery, Working Street, Cardiff. *Transactions of the Cardiff Naturalists' Society,* **26,** 107-109.

STRAHAN, A. 1885. The geology of the coasts adjoining Rhyl, Abergele and Colwyn. *Memoirs of the Geological Survey of England and Wales.* Explanation of Quarter-Sheet 79 N.W.

STRAHAN, A. 1890. The geology of the neighbourhoods of Flint, Mold, and Ruthin. *Memoirs of the Geological Survey.* Explanation of Quarter-sheet 79SE.

STRAHAN, A. 1899. The geology of the South Wales Coalfield. Part 1. The country around Newport, Monmouthshire. *Memoirs of the Geological Survey of England and Wales.*

STRAHAN, A. 1907. The Geology of the South Wales Coalfield, Part VIII. The Country around Swansea. *Memoirs of the Geological Survey of England and Wales,* Sheet 247.

STRAHAN, A., CANTRILL, T.C., DIXON, E.E.L., and THOMAS, H.H. 1909. The geology of the South Wales Coalfield. Part X. The Country around Carmarthen. *Memoirs of the Geological Survey of England and Wales.* Explanation of Sheet 229.

STRAHAN, A., GIBSON, W., CANTRILL, T.C., SHERLOCK, R.L. and DEWEY, H. 1920. Pre-Carboniferous and Carboniferous bedded ores of England and Wales. *Memoirs of the Geological Survey. Special Reports on the Mineral Resources of Great Britain,* **13.**

SYLVESTER-BRADLEY, P.C., and KING, R.J. 1963. Evidence for abiogenic hydrocarbons. *Nature,* **198,** 728-731.

TEALL, J.J.H. 1888. *British Petrography.* Dulau, London, 469pp.

THANASUTHIPITAK, T. 1974. *The relationship of mineralization to petrology at Parys Mountain, Anglesey.* Unpublished Ph.D. thesis, University of Aston in Birmingham.

THOMAS, H.H. 1909a. Orthite in North Wales. *Nature,* **81,** 487.

THOMAS, H.H. 1909b. Detrital andalusite in Tertiary and post-Tertiary sands. *Mineralogical Magazine,* **15,** 241-244.

THOMAS, T.M. 1968. A new occurrence of celestite, near Llantrisant, Mid Glamorgan. *Geological Magazine,* **105,** 185-186.

THORPE, R.S., WILLIAMS-THORPE, O., JENKINS, D.G., and WATSON, J.S. 1991. The geological sources and transport of the bluestones of Stonehenge, Wiltshire, U.K. *Proceedings of the Prehistoric Society,* **57,** 103-157.

TRAILL, T.S. 1821. Observation on the mineralogy of Halkin Mountain, in Flintshire; with particular account of the recently discovered Buhrstone and porcelain-clay of that place. *Edinburgh Philosophical Journal,* **4,** 246-261.

TRUEMAN, A.E. 1930. Wavellite in the cherts at Bishopston. *Swansea Scientific and Field Naturalists' Society Proceedings,* **1,** 98-99.

TRYTHALL, R.J.B. 1988. *The Mid-Ordovician Oolitic Ironstones of North Wales.* Unpublished D.Phil. thesis, Luton College of Higher Education.

TRYTHALL, R.J.B. 1989. The mid-Ordovician oolitic ironstones of North Wales: a field guide. *In:* Young, T.P., and Taylor, W.E.G. (eds) *Phanerozoic Ironstones.* Geological Society of London Special Publication, **46,** 213-220.

TRYHALL, R.J.B., ECCLES, C., MOLYNEUX, S.G., and TAYLOR, W.E.G. 1987. Age and controls of ironstone deposition (Ordovician), North Wales. *Geological Journal,* **22,** 31-43.

TUCKER, M.E. 1977. The marginal Triassic deposits of South Wales: continental facies and palaeogeography. *Geological Journal,* **12,** 169-188.

VIVIAN, S. 1885. The hematite deposits of the southern outcrop of the Carboniferous Limestone of South Wales. *Transactions of the South Wales Institute of Engineers,* **14,** 164-175.

VIVIAN, S. 1887. The hematite deposits of the southern outcrop of the Carboniferous Limestone of South Wales. *Transactions of the Cardiff Naturalists' Society,* **19,** 48-53.

VIVIAN, W. 1859. On arborescent native copper in the Great Ormeshead, North Wales. *Quarterly Journal of the Geological Society of London,* **15,** 109-110.

VIVIAN, W. 1876. Note on the paragenetic formations of carbonate of lime and oxide of iron, at the Mwyndy Iron Mines, Glamorganshire. *Mineralogical Magazine,* **1,** 18-19.

VIVIAN, W. 1877. Further notes on the oxides of iron, enclosed in quartz, at Mwyndy, Glamorganshire. *Mineralogical Magazine,* **1,** 117-118.

WARREN, P.T., PRICE, D., NUTT, M.J.C., and SMITH, E.G. 1984. Geology of the country around Rhyl and Denbigh. *Memoirs of the British Geological Survey.* Explanation of Sheets 95 and 107 and parts of Sheets 94 and 106, 217pp.

WATERS, R.A., AND LAWRENCE, D.J.D. 1987. Geology of the South Wales Coalfield, Part III, the Country around Cardiff. 3rd edition. *Memoirs of the Geological Survey of England and Wales.* Explanation of Sheet 263.

WATSON, J.J.W. 1859. The haematitic deposits of Glamorgan. *Geologist,* **2,** 241-256.

WEDD, C.B., SMITH, B., KING, W.B.R., and WRAY, D.A. 1929. The Country around Oswestry. *Memoirs of the Geological Survey of England and Wales.* Explanation of Sheet 137.

WEINBERG, R.M. 1973. *The petrology and geochemistry of the Cambro-Ordovician ironstones of North Wales.* Unpublished D.Phil. thesis, University of Oxford.

WESTHEAD, S.J. 1993. *The structural controls on mineralisation at Parys Mountain, Anglesey, North Wales.* Unpublished Ph.D. thesis, University of Wales.

WHEATLEY, C.J.V. 1971. *Economic geology of the Avoca mineralised belt, S.E. Ireland, and Parys Mountain, Anglesey.* Unpublished Ph.D. thesis, Imperial College, University of London.

WHITE, S.C. 1993. *The tectono-thermal evolution of the South Wales Coalfield.* Unpublished Ph.D. thesis, University of Wales.

WILLIAMS, D. 1924. On two olivine-dolerite dykes in Snowdonia. *Proceedings of the Liverpool Geological Society,* **14,** 38-47.

WILLIAMS, D. 1930. The geology of the country between Nant Peris and Nant Ffrancon (Snowdonia). *Quarterly Journal of the Geological Society of London,* **86,** 191-232.

WILLIAMS, H. 1922. The igneous rocks of the Capel Curig district (North Wales). *Proceedings of the Liverpool Geological Society,* **13,** 166-202.

WILLIAMS, H. 1927. The geology of Snowdon (North Wales). *Quarterly Journal of the Geological Society of London,* **83,** 346-431.

WILLIAMS, H. 1930. The Snowdon District: Report of the Easter field meeting of the Geologists' Association. *Proceedings of the Geologists' Association,* **41,** 190-205.

WILLIAMS, R.A. 1985. The Old Mines of the Llangynog District. *British Mining No. 26.* Northern Mine Research Society, 128pp.

WILLIAMS, W. 1802. *Observations of the Snowdon Mountains.* S. Collingwood, Oxford.

WILSON, M.J. 1978. Occurrence of thaumasite in weathered furnace slag, Merthyr Tydfil. *Mineralogical Magazine, 42,* 290-291.

WOODLAND, A.W. 1935. Spessartite in the Cambrian manganese ore of Merionethshire. *Geological Magazine, 72,* 384.

WOODLAND, A.W. 1938a. Petrological studies in the Harlech Grit Series of Merionethshire. I. Metamorphic changes in the mudstones of the Mangenese Shale Group. *Geological Magazine, 75,* 366-382.

WOODLAND, A.W. 1938b. Petrological studies in the Harlech Grit Series of Merionethshire. II: The petrography and petrology of some of the grits. *Geological Magazine, 75,* 440-454.

WOODLAND, A.W. 1938c. Some petrological studies in the Harlech Grit Series of Merionethshire. III: The development of pyrite in the grits and mudstones. *Geological Magazine, 75,* 529-539.

WOODLAND, A.W. 1939a. The petrography and petrology of the Lower Cambrian manganese ore of western Merionethshire. *Quarterly Journal of the Geological Society of London, 95,* 1-35.

WOODLAND, A.W. 1939b. The petrography and petrology of the manganese ore of the Rhiw district (Carnarvonshire). *Proceedings of the Geologists' Association, 50,* 205-222.

WOODLAND, A.W. 1956. The manganese deposits of Great Britain. *Symposium sobreyacimientos de manganeso, tomo 5, Europa. 20th International Geological Congress, Mexico,* 197-218.

WOODLAND, A.W., AND EVANS, W.B. 1964. Geology of the South Wales Coalfield, Part IV, Pontypridd and Maesteg. *Memoirs of the Geological Survey of the United Kingdom.*

YOUNG, T.P. 1989. Phanerozoic Ironstones: an introduction and review. *In:* Young, T.P., and Taylor, W.E.G. (eds) *Phanerozoic ironstones.* Geological Society of London Special Publications, **46,** 51-63.

YOUNG, T.P. 1991. The Ordovician ironstones of North Wales. *In:* Young, T.P. (ed.) *Jurassic and Ordovician ooidal ironstones.* 13th International Sedimentological Congress Fieldguides, 51-72.

INDEX

This index contains the names of minerals, localities, geological horizons, and collectors or collections referred to in the text. It does not include literature citations or personal communications.

Geological publications in the National Museum of Wales

GEOLOGICAL SERIES

'Formed stones', folklore and fossils. *By M.G. Bassett. Geological Series No. 1. 32pp. ISBN 0 7200 0264 8. 1982.*

Fossil plants from Wales. *By M.G. Bassett and D. Edwards. Geological Series No. 2. 42pp. ISBN 0 7200 0265 6. 1982.*

The Cambrian-Ordovician boundary: sections, fossil distributions, and correlations. *Edited by M.G. Bassett and W.T. Dean. Geological Series No. 3. 227pp. ISBN 0 7200 0253 2. 1982.*

Welsh minerals. *By R.E. Bevins and T. Sharpe. Geological Series No. 4. 28pp. ISBN 0 7200 0262 1. 1982.*

Mineralau Cymru. *Gan R.E. Bevins a T. Sharpe. Geological Series No. 5. 28pp. ISBN 0 7200 0263 X. 1983.*

Geology in museums: a bibliography and index. *By T. Sharpe. Geological Series No. 6. 128pp. ISBN 0 7200 0281 8. 1983.*

Trilobites in Wales. *By R.M. Owens, Geological Series No. 7. 22pp. ISBN 0 7200 0289 3. 1984.*

In search of fossil plants: the life and work of David Davies (Gilfach Goch). *By B.A. Thomas. Geological Series No. 8. 54pp. ISBN 0 7200 0303 2. 1986.*

A Global Standard for The Silurian System. *Edited by C.H. Holland and M.G. Bassett. Geological Series No. 9. 325pp. ISBN 0 7200 0308 3. 1989.*

Silurian field excursions: a geotraverse across Wales and the Welsh Borderland. *By D.J. Siveter, R.M. Owens and A.T. Thomas. Geological Series No. 10. 133pp. ISBN 0 7200 0329 6. 1989.*

Catalogue of the R.J. King Mineral Collection in the National Museum of Wales. *By R.E. Bevins and J.M. Horák. Geological Series No. 11. 1994.*

Catalogue of type, figured and cited fossils in the National Museum of Wales. *By R.M. Owens and M.G. Bassett. Geological Series No. 12. 1994.*

Silurian field excursions: Prague Basin (Barrandian), Bohemia. *By J. Kríz. Geological Series No. 13. 111pp. ISBN 0 7200 0373 3. 1992.*

Geological excursions in Powys. *Edited by N.H. Woodcock and M.G. Bassett. Geological Series No. 14. 366pp. ISBN 0 7083 1217 9. 1993.*

Ichthyosaurs: a history of fossil 'sea-dragons'. *By S.R. Howe, T. Sharpe and H.S. Torrens. 32pp. Geological Series No. 15. ISBN 0 7200 0232 X. 1993.*

OTHER GEOLOGICAL PUBLICATIONS

Bibliography and index of geology and allied sciences for Wales and the Welsh Borders, 1897-1958. *By D.A. Bassett, 376pp. 1961.*

Bibliography and index of geology and allied sciences for Wales and the Welsh Borders, 1536-1896. *By D.A. Bassett, 246pp. 1963.*

A source-book of geological, geomorphological and soil maps for Wales and the Welsh Borders (1800-1966). *By D.A. Bassett. x + 240pp. 1967.*

Catalogue of type, figured and cited fossils in the National Museum of Wales. *By M.G. Bassett. 114pp. ISBN 0 7200 0068 8. 1972.*

The Ordovician System: proceedings of a Palaeontological Association symposium, September 1974. *Edited by M.G. Bassett. 696pp. ISBN 0 7083 0582 2. 1976.*

Henry De la Beche: observations on an observer. *By P.J. McCartney. 77pp. ISBN 0 7200 0201 X. 1978.*

Geological excursions in Dyfed, south-west Wales. *Edited by M.G. Bassett. 327pp. ISBN 0 7200 0249 4. 1982.*

A catalogue of these publications, including full details of prices, can be obtained from the bookshop manager, National Museum of Wales, Cardiff, CF1 3NP.